finite
mathematics:
a liberal
arts
approach

finite
mathematics:
a liberal
arts
approach

Irving Allen Dodes

Professor of Mathematics
Kingsborough Community College
City University of New York

McGraw-Hill Book Company

New York   Mexico
St. Louis   Panama
San Francisco   Sydney
Düsseldorf   Toronto
London

This book was set in Laurel by Graphic Services, Inc., printed on permanent paper by Halliday Lithograph Corporation, and bound by The Maple Press Company. The designer was Marsha Cohen; the drawings were done by AYXA, Inc. The editors were E. M. Millman and Antonia Stires. William P. Weiss supervised the production.

Finite
Mathematics:
A Liberal
Arts
Approach

Library of Congress Catalog Card Number 71-95798

17250

1 2 3 4 5 6 7 8 9 0   HDMM   7 9 8 7 6 5 4 3 2 1 0

*This book is dedicated, with love, to
{Mom}, {'Cile}, {Dot}, {Pam and Eric},
{Lance and Connie}, and the set of friends
who appear in the problems*

One of the happy, unexpected consequences of writing books is the flood of letters from readers all over the world. Some of these letters contain problems to be solved, some contain constructive criticism very useful in revisions, and some contain suggestions for further books.

Many of the letters I have received as an author had concrete suggestions for the following topics: slide rule, computing, PERT, management mathematics, linear programming, and the theory of games. At first, the variety of topics seemed to preclude any unified treatment, but after a while they seemed to fall into a pattern. These topics represented, in the main, mathematical solutions of modern problems solved by the methods usually identified with *finite mathematics*.

"Finite mathematics" is not very well defined. *Books* on finite mathematics usually start with a lengthy treatment of symbolic logic, truth tables, sets, and probability and then proceed to problems in linear programming, the theory of games, and other noncalculus (hence *finite*) applications of mathematics to industry, commerce, and business. Unfortunately, most *courses* in finite mathematics do not get beyond the first half of books on the subject so that these courses are, in reality, largely devoted to problems in finite probability somewhat similar in content (if not in method) to the old unit in advanced algebra. The liberal arts aspect of "In how many ways can seven different flags be run up a flagpole?" eludes me.

In this book, I decided to cut to a minimum all those topics that are mainly of professional interest to a mathematics major. (If a mathematics major takes this course, he has probably had both probability and truth tables elsewhere or will take an advanced course in fields that discuss these professionally.) My purpose was to get to topics more relevant to a liberal arts or business student, e.g., linear programming, the theory of games, Markov chains, PERT, and computing.

The book therefore starts with a discussion of *linear programming* in Chap. 1. Included in this chapter are just those concepts of sets and graphs that are essential to the treatment. The *third* chapter deals with *Markov chains,* but in order to explain them it is necessary to teach, in Chap. 2, some of the elements of probability. With this basis, Markov chains are explainable in terms of the Kemeny tree. At the same time, the opportunity was seized to teach an indispensable tool, *matrices,* used in Chaps. 4 and 5 to illuminate the *theory of games* from what I believe to be a novel approach.

Thus ends the first half of the book. As you can see, it was designed to fit together economically and precisely, containing only those topics that are essential for the attainment of my goal: an understanding of the power of mathematics in solving problems by linear programming, Markov chains, and the theory of games.

The second half of the book emphasizes relevant computation of various kinds. I suppose that many teachers will skip Chap. 6 on the *slide rule,* but I predict that students will read it anyhow. Slide rules have their own fascination, and the engineer is more commonly seen at his desk with a "slipstick" than playing with a computer. I admit that the slide rule is not a modern invention, but its use is modern. At any rate, I retained the chapter because there were so many requests and because not one of the five professional reviewers who examined the manuscript objected to it.

Chapters 7 to 9 deal mainly with applications of mathematics to problems in industry and commerce: savings plans, annuities, amortization, PERT, and forecasting. The first three of these cannot be explained intelligently without logarithms, and so I included Chap. 7 on logarithms for students who have not been introduced to them or who, in the opinion of the teacher, need a review. At the present time it is fashionable to underestimate the power of logarithms in computation. Actually, logarithms were a tremendous achievement in the mathematics of computation. The tables for many business problems are logarithmic in nature, and computers use logarithms for computation. At any rate, most students will have had an exposure to logarithms and will need little more than a refresher. The chapter was included to make this convenient. At the same time, the book contains many optional topics so that time saved here can be devoted to some of those.

As for Chaps. 8 and 9, even mathematicians will find problems in *simulation, PERT,* and *forecasting* new, different, and fascinating.

The second half of the book concludes with Chap. 10 on FORTRAN. The programs are based upon the IBM 360/30. At this time in history, a chapter on computing in a book designed for liberal arts and business students needs no defense.

What was omitted? I deliberately omitted advanced set theory, complex problems in probability and statistics, and truth tables and switching circuits. (I, personally, like all these topics.) Truth tables and the application of truth tables to switching circuits, for example, are fascinating to a student of mathematics and the sciences, but experience leads me to believe that the usual short treatment (1) does not appear to be relevant to the liberal arts or business student and (2) is rarely or never carried through the stream of thought in the remainder of the book in which it is introduced.

No assumptions have been made about the previous training of the students. As I have pointed out, the book is self-contained in this respect, allowing the teacher to skip "old stuff" and substitute other topics wherever this is possible. There is enough material for a one-semester course or a one-year course.

No effort has been spared to make this book useful in a practical, educational situation. There are a great many illustrative problems completely worked out and explained in detail. Answers to the odd-numbered problems are given in the text, for the convenience of students. The Teachers' Manual contains answers to all problems and complete solutions for certain lengthy ones, for the convenience of the teacher. The Teachers' Manual also contains suggested syllabi for various lengths of courses at various levels and some other material which, it is hoped, will make life easier for the teacher.

The text has been read carefully by many teachers and mathematicians. I am especially grateful to my good friend Frank Hawthorne and to the editors and reviewers of McGraw-Hill for invaluable criticisms and suggestions.

Irving Allen Dodes

° In a short course, the sections preceded by an asterisk may be
omitted without loss of continuity.

contents

an
introduction
to
operations
research

A cafeteria near a college sells a delicious 80-item lunch (a plate of beans) for 35¢ at a profit of 32¢, and also sandwiches for 25¢ at a profit of 20¢. The storage bin for beans and sandwiches holds no more than 70 sandwiches and 40 plates of beans for each 40-minute lunch period. The manager must have at least 10 plates of beans and 30 sandwiches to be sold each lunch period in order to meet the minimum requirements of the supplier. There are 90 students in the lunchroom each lunch period, and each one may buy either a sandwich or a plate of beans, but not both. In order to increase his profit, the manager puts in a line of 10¢ candy, each piece of which has a 5¢ profit. He discovers that, in each lunch period, each of the three cashiers spends 1 minute collecting for each sandwich and 2 minutes collecting for each plate of beans (the cashier needs the time to count the beans). If there is any time left over, the cashiers are supposed to sell candy. Each piece of candy takes ½ minute to sell. What combination of beans, sandwiches, and candy will bring about the maximum profit for the cafeteria?

By the end of this chapter, you will know how to solve this involved problem by a very simple method (it sounds harder than it really is). It is one of the kinds of problems solved by a method called *linear programming* in a fairly new field of mathematics called *operations research*. Some other problems involved in operations research are:

Nutrition problems: What is the cheapest way to feed livestock to get the best results?

Transport problems: What is the cheapest way to route ships to pick up cargo and make the largest profit?

Production problems: How many toys shall a manufacturer make each month to avoid excessive storage and yet meet the probable demand?

Buying problems: How much perishable stock, such as eggs, should a store keep to avoid loss of goodwill and yet not lose money on leftovers?

Other problems deal not only with business but also with military strategy, logistics, game strategy, science, and the social sciences. Most of these require rather advanced methods, and we shall not be able to illustrate them. However, the problems we shall demonstrate will show you the general thought behind the solution. That is all we want to do.

First, we shall teach you some exact mathematical language and review some not-too-difficult algebra, so that our conversation can continue pleasantly. (If you know the language of sets and how to plot inequalities, you can skip to Sec. 1.5, where we start the discussion of linear programming.)

1.1   THE LANGUAGE OF SETS

Any collection of objects, people, things, or ideas is called a *set*. For example, {Peter, Paul, Mary} is a set. The members of a set are called its *elements*, and the number of elements in a set is called its *cardinal number*. In this case, the cardinal number of the set is 3. This set is said to be a *finite set*.

From the viewpoint of a mathematician, the important property of a set is that we can determine what is in it and what is not in it. For example, if we consider the set of even numbers, written symbolically as {even numbers},[1] we know that 2 is in it, but 3 and 6½ are not in it. (Therefore, it is a set.)

In some cases we can determine the cardinal number of a set by counting. In the case of the set of even numbers, {even numbers}, we can start counting but we can never finish. Mathematicians call this an *infinite set* and say that its cardinal number is $\aleph_0$ (aleph-null). The Hebrew letter with subscript zero is used to represent the cardinal number of sets in which one can count but never finish counting.[2] We shall deal with finite sets and infinite sets in this book, but not in detail.

Two or more sets may have some elements in common. For example, consider the sets,

Set A = {Peter, Paul, Mary, Pam, Lance}

Set B = {Pam, Eric, Lance, Dorothy}

Lance and *Pam* are in both sets. We call them *common elements* for sets A and B, and we define a new set

Set C = {Pam, Lance}

which is composed only of the common elements. This is called the *intersection* of A and B. We write

$$C = A \cap B$$

which is read "Set C is the intersection of set A and set B," or, more briefly, "C is A intersection B."

We can also define a new set composed of all the *different* elements of sets A and B:

Set D = {Peter, Paul, Mary, Pam, Lance, Eric, Dorothy}

---

[1] Braces, {   }, are used to abbreviate "the set of."

[2] There are other infinities, such as the number of points on a line, which cannot even be counted. You can read more about infinities in a remarkable book by Richard Courant and Herbert Robbins, "What Is Mathematics?", pp. 77–88, Oxford University Press, Fair Lawn, N.J., 1941.

This new set contains all the elements of sets A and B, but no others. It is called the *union* of A and B. We write

$$D = A \cup B$$

which is read "Set D is the union of set A and set B" or "D is A union B." Notice that the symbol $\cup$ looks like the letter U.

definition: intersection

The *intersection* (set) of two or more sets is the smallest set of all *common* elements.

definition: union

The *union* (set) of two or more sets is the smallest set of all *different* elements.

The five illustrative problems that follow are intended to clarify the ideas presented so far.

illustrative problem 1

Two sets are $A = \{$snakes, hedgehogs, newts, worms$\}$ and $B = \{$spiders, beetles, newts, worms, snails$\}$.
(*a*) Draw a diagram for the two sets.
(*b*) What is the intersection set, $A \cap B$?
(*c*) What is the union set, $A \cup B$?
(*d*) What is the cardinal number of each set?

solution

(*a*) See Fig. 1-1.
(*b*) $A \cap B = \{$newts, worms$\}$.
(*c*) $A \cup B = \{$snakes, hedgehogs, newts, worms, spiders, beetles, snails$\}$.
(*d*) The cardinal numbers are A, 4; B, 5; $A \cap B$, 2; $A \cup B$, 7.

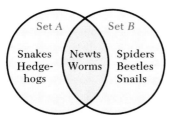

Fig. 1-1   *Illustrative Problem 1.*

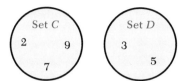

Fig. 1-2   Illustrative Problem 2.

illustrative problem 2

Two sets are $C = \{2,7,9\}$ and $D = \{3,5\}$. Draw a diagram, and find the intersection and union and the cardinal numbers.

solution

(*a*) See Fig. 1-2.

(*b*) $C \cap D = \{\quad\}$. There is nothing in this set. It is called the *null set* or *empty set,* often symbolized by the symbol $\varnothing$. We write $C \cap D = \varnothing$ ("The intersection of sets C and D is the null set").

(*c*) $C \cup D = \{2,7,9,3,5\}$.

(*d*) The cardinal numbers are as follows: C, 3; D, 2; $C \cap D$, 0; $C \cup D$, 5.

illustrative problem 3

Two sets are $F = \{2,4,6,8,10\}$ and $E = \{2,4\}$. Draw a diagram, and find the union and intersection and the cardinal numbers of all the sets involved.

solution

(*a*) See Fig. 1-3.

(*b*) $E \cap F = \{2,4\}$. Note that this is set E, so that $E \cap F = E$.

(*c*) $E \cup F = \{2,4,6,8,10\}$. Note that this is set F, so that $E \cup F = F$.

(*d*) The cardinal numbers are as follows: E, 2; F, 5; $E \cap F$, 2; $E \cup F$, 5.

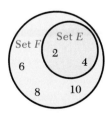

Fig. 1-3   Illustrative Problem 3.

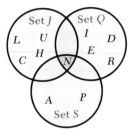

Fig. 1-4 *Illustrative*
Problem 4.

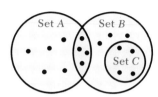

Fig. 1-5 *Illustrative*
Problem 5.

illustrative problem 4

Three sets are $J = \{L,U,N,C,H\}$, $Q = \{D,I,N,E,R\}$, and $S = \{N,A,P\}$. Draw a diagram, and find the intersection and union and the cardinal numbers of the sets.

solution

(*a*) See Fig. 1-4.
(*b*) $J \cap Q \cap S = \{N\}$.
(*c*) $J \cup Q \cup S = \{L,U,N,C,H,D,I,E,R,A,P\}$.
(*d*) The cardinal numbers are J, 5; Q, 5; S, 3; $J \cap Q \cap S$, 1; $J \cup Q \cup S$, 11.

illustrative problem 5

In Fig. 1-5, each dot represents a different element of a set. Find the cardinal number of each set and of the union and intersection of the sets.

solution

Set A has 9 elements. Set B has 11 elements. Set C has 4 elements. The union, $A \cup B \cup C$, has 16 elements. The intersection, $A \cap B \cap C$, is the null set. It has no elements, and its cardinal number is zero.

PROBLEM SECTION 1.1

Part A. Draw diagrams, and find the union, and the intersection, of the following sets.

1. $\{A,B,C\}$, $\{B,C,D\}$
2. $\{F,X,L\}$, $\{X,L,P\}$
3. $\{A,B\}$, $\{C,E,M\}$
4. $\{P,Q\}$, $\{D,R,S\}$
5. $\{A,B,C\}$, $\{C,B,A\}$
6. $\{M,N,R\}$, $\{R,N,M\}$
7. $\{A,B,C,D\}$, $\{B,C\}$
8. $\{R,S\}$, $\{P,Q,R,S\}$
9. $\{A,B\}$, $\{B,C\}$, $\{C,D\}$
10. $\{M,N,R\}$, $\{N,R,S\}$, $\{R,S,T\}$

Part B. In each of the following, find the number of elements in each set (including the union, and intersection sets). Each dot represents an element.

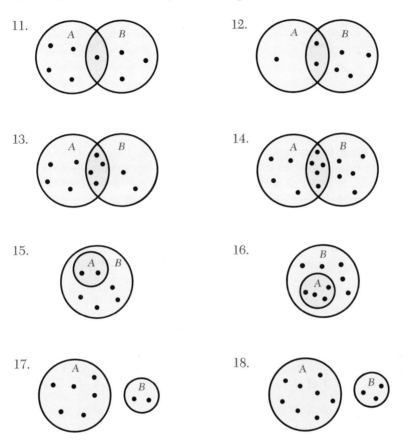

11.

12.

13.

14.

15.

16.

17.

18.

Part C. In each of the following, find the number of elements in each set (including the union, and intersection sets). Each dot represents an element.

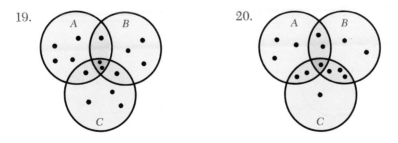

19.

20.

21.

22.

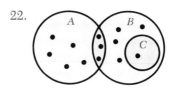

1.2   INCOMPLETE POLLS

Before getting to our main business, we are going to use the ideas of union and intersection to solve a puzzle type of problem. We are doing this in order to practice with overlapping sets.

   The problem is as follows. Someone takes a poll and does not get all the information. Something is missing. If, however, a certain amount of information has been gathered, a mathematician can fairly easily calculate the remaining bit of information. The easiest way to show you exactly what we mean is to show you some illustrative problems and solutions.

illustrative problem 1

An investigator was paid 50¢ per person to ask how many liked the policy of the Republicrats, and how many liked the policy of the Democans. He reported that 15 liked the Republicrats, 24 liked the Democans, and 4 of these liked both. How much money did he earn?

solution (Fig. 1-6)

A diagram shows that there were $15 + 4 + 20 = 39$ elements in the union set. He earned $19.50.

illustrative problem 2

An investigator found, in a poll of 30 people, that 12 people liked only Brand X and 5 people liked both Brand X and Brand Y. Everyone liked

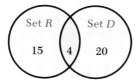

Fig. 1-6   *Illustrative Problem 1.*

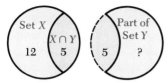

Fig. 1-7   Separating the sets.

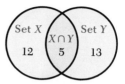

Fig. 1-8   Sets X and Y.

at least one brand. He forgot to find out how many people liked only Brand Y. How many people liked Brand X, how many liked Brand Y, and how many liked both?

solution

From the information we have, we know that the cardinal number of set X is $12 + 5 = 17$. Therefore, there are $30 - 17 = 13$ people unaccounted for (Fig. 1-7). When the information is put together, the result is as shown in Fig. 1-8. From this diagram, we see that 17 liked Brand X, 18 liked Brand Y, and 5 liked both Brand X and Brand Y.

illustrative problem 3

A market investigator found, in a study of 1,200 people, that 582 bought utilities stock, 627 bought automation stock, and 543 bought transportation stock. Of these, 217 bought both utilities and automation, 307 bought both utilities and transportation, and 250 bought both automation and transportation. How many bought all three?

solution

Figure 1-9 shows the number of elements in the "large" sets. Figure 1-10 shows the number of elements in the sets of "pairs." We are interested in the intersection set, which is labeled X.

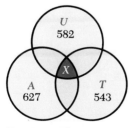

Fig. 1-9   Elements in the large sets.

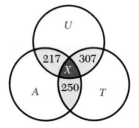

Fig. 1-10   Elements in the sets of pairs.

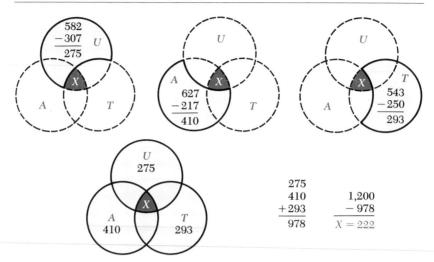

Fig. 1-11   Separating the sets to find set X.

If we separate the sets very carefully, as in Fig. 1-11, we find that the three separated sets account for $275 + 410 + 293 = 978$ of the elements. All the other elements, $1,200 - 978 = 222$, must be in X.

In other words, 222 people bought all three stocks.

PROBLEM SECTION 1.2

Part A

1. In a poll, 12 people voted that they liked round containers, 15 voted that they liked square containers, and 5 of them said that they liked both. If everyone voted, how many people were interviewed?
2. In a certain class, 21 men wore bow ties, 19 wore white shirts, and 3 of these wore both white shirts and bow ties. How many men were there?

Problem 1   *Problem 2*

3. A cafeteria serves one or two vegetables to customers, as they request. On a certain day, the counterman served 16 orders of beans and 14 orders of carrots; he noticed that 4 of these had both beans and carrots. How many customers were there?

Problem 3   Problem 4

4. A dealer found that 25 of his customers looked at four-door cars and 18 looked at two-door cars. Ten of them looked at both. How many customers were there?

Part B. Make your own diagrams for the following:

5. A questionaire study showed that 19 people liked brand A, 18 liked brand B, and 20 liked brand C. Five of these people liked A and B, eight liked B and C, and seven liked A and C. Two people liked all three. How many people were there?

6. A travel bureau reported that, on a certain day, 63 people inquired about trips to Europe, 52 people inquired about trips to the West Indies, and 87 people inquired about trips within the United States. Some inquired about more than one trip; 27 inquired about both Europe and the United States; 25 about the West Indies and the United States; and 12 about both the West Indies and Europe. Ten people inquired about all three. How many people asked questions that day?

Part C

7. A sociology class was asked to interview 52 businessmen to find out whether they would advertise in the college newspaper (set A), the college magazine (set B), or in the Yearbook (set C). The results were as follows: A: 35; B: 23; C: 28; A and B: 15; A and C: 13; B and C: 11. How many businessmen would advertise in all three?

8. Forty-six chemical samples were tested for arsenic (As), lead (Pb), and iron (Fe). It was found that 27 had As, 25 had Pb, and 16 had Fe. Of these, 8 had both As and Pb, 7 had As and Fe, and 10 had both Pb and Fe. How many had all three?

1.3   LINEAR GRAPHS

Most of this section is a review of material you have learned in previous courses. Because graphs are essential throughout our work, we decided to refresh your memory by starting at the beginning and going through the material quickly. You may be able to skip some of it after a brief glance.

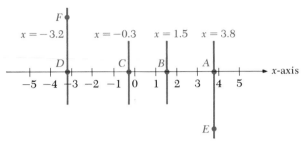

Fig. 1-12   *A real-number line.*

Coordinates

You are probably familiar with the idea of a *real-number line*, such as the one shown in Fig. 1-12. On this line, which extends in both directions without end, each point corresponds to a real number, and each real number corresponds to a point.[1] For example, point A corresponds to the number 3.8 and point D corresponds to the number -3.2. For our own purposes, we shall call this line the *x-axis*.

If we erect perpendiculars at A, B, C, D (these also are endless), we shall agree that every point on each of these lines shares the same x-value. For example, at point E, $x = 3.8$; and, at point F, $x = -3.2$. We can also say that the *x-coordinate* of A or E is 3.8, and the x-coordinate of D or F is -3.2.

Using the same assumptions, we shall draw another real-number line (Fig. 1-13) at right angles to the x-axis. We shall call this the *y-axis*. (It does not matter what the letters are, as long as the diagram is marked properly.) This line is also endless; only parts of lines can be shown in diagrams. The point at which the x-axis and the y-axis meet is called the *origin*.

In Fig. 1-13, point G corresponds to 2.5. At point H, $y = 3.3$. Point I corresponds to -2.7. We shall make the same assumption as we did before and say that, if perpendiculars are erected to the y-axis, every point on each line shares the same y-value. For example, at point F, $y = 2.5$. At point E, $y = -2.7$. We can also say that the *y-coordinate* of points G and F is 2.5, and the y-coordinate of points E and I is -2.7.

Now we shall put the two number lines together (Fig. 1-14). In the figure, we have reproduced points E and F. At point E, $x = 3.8$ and $y = -2.7$ simultaneously. We say that the *coordinates* of point E are $(3.8, -2.7)$. Similarly, the coordinates of point F are $(-3.2, 2.5)$. Note that a *pair* of numbers is needed to locate a point in this figure.

---

[1] Real numbers are the integers (whole numbers), both positive and negative, and all the numbers between them. Some examples are 5.8, π, $-3\frac{3}{4}$.

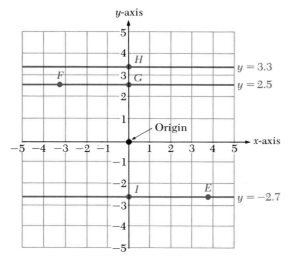

Fig. 1-13   *The two number lines meet at the origin.*

The arrangement shown in Fig. 1-14 is called a *cartesian lattice* (network) in honor of the great French mathematician René Descartes (1596–1650). The figure shows the four *quadrants* into which the plane (flat surface) is divided by the two axes.

We remind you that *every* real-number pair exists on a cartesian lattice. For example, (427, 856) exists on it. The lattice is, in fact, endless even though an actual diagram cannot show this.

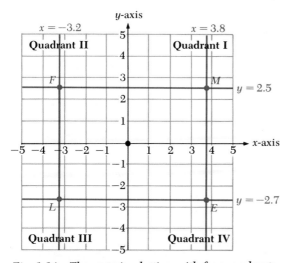

Fig. 1-14   *The cartesian lattice, with four quadrants.*

illustrative problem 1

Give the coordinates of the points marked A, B, C, D, and E in the figure.

solution

A: $(1,2)$; B: $(2,2)$; C: $(3,1)$; D: $(3,4)$; E: $(4,3)$.

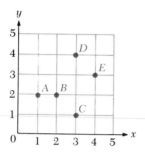

illustrative problem 2

Make a lattice on graph paper and find the following: (a) the line for an x value of 3; (b) the line for a y value of 4; (c) the point $(2,5)$.

solution

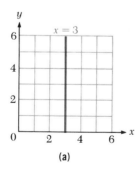

(a)

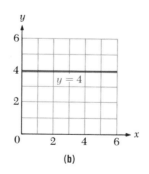

(b)

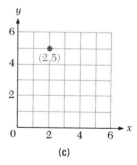

(c)

illustrative problem 3

Find the following lines:

(a) $x = -2$ (b) $x = -1$ (c) $x = 0$
(d) $x = 2.5$ (e) $x = -3\frac{1}{3}$

solution

(See diagram, on page 15, top left.)

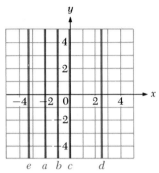

e   a b c   d

Illustrative Problem 3

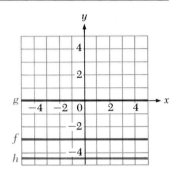

Illustrative Problem 4

illustrative problem 4

Find the following lines:

$(f)\ y = -3$ $(g)\ y = 0$ $(h)\ y = -4\frac{1}{2}$

solution

(See diagram, at right, above.)

illustrative problem 5

Find the following points:

$(i)\ (-2, 3)$ $(j)\ (-4, -1)$ $(k)\ (2.5, -3)$ $(l)\ (3, 4)$

and name their quadrants.

solution

Point i is in quadrant II. Point j is in quadrant III. Point k is in quadrant IV. Point l is in quadrant I.

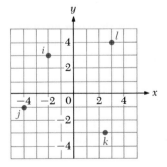

illustrative problem 6

Find the coordinates of the points marked on the lattice in the figure and name the quadrants.

solution

Point m: $(3.5, 1)$, in quadrant I; point n: $(-1, 2.5)$, in quadrant II; point p: $(-3.5, -3)$, in quadrant III; point q: $(4.5, -0.5)$, in quadrant IV; point r: $(2, 0)$, in quadrants I and IV; point s: $(0, -4)$, in quadrants III and IV.

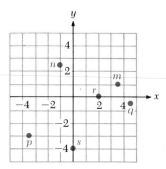

Let us think of one set of numbers, which we shall call y numbers, which depends on some other set of numbers, which we shall call x numbers. For example, here are two sets of numbers which are related:

x	...	0	1	2	3	4	5	...	15	...	1,257	...
y	...	0	2	4	6	8	10	...	30	...	2,514	...

In this example, you can see that the y number is always twice the x number. The mathematician writes this as a *rule* or *formula*:

$$y = 2x$$

Notice that this rule associates *pairs* of numbers: 0 with 0, 1 with 2, 2 with 4, 3 with 6, and so on. These can be written (0,0), (1,2), (2,4), (3,6), and so on. If these are considered to be coordinates, they can be drawn on a graph (Fig. 1-15). The graph turns out to be a straight line. This straight line is called the *graph of the formula* $y = 2x$.

We started with the idea that the value of the y number is double the value of the x number. Let us see how the graph can be used to find a y number if we know the x number. Suppose the x number is $1\frac{1}{2}$, or $x = 1\frac{1}{2}$. Find the line for $x = 1\frac{1}{2}$ on the x-axis (Fig. 1-16); then read up to the graph of $y = 2x$, and across to the y-axis. The correct y number is 3 for this x number.

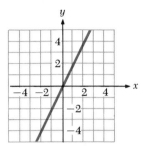

Fig. 1-15 $y = 2x$.

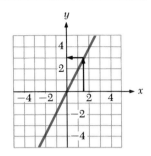

Fig. 1-16   Finding a y
number.

Suppose we *go above* the graph (Fig. 1-17) to position A. Then the value for y will be 4. In other words, y will not be twice x at point A. It will be *greater* than $2x$. The mathematician writes this as

$y > 2x$ (*y is greater* than $2x$)

Figure 1-18 shows the region for which $y > 2x$ always holds. All the y numbers in the region marked are too great for the formula $y = 2x$. (The line in Fig. 1-18 is dashed to show that it does not belong to $y > 2x$.)

Going back to Fig. 1-17, what happens if we travel on the line for $x = 1\frac{1}{2}$ but do not get up to the line? If we stop at point B, this corresponds to a y number of $1\frac{1}{2}$ which is not double the x number. It is too small. In other words, if we are *under* the line,

$y < 2x$ (*y is less* than $2x$)

The graph for this condition is shown in Fig. 1-19.

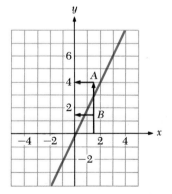

Fig. 1-17   *Going above the
line or below the line.*

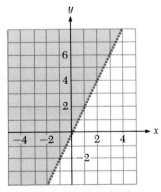

Fig. 1-18   *The graph of
$y > 2x$.*

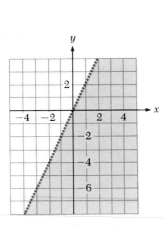

Fig. 1-19   The graph of
$y < 2x.$

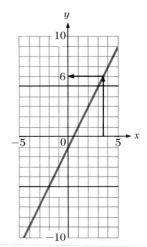

Fig. 1-20 $y = 2x - 1.$

illustrative problem 7

The following table shows how y varies with x:

x	0	1	2	3	4	5	etc.
y	−1	1	3	5	7	9	etc.

(a) What is the rule or formula? (b) Make a graph for this rule. (c) Using the graph, find y when $x = 3\frac{1}{2}$.

solution

(a) The y number is found by doubling the x number, then subtracting 1. In mathematical language, this is written

$$y = 2x - 1 \qquad (y \text{ is 1 less than twice } x)$$

(b) Plotting the points given in the table, the straight line in Fig. 1-20 is obtained. This is the graph of $y = 2x - 1$.

(c) To find the y number when the x number is $3\frac{1}{2}$, locate $3\frac{1}{2}$ on the x-axis, and then read up to the line and across to the y-axis. The correct y number is 6.

illustrative problem 8

Draw the graphs for $y > 2x - 1$, and $y < 2x - 1$.

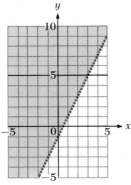

Fig. 1-21 $y > 2x - 1$.

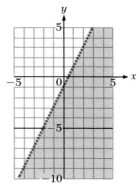

Fig. 1-22 $y < 2x - 1$.

solution

First draw the graph for $y = 2x - 1$ (as done in Illustrative Problem 7). The part *above* the straight line is $y > 2x - 1$. The part *below* the straight line is $y < 2x - 1$. These are shown in Figs. 1-21 and 1-22.

PROBLEM SECTION 1.3

Part A. Make a lattice extending from -6 to $+6$ in both directions, and draw the following lines:

1. $x = 3$ 2. $x = -2$ 3. $y = 5$
4. $y = -2$ 5. $x = 5.5$ 6. $x = -3.5$
7. $y = 4.5$ 8. $y = -1.5$ 9. $x = 0$
10. $y = 0$
11. Find the coordinates of each point in the following lattice, and name its quadrant.

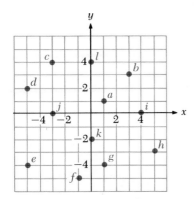

Make a lattice extending from -6 to $+6$ in both directions, and find the following points. Name their quadrants.

12. $(2,5)$ 13. $(3, 4)$ 14. $(-3, +5)$
15. $(-5, 6)$ 16. $(4, 6)$ 17. $(5, -5)$
18. $(-2, -3)$ 19. $(-5, -6)$ 20. $(-2, 0)$
21. $(0, -5)$ 22. $(3.5, -4.5)$ 23. $(-2.5, 5.5)$
24. $(-4.5, -2.5)$ 25. $(-0.5, +0.5)$

Part B. In the following, (a) plot the graph, (b) identify the region where y is too great, and (c) identify the region where y is too small.

26. $y = x + 1$

x	0	1	2	3	4	5
y	1	2	3	4	5	6

27. $y = x - 1$

x	0	1	2	3	4	5
y	-1	0	1	2	3	4

28. $y = 2x + 3$

x	0	1	2	3	4	5
y	3	5	7	9	11	13

29. $y = 2x - 3$

x	0	1	2	3	4	5
y	-3	-1	1	3	5	7

30. $y = -x + 2$

x	-3	-2	-1	0	1	2	3
y	5	4	3	2	1	0	-1

31. $y = -x - 3$

x	-3	-2	-1	0	1	2	3
y	0	-1	-2	-3	-4	-5	-6

32. $y = -3x + 5$

x	0	1	2	3	4	5
y	5	2	-1	-4	-7	-10

33. $y = -3x - 2$

x	0	1	2	3	4	5
y	-2	-5	-8	-11	-14	-17

Part C. In the following, (*a*) discover the rule and (*b*) plot the graph.

34.

x	-5	-3	-1	1	2	4
y	-5	-3	-1	1	2	4

35.

x	-5	-3	-1	0	1	2	4
y	5	3	1	0	-1	-2	-4

36.

x	-3	-2	-1	0	1	2	3
y	-6	-4	-2	0	2	4	6

37.

x	-3	-2	-1	0	1	2	3
y	-9	-6	-3	0	3	6	9

38.

x	-3	-2	-1	0	1	2	3
y	-7	-5	-3	-1	1	3	5

39.

x	-3	-2	-1	0	1	2	3
y	-8	-5	-2	1	4	7	10

1.4 POLYGON GRAPHS

We shall be interested in combinations of statements, of which the following are typical:

1. The amount of V is more than or equal to that of C.
2. The amount of V plus the amount of C is less than or equal to 8.

These two sentences, and others, can (most unfortunately) be said in many different ways in English, and sometimes it is hard to translate from English into mathematical language. To help you, we provide a short "dictionary" of some of the common expressions.

$V \geq C$ (This means $V > C$ or $V = C$.)
     V is greater than or equal to C.
     V is not less than C.
     V is at least as great as C.
$V \leq C$ (This means $V < C$ or $V = C$.)
     V is less than or equal to C.
     V is not more than C.
     V is at least as small as C.
$V \geq 0$ (This means $V > 0$ or $V = 0$.)
     V is greater than or equal to zero.
     V is positive or zero.
     V is not negative.
$V \leq 0$ (This means $V < 0$ or $V = 0$.)
     V is less than or equal to zero.
     V is negative or zero.
     V is not positive.

Before continuing our "dictionary," we shall need to discuss one more graph. We start with the statement that *the sum of V and C is 8*, where V and C are not negative. Some typical values are

V	0	1	2	3	4	5	6	7	8
C	8	7	6	5	4	3	2	1	0

These are graphed in Fig. 1-23. As you can see, this kind of statement leads to a straight-line graph, and so only two points are needed to draw it with a ruler. Usually, the easiest way to find two points is to ask two questions:

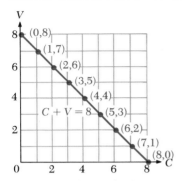

Fig. 1-23 The graph of
$C + V = 8$.

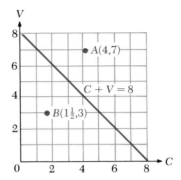

Fig. 1-24 At A, $C + V = 11$;
thus $C + V > 8$. At B,
$C + V = 4½$; thus $C + V < 8$.

1. When $C = 0$, how much is V?   Answer: 8
2. When $V = 0$, how much is C?   Answer: 8

Therefore, $(0,8)$ and $(8,0)$ are on the graph. This is enough information to draw the line.

Now look at Fig. 1-24. We choose a point, A, *above* the line. Notice that for this point $C + V > 8$. If we choose a point such as B, we find that for any point *under* the line $C + V < 8$. If we choose a point *on* the line, of course $C + V = 8$, as shown in Fig. 1-23.

We shall complete our brief dictionary before continuing our discussion of graphs.

$V + C \geq 8$
     The sum of V and C is greater than or equal to 8.
     The sum of V and C is at least 8.
     The sum of V and C is not less than 8.
$V + C \leq 8$
     The sum of V and C is less than or equal to 8.
     The sum of V and C is at most 8.
     The sum of V and C is not more than 8.

illustrative problem 1

Translate into mathematical language and draw the graphs:

(a) There is at least 3 ounces of petroleum jelly (V).
(b) There is no more than 3½ ounces of chopped liver (C).
(c) The chopped liver and petroleum jelly, together, weigh no more than 8 ounces.

Note: From the nature of the problem, V and C cannot be negative.

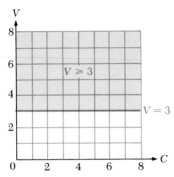

Fig. 1-25 *The shaded region, including the boundary lines, represents V ≥ 3. Note that V is not negative.*

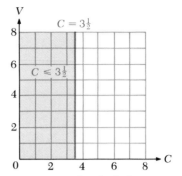

Fig. 1-26 *The shaded region, including the boundary lines, represents C ≤ 3½. Note that C is not negative.*

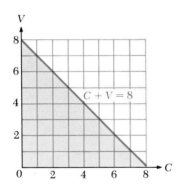

Fig. 1-27 *The shaded region, including the boundary lines, represents C + V ≤ 8.*

solution

(a) $V \geq 3$ (Fig. 1-25)
(b) $C \leq 3½$ (Fig. 1-26)
(c) $C + V \leq 8$ (Fig. 1-27)

illustrative problem 2

Translate into mathematical language and into English the information given by the graphs in Fig. 1-28.

solution

(a) $y \geq 0$; y is not negative.
(b) $y \geq 2$; y is at least 2.

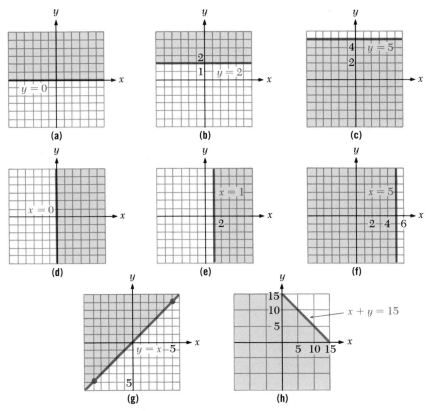

Fig. 1-28   *Illustrative Problem 2.*

(c) $y \leq 5$; y is not more than 5.
(d) $x \geq 0$; x is at least 0.
(e) $x \geq 1$; x is 1 or more.
(f) $x \leq 5$; x is 5 or less.
(g) $x + y \geq 5$; the sum of x and y is at least 5.
(h) $x + y \leq 15$; the sum of x and y is not more than 15.

By making combinations of these graphs, we obtain what are called *polygon graphs*. This is what we have been leading up to throughout the chapter, in preparation for the final problems in the last sections of the chapter. We shall illustrate by three problems.

illustrative problem 3

Assume that condition 1 is $Q \geq 2P$, and condition 2 is $P + Q \leq 75$, where P and Q are not negative. Draw a graph that satisfies *both* conditions, and find some values of P and Q which are satisfactory.

solution (Fig. 1-29)

First we draw one of the graphs, say $Q = 2P$. We can do this easily by finding two points such as $(0,0)$ and $(20,40)$, where the first coordinate is P and the second coordinate is Q. Then we draw the other graph, $P + Q = 75$. We have to decide which region is the correct one. Note that we must be *above* the graph for $Q = 2P$ (including the line, however) and *below* the graph for $P + Q = 75$ (also including the line). In other words, it is quite the same as the intersection of sets which we studied before. The crosshatched part, including the boundary lines, has all the answers. Before giving some samples of answers, let us check one value in each of the four regions to be sure we have the right region. It is very easy to become confused in this kind of work, and checking is so simple that we recommend it for every case. Four points, A, B, C, and D, were chosen, with one in each region of the graph in Fig. 1-29. Let us examine them.

Point A: $(20,15)$. $P = 20$, $Q = 15$. Note that Q is not $\geq 2P$ because 15 is not at least twice 20. Therefore, region A is definitely unsatisfactory.

Point B: $(10,50)$. $P = 10$, $Q = 50$. Note that 50 is more than twice 10, so that condition 1 is satisfied. Also, the sum of P and Q is 60, which is less than 75, so that condition 2 is satisfied. Point B is satisfactory.

Point C: $(20,70)$. $P = 20$, $Q = 70$. Condition 2 is not satisfied.

Point D: $(60,50)$. Neither condition is satisfied.

This quick check shows that the crosshatched region is really the right one. Some other satisfactory points in the region (including the border) are $(20,40)$, $(20,50)$, $(20,55)$, $(5,60)$, and so on.

In the next problem, we show the crosshatched region and leave details (and the check) to the reader.

illustrative problem 4

Make a graph satisfying the following conditions: $y \geq 1$, $y \leq 10$, $x \geq 2$, $x \leq 8$, $x + y \leq 13$, and find the coordinates of the corners (*vertices*) of the figure formed. The figure is called a *polygon*. Without our going into details, a polygon is a flat figure bounded by straight-line segments.

solution (Fig. 1-30)

A check shows that the points *in* and *on* the polygon satisfy all the conditions. The vertices are $A(2,1)$, $B(2,10)$, $C(3,10)$, $D(8,5)$, and $E(8,1)$, and these are also satisfactory, of course.

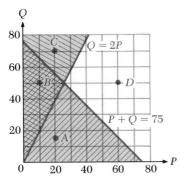

Fig. 1-29   The crosshatched
region represents the intersection
of two sets, {Q ≥ 2P} and
{P + Q ≤ 75}, where P and Q
are not negative.

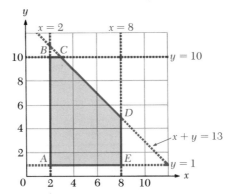

Fig. 1-30   Illustrative Problem 4.

The last of the illustrative problems for this section is much more difficult than anything we shall really need in our operations-research problem. We are using it for review and summary of important procedures and techniques in graphing. We remind you that we are working only in quadrant I simply because our problems (later) will deal only with nonnegative numbers. However, all the techniques we are describing apply just as well to the other quadrants.

illustrative problem 5

Graph the following:

$$y \geq x + 2$$
$$y \leq 3x - 1$$
$$x + y \leq 8$$
$$5x + 2y \geq 20$$

Then find the coordinates of the vertices and one interior point of the polygon.

solution (Figs. 1-31 to 1-35)

We shall do this step by step for a final review. Figure 1-31 is the graph of $y \geq x + 2$. To draw it, we found two points on $y = x + 2$. Any two points would serve (provided they are on the paper). We happened to notice that (1) when $x = 0$, $y = 2$, and (2) when $x = 8$, $y = 10$. We could, just as well, have chosen (1,3) and (5,7) or (2½,4½), or an infinity

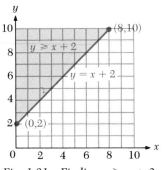

Fig. 1-31   Finding $y \geq x + 2$.

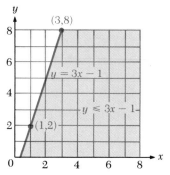

Fig. 1-32   Finding $y \leq 3x - 1$.

of other pairs of points. We could not choose $x = 11$, $y = 13$ only because this point would not fit on the paper as we drew the axes. However, if we had used larger paper, these values would have been perfectly satisfactory. Then we went *above* the graph and crosshatched the region. In actual practice, we would not, of course, separate the graphs like this. We might make a mark or draw arrows to show in which "direction" to go, later on, in forming the polygon.

Figure 1-32 is the graph of $y \leq 3x - 1$. To draw it, we had to find two points for $y = 3x - 1$. We happened to choose (1) $x = 1$, $y = 2$; and (2) $x = 3$, $y = 8$. We might just as well have chosen points like $(2,5)$ or $(2\frac{1}{2},6\frac{1}{2})$. What we are emphasizing is that *any* values you choose are all right. From time to time, you may find it necessary to redraw the axes in order to fit convenient points on it.

Figure 1-33 is the graph of $x + y \leq 8$. First, we drew $y = 8 - x$ (which is the same as $x + y = 8$, of course) by locating the two points $(0,8)$ and $(8,0)$. Other possible points were $(1,7)$, $(2,6)$, $(3,5)$, and so on. Then we crosshatched *under* it. Figure 1-34 is the graph for the last of

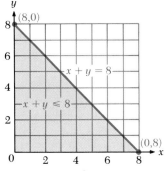

Fig. 1-33   Finding $x + y \leq 8$.

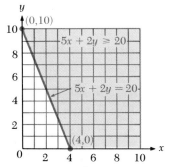

Fig. 1-34   Finding $5x + 2y \geq 20$.

the four conditions, $5x + 2y \geq 20$. We tried to find two easy points by asking (1) when $x = 0$, what does y equal? (*Answer:* $y = 10$ on the graph of $5x + 2y = 20$); (2) when $y = 0$, what does x equal? (*Answer:* $x = 4$ on the graph of $5x + 2y = 20$). To illustrate how to find a point, let us find out what y equals (on the graph of $5x + 2y = 20$) when $x = 1$.

$$5x + 2y = 20$$
$$5(1) + 2y = 20$$
$$5 + 2y = 20$$
$$2y = 15$$
$$y = 7\frac{1}{2}$$

From this, we know that, when $x = 1$, $y = 7\frac{1}{2}$ on the graph of $5x + 2y = 20$. In other words, $(1,7\frac{1}{2})$ is a point on that line. If you check Fig. 1-34, you will see that this is correct. You may wish to practice by finding what y equals when $x = 2$. Check by looking at Fig. 1-34.

In Fig. 1-35, all the graphs are put together, and the intersection of the sets is marked by crosshatching. The vertices are

$A(2,5)$, $B(2\frac{1}{4},5\frac{3}{4})$, $C(3,5)$, $D(2\frac{2}{7},4\frac{2}{7})$

and an interior point is

$E(2\frac{1}{2},5)$

We found point D algebraically by solving a pair of simultaneous equations. Using only the graph, you could probably estimate $D(2.4,4.4)$ which is close.

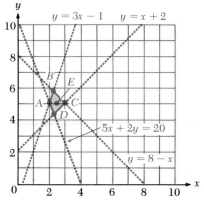

Fig. 1-35   The polygon for Illustrative Problem 5.

The reader should check that all these points (and others in and on the polygon) really do satisfy all the conditions of the problem.

PROBLEM SECTION 1.4

Part A. Graph the following and check the vertices.

1. $y \geq 0$
   $x \geq 0$
   $x + y \leq 1$

2. $x \geq 0$
   $y \geq 0$
   $x + y \leq 2$

3. $y \geq 0$
   $y \leq x$
   $x + y \leq 1$

4. $y \geq 0$
   $y \leq x$
   $x + y \leq 2$

Part B. Translate into mathematical language, graph the result, and check the vertices to see that they satisfy all the conditions.

5. y is not less than x, y is not more than twice x, and the sum of twice x and (one) y is less than or equal to 3.

6. y is at least as large as x, y is not more than three times x, and the sum of x and y is not more than 5.

7. y is at least twice x, y is not more than four times x, and the sum of y and twice x is no more than 7.

8. y is greater than or equal to two times x, y is not more than three times x, and the sum of y and three times x is less than or equal to 6.

Part C. Translate into mathematical language, graph the result, and check the vertices to see that they satisfy all the conditions.

9. y is at least one more than x, y is less than or equal to one less than twice x, the sum of x and y is more than 7, the sum of y and three times x is not more than 18.

10. y is at least one less than x, y is not more than 3 less than three times x, y is less than or equal to 8 more than x, the sum of x and y is not more than 12.

1.5   LINEAR PROGRAMMING (PART I)

We shall introduce this topic by posing a problem which will give us a chance to illustrate and explain, in detail, what linear programming is all about before defining it. In the following problem, the statements are labeled for convenience in the discussion.

illustrative problem 1

(*a*) John Q. Student wants to buy some 10¢ pencils (*P*) and some 5¢ erasers (*E*). (*b*) In the store, for no good reason except that we need it in this problem, he must buy at least 5 pencils and 3 erasers, but (c) no more than 11 pencils and 7 erasers. Also (don't ask us why), (d) the number of pencils and erasers, together, must not exceed 16. (e) Besides this, he decides to get at least as many pencils as erasers. (f) How can he satisfy all the conditions at least cost?

solution

Our first job is to list all the statements in mathematical form. We omit (a) and (f) for the moment; these are *cost* statements which will be used later. The following are the translations of (b) to (e):

(b) $P \geq 5, E \geq 3$
(c) $P \leq 11, E \leq 7$
(d) $P + E \leq 16$
(e) $P \geq E$

This list of inequalities should begin to give you some interesting thoughts. We have graphed them in Fig. 1-36. In the language of operations research, the restrictions on the *numbers* of items are called *constraints*. Figure 1-36, therefore, is a picture of the constraints in this problem.

    We already know that points *in* or *on* the polygon will satisfy the constraints. In this particular case, P and E must be whole numbers because one cannot buy a part of a pencil or a part of an eraser. This means that in Fig. 1-36 there are 29 possible combinations that satisfy the constraints. For example, (4 erasers, 10 pencils) and (5 erasers, 8 pencils) are possibilities. We could solve this problem by finding the cost for the 29 possibilities. The combination (4 erasers, 10 pencils) costs $20¢ + 100¢ = 120¢$, and the combination (5 erasers, 8 pencils) costs $25¢ + 80¢ = 105¢$.

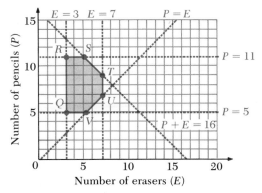

Fig. 1-36   *Illustrative Problem 1: the effect of constraints b, c, d, and e.*

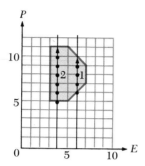

Fig. 1-37 *Traveling up chords 1 and 2.*

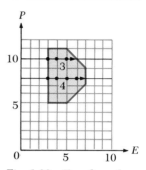

Fig. 1-38 *Traveling along chords 3 and 4.*

We pause for a moment to remark that problems like this one, in which the constraints and costs are on straight lines, are called *linear-programming* problems. They usually (but not always) lead to polygons like Fig. 1-36, at least in practical problems, if there are only two factors involved (here, pencils and erasers).

Instead of proceeding by brute force to test the 29 possibilities, let us make a small investigation of how the costs change in and on the polygon. In Fig. 1-37, we have drawn two vertical lines through the polygon. We are going to travel *up* each of the lines and see what happens. We are interested only in the part of the line that extends from one side of the polygon to another, because the points outside the polygon do not satisfy the constraints. The part of the line that is not outside the polygon is called a *chord*.

As we travel up chord 1, we pass through the points listed in Table I. Notice that along chord 1 the *minimum* cost is at one end and the *maximum* cost is at the other.

Now let us try chord 2 (Fig. 1-37). The results are shown in Table II. Notice that along chord 2 the minimum is, again, at one end and the maximum at the other.

Now, in Fig. 1-38, we consider chords 3 and 4. The results for chord 3 are shown in Table III. You see that the minimum cost is at one

TABLE I. *TRAVELING UP CHORD 1*

Erasers	Pencils	Costs (E)	Cost (P)	Total Cost
6	6	$0.30	$0.60	$0.90
6	7	0.30	0.70	1.00
6	8	0.30	0.80	1.10
6	9	0.30	0.90	1.20

TABLE II.   *TRAVELING UP CHORD 2*

Erasers	Pencils	Cost (E)	Cost (P)	Total Cost
4	5	$0.20	$0.50	$0.70
4	6	0.20	0.60	0.80
4	7	0.20	0.70	0.90
4	8	0.20	0.80	1.00
4	9	0.40	0.90	1.10
4	10	0.20	1.00	1.20
4	11	0.20	1.10	1.30

TABLE III.   *TRAVELING ALONG CHORD 3*

Erasers	Pencils	Cost (E)	Cost (P)	Total Cost
3	10	$0.15	$1.00	$1.15
4	10	0.20	1.00	1.20
5	10	0.25	1.00	1.25
6	10	0.30	1.00	1.30

end of the chord, and the maximum cost is at the other. We leave a detailed investigation of chord 4 to the reader. The result is the same: minimum at one end and maximum at the other.

We may suspect, from this small investigation, that the search for minimum or maximum can be simplified by testing only the boundary lines of the polygon, i.e., points *on* the polygon. We did not *prove* this; we did only a demonstration, but it can be proved. We express this fact as a mathematical theorem.

theorem

If a polygon is formed in a linear-programming problem, with all the constraints satisfied by points inside and on the polygon, then the minimum and maximum values (if they exist) are *on* the polygon.

According to this theorem, we do not have to test 29 values in Illustrative Problem 1. We need test only the values on the boundary lines, namely, 16 values. Let us see whether we can cut this down a little more.

Referring to Fig. 1-36, let us go from R to S and see what happens, and then from S to T and see what happens. The results are shown in Tables IV and V. In each case, you see that one end of a side of the polygon, a *vertex*, is a minimum and the other is a maximum. This is a demonstration of the following theorem:

TABLE IV.   FROM R TO S

Erasers	Pencils	Cost (E)	Cost (P)	Total Cost
3	11	$0.15	$1.10	$1.25
4	11	0.20	1.10	1.30
5	11	0.25	1.10	1.35

TABLE V.   FROM S TO T

Erasers	Pencils	Cost (E)	Cost (P)	Total Cost
5	11	$0.25	$1.10	$1.35
6	10	0.30	1.00	1.30
7	9	0.35	0.90	1.25

vertex theorem

If a polygon is formed in a linear-programming problem, with all the constraints satisfied by points inside and on the polygon, then the maximum values and minimum values (if they exist) are at the vertices.

The parenthetical remark "if they exist" refers to the fact that there are problems in which some values inside the polygon or inside a side of the polygon (not at a vertex) are just as low or just as high as the ones at the vertex, but there are never better or worse choices than those at the vertex points. In other words, it is sometimes possible to do as well (either maximum or minimum) at a point not at a vertex, but never better, if the other conditions of the theorem are met.

According to the vertex theorem, we do not have to test 29 values *in* or *on* the polygon, or the 16 possibilities *on* the polygon, but only 6, at the vertices. This is done in Table VI. The *minimum* is at *Q*. Under all the constraints, and with the costs as given, John Q. Student will

TABLE VI.   TESTING THE VERTICES FOR ILLUSTRATIVE PROBLEM 1

Point	Erasers	Pencils	Cost (E)	Cost (P)	Total Cost	
Q	3	5	$0.15	$0.50	$0.65	✔
R	3	11	0.15	1.10	1.25	
S	5	11	0.25	1.10	1.35	
T	7	9	0.35	0.90	1.25	
U	7	7	0.35	0.70	1.05	
V	5	5	0.25	0.50	0.75	

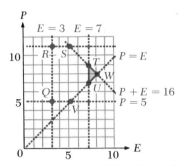

Fig. 1-39   *Case 1: E ≥ 7 instead of E ≤ 7.*

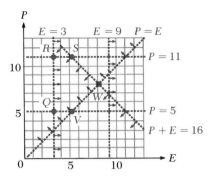

Fig. 1-40   *Case 2: E ≥ 9.*

spend the least by purchasing three erasers and five pencils. The reader should check to see that this solution really satisfies the constraints.

Before leaving this problem (now solved), let us see what would have happened if some of the constraints had been changed.

Case 1. Suppose that, instead of having the number of erasers *less than* 7, the problem had asked for $E \geq 7$. Then the permissible region would be the small triangle shown in Fig. 1-39. Notice carefully that, in this case, three of the constraints, $E \geq 3$, $P \geq 5$, and $P \leq 11$, were *unnecessary*. In fact, for this case, it would have been sufficient to have just three constraints: $P + E \leq 16$, $P \geq E$, and $E \geq 7$. In practical problems, this situation is fairly common. Many of the problems occurring in practical situations are of this kind. In such cases, the effect of this kind of analysis is to simplify the problem by removing unnecessary conditions. In Fig. 1-39, the possible solutions are at points T, U, and W.

Case 2. Instead of having $E \leq 7$, which leads to Fig. 1-36, or $E \geq 7$, which leads to Fig. 1-39, suppose we have $E \geq 9$. The graph is shown in Fig. 1-40. The arrows show on which side of each line the permissible values are found. In this case, there is no polygon that contains the solutions and, in fact, *there are no solutions*. The constraints, in this case, are *contradictory*.

There are other possibilities. The point in discussing these two special cases was merely to emphasize the importance of checking to see that the points chosen really satisfy the constraints.

We are now ready to attack the first half of the problem with which we started the chapter. (We postpone the second half to the next section.) We shall, of course, use the vertex theorem which was demonstrated previously.

illustrative problem 2

(*a*) A cafeteria near a college sells a delicious 80-item lunch (a plate of beans) for 35¢, at a profit of 32¢, and also sandwiches for 25¢, at a profit of 20¢. (*b*) The storage bin for beans and sandwiches holds no more than 70 sandwiches and 40 plates of beans for each lunch period. (*c*) The manager must have at least 10 plates of beans and 30 sandwiches to be sold each lunch period, in order to meet the minimum requirements of the supplier. (*d*) There are 90 students in the lunchroom each lunch period, and each one may buy either a sandwich or a plate of beans, but not both. (*e*) What combination of beans and sandwiches will bring about the maximum profit for the cafeteria? (This is the first part of the introductory problem.)

solution

We start by rewriting the constraints in mathematical language:

(*b*) $S \leq 70, B \leq 40$
(*c*) $S \geq 30, B \geq 10$
(*d*) $B + S \leq 90$

    Figure 1-41 shows the constraints and the permissible polygon. (The reader should check one point inside the polygon to make sure that the three constraints are satisfied.) Table VII shows the calculation of profit at each vertex. In the first line of the table, 10 plates of beans at 32¢ profit yields a profit of $3.20, and 70 sandwiches at 20¢ profit yields a profit of $14.00. The total profit at point A is $3.20 + $14.00 = $17.20 for the lunch period.

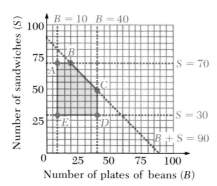

Fig. 1-41   *Illustrative Problem 2.*

TABLE VII

Point	Beans	Sandwiches	Profit (B)	Profit (S)	Total Profit	
A	10	70	$ 3.20	$14.00	$17.20	
B	20	70	6.40	14.00	20.40	
C	40	50	12.80	10.00	22.80	✔
D	40	30	12.80	6.00	18.80	
E	10	30	3.20	6.00	9.20	

Answer: The largest profit is made by selling 40 plates of beans and 50 sandwiches. (Notice that the *least* profit is at point E, with 10 plates of beans and 30 sandwiches, which still satisfies all the constraints.)

PROBLEM SECTION 1.5

Part A °

1. A student is given two sets of problems (S and L). Set S contains short-answer questions worth 3 credits each, and set L contains longer questions worth 7 credits each. The instructions are as follows. Do no more than 14 problems from the two sets ($L + S \leq 14$). Do at least 5 problems from set S ($S \geq 5$) and at least 3 problems from set L ($L \geq 3$). How can the student get the best score if he does not wish to do more than 10 short-answer questions ($S \leq 10$) or more than 6 long-answer questions ($L \leq 6$)?

2. Pam is interested in investing up to $2,000 worth of trust funds in two stocks, Good Gosh Gold and Hello Sucker ($G + H \leq 2,000$). The broker advises her that she can buy $200 to $600 worth of Good Gosh Gold stock ($G \geq 200$, $G \leq 600$), and $600 to $1,500 worth of Hello Sucker stock ($H \geq 600$, $H \leq 1,500$), but she must buy at least twice as much of Hello Sucker stock as of Good Gosh stock ($H \geq 2G$). Hello Sucker stock pays $7 dividend for each $100 of stock, and Good Gosh Gold stock pays $7.50 dividend for each $100 of stock. How should Pam invest her money?

Part B

3. Lance has two tests to study for and cannot spend more than 2 hours (120 minutes) doing the studying. He must use at least 20 minutes for Sanskrit (S) but cannot stand more than 80 minutes of this. He must spend at least 10 minutes on Advanced Sandbox (X), but it does not pay him to use more than 50 minutes on it. He thinks he ought to spend at least as much time on Sanskrit as he does

on Advanced Sandbox, because he dislikes each subject equally. His present average in Sanskrit is a high 55 percent. He estimates that every minute of study will push his Sanskrit average up by ½ point. His present average in Advanced Sandbox is 80 percent (he has a natural talent), and he estimates that every minute of study will raise his Advanced Sandbox average by ⅕ point. What combination of study will raise his average most?

4. An ordinary farmer raises lions (L) and whales (W) on his little farm. He wants to have no more than 400 of these livestock because it takes time to wash them and brush their teeth. Also, he does not want to have fewer than 100 lions or more than 200, and he wants at least 150 whales but not more than 250. Furthermore, the number of whales should be no more than twice the number of lions. It costs $10 a day to raise a lion and $30 a day to raise a whale. Using all these absurd conditions, find the smallest cost per day of running this farm.

Part C

5. A company produces the well-known Beauty and the Beast Skin Ointment which sells for $16.27 (plus tax) for an 8-ounce bottle. Its ingredients are chopped liver (C) and petroleum jelly (V). The chopped liver costs 5¢ an ounce, and the petroleum jelly costs 2¢ an ounce. According to the Poor Food Law, 8 ounces of ointment must have at least 3 ounces of petroleum jelly but not more than 5 ounces, and 8 ounces of ointment must have at least 1 ounce of chopped liver but not more than 3½. The rest is water and does not cost anything. It is found that if there is more than twice as much petroleum jelly as chopped liver the ointment slides out of the bottle, and so the company always makes sure that there is less than twice as much petroleum jelly as liver. On the other hand, if there is less petroleum jelly than chopped liver, it tastes too good and the customers eat it instead of putting it on their skins. This is bad for business, because hardly anyone cares about a beautiful inside stomach. Therefore the company always puts in at least as much petroleum jelly as chopped liver. What is the cheapest mixture that will fulfill all the requirements?

6. A company is supporting a terrible 30-minute TV program called "The Terrible Half Hour." On this program, there is a comedian who tells terrible jokes for a certain number of minutes (J) and a series of commercials for a certain number of minutes (C). According to the station, not more than 20 minutes can be devoted to commercials, but the company insists upon at least 10 minutes of

commercials. The comedian, Mr. Terrible, is worried about his image, and so he insists upon at least 8 minutes on camera, but the sponsor will not let him be on for more than 18 minutes. According to station rules, the company must provide at least 24 minutes of commercials plus jokes, and the time for jokes must not be less than the time for commercials. If any time is left over, the station fills in with harmless announcements which do no good and no harm. A survey shows that every minute of jokes (such as they are) loses 75 customers and every minute of commercials loses 100 customers. What arrangement of time will lose fewest customers?

1.6 LINEAR PROGRAMMING (PART II)

All the problems we have discussed have had two factors: pencils and erasers, sandwiches and beans, and so on. From time to time, it is possible to investigate the effect of a third factor *provided that there are no additional constraints associated with the new factor.* We shall illustrate with two examples, the first of which completes the problem that opened the chapter.

illustrative problem 1

(This is a continuation of the sandwich-bean problem, page 36.) (*f*) In order to increase his profit, the manager decides to sell some 10¢ candy, each piece yielding a 5¢ profit. (*g*) He discovers that, in each 40-minute period, each of the three cashiers spends 1 minute collecting for each sandwich and 2 minutes collecting for each plate of beans (the cashier needs the time to count the beans). (*h*) In the time left over, if any, the cashiers are supposed to keep busy by selling candy. Each piece of candy takes ½ minute to sell. (*i*) What combination of beans, sandwiches, and candy will yield the maximum profit?

solution

First, we note that there is an additional constraint, namely, (*g*), which may limit the sales. Fortunately, this deals only with the beans and sandwiches, and so it must be added to the other constraints on beans and sandwiches. [Statement (*h*) does not constrain the sale of candy because there are no limits, in either direction, on how much candy may be sold. If we were told that the amount of candy had to be restricted in some way, this would have to be taken into account, but then we might not be able to do the problem by a two-dimensional graph.]

Consider that the three cashiers have only 120 minutes of working time for the 40-minute lunch period, so that the time spent selling

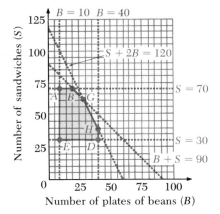

Fig. 1-42 The bean-sandwich-candy problem, completed.

beans and sandwiches cannot be more than 120. But there are 2 minutes spent selling each plate of beans and only 1 minute for each sandwich, so that our new constraint is $1S + 2B \leq 120$. The revised graph, using this constraint, is shown in Fig. 1-42. If you compare this with Fig. 1-41, you will notice that solution C has disappeared. This is so because the cashiers would not have time to collect for 40 plates of beans and 50 sandwiches. This would take 130 minutes (80 for the beans and 50 for the sandwiches) and the cashiers have only 120 minutes.

Now consider point A, where 10 plates of beans and 70 sandwiches are sold. The beans take 20 minutes to sell, and the sandwiches take 70 minutes. This means that the cashiers have used up 90 minutes of the 120 minutes possible. They have 30 "free" minutes. In this time, they can sell 60 pieces of candy. The profit from beans is $10 \times 32¢ = \$3.20$; the profit from sandwiches is $70 \times 20¢ = \$14.00$; and the profit from candy is $60 \times 5¢ = \$3.00$. The total profit is $\$3.20 + \$14.00 + \$3.00 = \$20.20$.

TABLE VIII

Point	B	S	B	S	C	C	Profit (B)	Profit (S)	Profit (C)	Total
			Minutes							
A	10	70	20	70	30	60	$ 3.20	$14.00	3.00	$20.20
B	20	70	40	70	10	20	6.40	14.00	1.00	21.40
G	30	60	60	60	0	0	9.60	12.00	0	21.60 ✔
H	40	40	80	40	0	0	12.80	8.00	0	20.80
D	40	30	80	30	10	20	12.80	6.00	1.00	19.80
E	10	30	20	30	70	140	3.20	6.00	7.00	16.20

The calculation for each point is shown in Table VIII. According to the table, the best result is at point G, where 30 plates of beans, 60 sandwiches, and no pieces of candy are sold, with a total profit of $21.60 for the lunch period. (Of course, if the manager hired another cashier, there would be an additional 40 minutes of time available. In this time, 80 more pieces of candy could be sold.)

illustrative problem 2

Mr. William E. Goat was put on a special diet of cans (C), glasses (G), and old shoes (S) by his kindly doctor. He could mix them to his taste, said the kindly doctor, except that he had to follow certain rules:

1. For the proper mineral content, he had to have at least four cans per day and at least three glasses.
2. He was advised not to have more than nine cans per day, since these would make him rattle, nor more than seven glasses per day, since these would allow people to see through him.
3. The doctor did not want him to stuff himself with more than 14 cans and glasses (together) per day.
4. The doctor insisted that Mr. Goat get at least the minimum vitamin content of 120 units per day. As everyone knows, a can has 15 units and a glass has 10 units, but a shoe has none.
5. To obtain the maximum number of calories, Mr. Goat could eat any combination of cans, glasses, and old shoes, but he could not have more than 17 items of the three per day. As everyone knows, the calorie content of a can is 25, of a glass 20, and of an old shoe 40.

How can Mr. Goat obtain the maximum number of calories and still follow all the rules?

solution

The key to this problem is the fact that the old shoes are not restricted. Therefore, we can concentrate on cans (C) and glasses (G). Figure 1-43 shows the constraints for these two factors.

Table IX investigates each vertex. According to the table, Mr. Goat

TABLE IX

Point	C	G	S	Cal (C)	Cal (G)	Cal (S)	Total Calories	
A	4	6	7	100	120	280	500	✔
B	4	7	6	100	140	240	480	
C	7	7	3	175	140	120	435	
D	9	5	3	225	100	120	445	
E	9	3	5	225	60	200	485	
F	6	3	6	150	60	240	450	

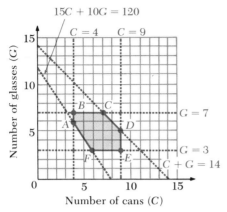

Fig. 1-43   *Illustrative Problem 2.*

will obtain most calories by eating four cans, six glasses, and seven old shoes.

PROBLEM SECTION 1.6

Part A

1. (Continuation of Prob. 1, Problem Section 1.5). Upon thinking it over, the teacher decided to hand out a third set, set P, containing problems worth 12 credits each. Students may take as many of these as they have time for, but the entire test is limited to 120 minutes. If set S questions take 4 minutes each, set L questions take 10 minutes each, and set P problems take 13 minutes each, what is the best combination for the student?

2. (Continuation of Prob. 2, Problem Section 1.5). Just before buying the two stocks, Pam discovers another stock (X) paying $8 for each $100. The broker will sell it to her provided she follows the same rules as before. How should she diversify her investment now?

Part B

3. (Continuation of Prob. 3, Problem Section 1.5). Before sitting down to study, Lance suddenly remembers that he has a little quiz in Chicken Plucking (P) where he has an average of 65 percent. He estimates that every minute spent on this will raise his mark by ⅓ point. Since he has only 120 minutes to study, how can he redistribute his study time to raise his marks the most?

4. (Continuation of Prob. 4, Problem Section 1.5). The farmer finds that

it takes 3 minutes a day per lion and 2 minutes a day per whale. He wants his three helpers to work a full 8-hour day each (a total of 1,440 available minutes of work per day), and so he has to look around for a profitable sideline. After an investigation, he decides to raise unicorns (U) which take 10 minutes a day (they are hard to catch) and cost $50 a day to feed (they have an exotic diet). What is his best plan now?

Part C

5. (Continuation of Prob. 5, Problem Section 1.5). A new law is passed which states that each ounce of water added to the 8-ounce mixture shall be taxable at 12¢ per ounce. What is the cheapest mixture now?
6. (Continuation of Prob. 6, Problem Section 1.5). After thinking it over, the company decides to discontinue station announcement time and add a cultural element. A singing group called "The Fleas" (mostly because of their hair style) is hired. This group can use any time not used elsewhere. This is a tremendous success. Every minute of Flea time (F) loses only 80 customers (the older generation). What is the best arrangement now?

the
mathematics
of
gambling

2222222222

It is the year 1654. The room is large and ornate, and there is a bright shine from hundreds of candles set into chandeliers and wall candlesticks. As you look about, you see many cheerful gambling tables where some less cheerful noblemen, dressed in satins and silks, are playing at such games as dice and cards. One of the gamblers, the Chevalier de Méré, has been taking careful notes, over the years, concerning the "odds" in various games, but now he looks puzzled. He says to himself (in French), "Well, that's a humdinger! I wonder how that is figured out. I think I had better write to some mathematicians."

Students are frequently surprised to find that mathematicians are interested in studying dice throwing, coin tossing, poker, and other games of chance. There is nothing to be surprised about. Life often appears to be a series of events affected by chance. A mathematician merely tries to make some sense out of life by finding out as much as he can about the way chance operates.

We do not know how far back this interest goes (perhaps cavemen bet on sabertooth-tiger races), but the first published works on chance were those by Benvenuto d'Imola (1477), Paciola (*Suma*, 1494), Girolamo Cardano (*Practica*, 1539), and Nicolo Tartaglia (1556). The first systematic study of probability came about when the Chevalier de Méré raised certain gambling questions. It is really remarkable that he realized this was a mathematical problem. The resulting correspondence between Pierre Fermat and Blaise Pascal, in 1654, established the mathematical foundations of the laws of probability. Interest continued and led to such works as those by Christiaan Huygens (*De ratiociniis in ludo aleae*, 1657), Jacques Bernoulli (*Ars conjectandi*, 1713), Abraham DeMoivre ("Doctrine of Chances," 1718), Thomas Simpson ("Laws of Chance," 1740), and Pierre-Simon Laplace (*Théorie analytique des probabilités*, 1812). The number and extent of works since then have grown so much that it is impractical even to list what has happened in the nineteenth and twentieth centuries. Almost every important mathematician, scientist, and social scientist has used the laws of chance to explain the laws of nature.

At least some good has come out of shooting "craps."

2.1 DICE COMBINATIONS

Isolated Events

The easiest game to start with is the dice game. In this game, two dice are shaken (or shuffled) and thrown onto a hard surface. When they bounce back, each die rolls *at random* (if the dice are *fair*). When each die stops rolling, the top face may show any number of spots from a 1 to a 6. The numbers of spots showing on the two dice are now added. The possible results are shown in the following table.

		Second Die					
+		1	2	3	4	5	6
	1	2	3	4	5	6	7
	2	3	4	5	6	7	8
First	3	4	5	6	7	8	9
Die	4	5	6.	7	8	9	10
	5	6	7	8	9	10	11
	6	7	8	9	10	11	12

As you can see, there are $6 \times 6 = 36$ ways the dice can settle down. We say that

Total ways $= 36$

You can also see that each die is *equally likely* to turn up 1, 2, 3, 4, 5, or 6; but the combinations are *not* equally likely. There is little *chance* or *probability* of getting a 2, because there is only one way to get it. There is a much higher *chance* or *probability* of getting a 7, because there are many ways of getting it. If you look at the table, you will see that you can get a 7 by the following possible tosses: $6 + 1$, $5 + 2, 4 + 3, 3 + 4, 2 + 5,$ or $1 + 6$. There are *six* ways of getting a 7. The ways that you get what you are looking for are called *favorable ways,* and so we say

Favorable ways to get a 7 $= 6$

A mathematician measures chance or probability by dividing *favorable ways* by *total ways.*

definition: probability

Probability (or chance) $= \dfrac{\text{favorable ways}}{\text{total ways}}$

It should be fairly obvious that this fraction is always a number from 0 up to 1, or (in percent) from 0 to 100 percent.

illustrative problem 1

What is the chance of rolling a 7?

solution

From the table, the number of favorable ways is 6, and there are 36 total ways. Therefore, the probability is ⁶⁄₃₆ or ⅙. One-sixth is about 17 percent, and so we can say that the probability of rolling a 7 with two fair dice is ⅙ or about 17 percent. One way to think about this is that if you rolled the dice 100 times you would probably get a 7 about 17 times.

Alternative Events

In the previous paragraphs, we were interested in the probability of having one thing happen one time. This is called an *isolated event*. However, we may also be interested in the probability of *alternative* events, i.e., situations where more than one outcome can be considered "favorable." The next problem shows how to deal with this situation.

illustrative problem 2

What is the probability of rolling either a 7 or an 11?

solution

There are six ways of rolling a 7 and two ways of rolling an 11. This makes eight *favorable ways* in all. The total number of ways of rolling two dice is still 36. The probability is now ⁸⁄₃₆ or ²⁄₉. Two times out of nine, the dice should come up *either* 7 *or* 11. This is about 22 percent probability; in 100 rolls of the dice, a 7 or an 11 will turn up about 22 times.

Sequences of Events

Now we can consider a situation where one event follows another, forming a *sequence*. Two successive events may or may not depend on each other. At this point, we are concerned only with *independent events*, i.e., events in which the outcome of the first event does not influence that of the second one. To take a simple example, suppose that there are two roads, road *A* and road *B*, from point 1 to point 2 (Fig. 2-1), and three roads, road *C*, road *D*, and road *E*, from point 2 to point 3. Suppose that the choice of a road in each case is *equally likely;* i.e., it is just as likely that a person will take road *A* as road *B* to get from point 1 to point 2, and it is just as likely that he will take road *C*, road *D*, or road *E* to get from point 2 to point 3, *and his choice of road from point 1 to point 2 does not influence his choice of road from point 2 to point 3.* A list of the sequences is

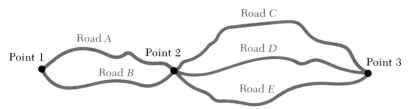

Fig. 2-1   Independent successive events.

$$
\begin{array}{ll}
A \rightarrow C & B \rightarrow C \\
A \rightarrow D & B \rightarrow D \\
A \rightarrow E & B \rightarrow E
\end{array}
$$

making a *total* of six ways. Now we ask about the chance that he will take road *B* followed by road *E*. The answer is obviously ⅙, because there is only *one* favorable way and there is a total of *six* ways, all of them equally likely.

Instead of going about it this way, we might have reasoned as follows:

1. The probability that he will take road *B* is ½.
2. The probability that he will take road *E* is ⅓.
3. The *joint probability* that he will take road *B* followed by road *E* is ½ of ⅓, or ½ × ⅓ = ⅙.

There is an important theorem in the theory of probability which says that we multiply independent probabilities in order to obtain *joint probability*.

theorem for successive independent events

The joint probability of two or more successive independent events is the product of their probabilities.

Remember that for *alternative* events we add, because we are increasing the number of favorable ways.

In order to emphasize the importance of the word *independent* in this discussion, let us change the problem a little so that the two events are *not* independent. Suppose, for example, there is a sign on road *B* which says, "Take road *E*." Suppose, also, that the traveler believes in signs. Then the possibilities are

$A \to C$
$A \to D$
$A \to E \qquad B \to E$

We have removed $B \to C$ and $B \to D$ because they are no longer possibilities. Then the probability of taking road B followed by road E is ¼ instead of ⅙.

illustrative problem 3

What is the probability of getting two 7s in two rolls of the dice?

solution

The probability of getting the first 7 is ⁶⁄₃₆ or ⅙. The probability of getting the second 7 is also ⅙. (Dice have no memory.) The joint probability is ⅙ × ⅙ = ¹⁄₃₆, which is about 2.8 percent. In 100 throws of two dice, we would expect to get two successive 7s about three times.

illustrative problem 4

What is the probability of getting a 2 followed by a 2 followed by a 7?

solution

$$\frac{1}{36} \times \frac{1}{36} \times \frac{1}{6} = \frac{1}{7{,}776}$$

This is approximately 0.00013, or about 13 times in 100,000.

To save you time in doing the problems which follow, we are happy to give you some decimal equivalents which will permit you to use multiplication (instead of division) to convert your fractional answers to percent form, if you are so inclined.

$\dfrac{1}{36}$ 　　　　　　　　　 0.027,777,78

$\dfrac{1}{36} \times \dfrac{1}{36}$ 　　　　　　 0.000,771,604,9

$\dfrac{1}{36} \times \dfrac{1}{36} \times \dfrac{1}{36}$ 　　　 0.000,021,433,47

$\dfrac{1}{36} \times \dfrac{1}{36} \times \dfrac{1}{36} \times \dfrac{1}{36}$ 　 0.000,000,595,374,2

For example, to find ⁶⁄₃₆ × ⁵⁄₃₆, you would multiply 30 by 0.000,771,604,9 and obtain 0.023 . . . or about 2.3 percent.

PROBLEM SECTION 2.1

Part A. How many favorable ways are there of rolling a pair of dice to obtain the sum shown below? What is the probability of doing this?

1. 2	2. 3	3. 4	4. 5	5. 6
6. 8	7. 9	8. 10	9. 11	10. 12

Part B. How many ways are there of obtaining either of the two sums given below? What is the probability of doing this?

11. 5 or 7	12. 8 or 3	13. 2 or 12
14. 6 or 9	15. 4 or 8	16. 2, 4, 6, 8, or 10
17. 3, 5, 7, 9, or 11	18. 3, 6, 9, or 12	19. 4, 8, or 12
20. 5 or 10		

Part C. What is the probability of the following sequences?

21. 3, 5, 11	22. 7, 7, 5
23. 8, 11, 3, 4	24. 12, 9, 6, 3

2.2   TOSSING COINS

Fair Coins

A coin has a *head* and a *tail*. There are two ways a single coin can turn up when you toss it. If the coin is *fair*, the probability of a head is ½ and the probability of a tail is ½. Figure 2-2 shows the situation diagrammatically for a single toss of a single coin. This kind of diagram is often called a *Kemeny tree*, in honor of Prof. John Kemeny of Dartmouth College, who used it to such great advantage in his work on probability.

Now suppose that the coin is tossed twice. You can get two heads (*HH*), a tail and a head (*TH*), a head and a tail (*HT*), or two tails (*TT*). The resulting Kemeny tree is shown in Fig. 2-3.

$$H(\tfrac{1}{2})$$
$$T(\tfrac{1}{2})$$

Fig. 2-2   Kemeny tree for a single toss of a single fair coin.

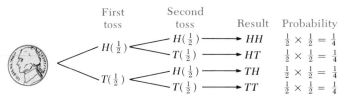

First toss   Second toss   Result   Probability

$H(\frac{1}{2})$ → HH $\frac{1}{2} \times \frac{1}{2} = \frac{1}{4}$

$H(\frac{1}{2})$ → HT $\frac{1}{2} \times \frac{1}{2} = \frac{1}{4}$

$T(\frac{1}{2})$ → TH $\frac{1}{2} \times \frac{1}{2} = \frac{1}{4}$

$T(\frac{1}{2})$ → TT $\frac{1}{2} \times \frac{1}{2} = \frac{1}{4}$

Fig. 2-3   Kemeny tree for two tosses of a fair coin.

illustrative problem 1

In two tosses of a fair coin, what is the chance of getting (*a*) two tails, (*b*) a head and a tail in either order, (*c*) at least one head?

solution (Fig. 2-3)

(*a*) The probability for two tails is ¼, or 25 percent. (*b*) The probability for a head and a tail in either order is ¼ + ¼ = ½, or 50 percent. (*c*) The probability for at least one head is that for $HT + TH + HH =$ ¾ = 75 percent.

    From a mathematical viewpoint, it makes no difference whether you toss *one* coin *twice*, or *two* coins *once*. The Kemeny tree looks the same, but the labels are a little different (Fig. 2-4).

    The Kemeny tree for *three* coins tossed at the same time is shown in Fig. 2-5.

illustrative problem 2 (Fig. 2-5)

In a toss of three fair coins, what is the probability of (*a*) three heads, (*b*) two heads and a tail, (*c*) at least two tails?

solution

(*a*) This is the *HHH* case. The probability is ⅛, or 12.5 percent. (*b*) This is *HHT + HTH + THH*, or ⅜, which is 37.5 percent. (*c*) This is *HTT + THT + TTH + TTT*, or 4⁄8, which is 50 percent.

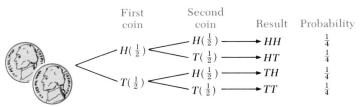

First coin   Second coin   Result   Probability

$H(\frac{1}{2})$ → HH $\frac{1}{4}$

$H(\frac{1}{2})$ → HT $\frac{1}{4}$

$T(\frac{1}{2})$ → TH $\frac{1}{4}$

$T(\frac{1}{2})$ → TT $\frac{1}{4}$

Fig. 2-4   Kemeny tree for a single toss of two fair coins.

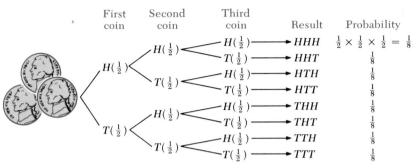

First coin	Second coin	Third coin	Result	Probability
$H(\frac{1}{2})$	$H(\frac{1}{2})$	$H(\frac{1}{2})$ →	HHH	$\frac{1}{2} \times \frac{1}{2} \times \frac{1}{2} = \frac{1}{8}$
		$T(\frac{1}{2})$ →	HHT	$\frac{1}{8}$
	$T(\frac{1}{2})$	$H(\frac{1}{2})$ →	HTH	$\frac{1}{8}$
		$T(\frac{1}{2})$ →	HTT	$\frac{1}{8}$
$T(\frac{1}{2})$	$H(\frac{1}{2})$	$H(\frac{1}{2})$ →	THH	$\frac{1}{8}$
		$T(\frac{1}{2})$ →	THT	$\frac{1}{8}$
	$T(\frac{1}{2})$	$H(\frac{1}{2})$ →	TTH	$\frac{1}{8}$
		$T(\frac{1}{2})$ →	TTT	$\frac{1}{8}$

Fig. 2-5   Kemeny tree for one toss of three fair coins.

Unfair Coins

Suppose that in some way a coin is "loaded" so that it comes up heads most of the time, say, three-fourths of the time. Then the coin is no longer a "fair" coin. On a single toss, we would get the Kemeny tree shown in Fig. 2-6. The numbers in parentheses show, as usual, the probability of the outcome.

$H(\frac{3}{4})$
$T(\frac{1}{4})$

Fig. 2-6   Kemeny tree for a single toss of a loaded coin.

Now, let us toss the same coin again (Fig. 2-7).

illustrative problem 3

In two tosses of a coin loaded so that it comes up heads three-fourths of the time, what is the probability of (*a*) a head and a tail in either order and (*b*) at least one head?

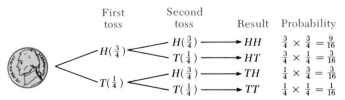

First toss	Second toss	Result	Probability
$H(\frac{3}{4})$	$H(\frac{3}{4})$ →	HH	$\frac{3}{4} \times \frac{3}{4} = \frac{9}{16}$
	$T(\frac{1}{4})$ →	HT	$\frac{3}{4} \times \frac{1}{4} = \frac{3}{16}$
$T(\frac{1}{4})$	$H(\frac{3}{4})$ →	TH	$\frac{1}{4} \times \frac{3}{4} = \frac{3}{16}$
	$T(\frac{1}{4})$ →	TT	$\frac{1}{4} \times \frac{1}{4} = \frac{1}{16}$

Fig. 2-7   Kemeny tree for two tosses of a loaded coin.

solution (Fig. 2-7)

(*a*) This is *HT* + *TH*, or ⁶⁄₁₆, which is 37.5 percent. (*b*) This is *HH* + *HT* + *TH*, or ¹⁵⁄₁₆, which is 93.75 percent.

illustrative problem 4

What is the probability of getting at least two heads when three unfair coins are tossed, if the coins have been loaded so that heads come up three-fourths of the time?

solution

(The diagram is left to the reader.) The favorable outcomes are on the "branches" of the Kemeny tree which result in *HHH*, *HHT*, *HTH*, and *THH*. The probability is ²⁷⁄₆₄ + ⁹⁄₆₄ + ⁹⁄₆₄ + ⁹⁄₆₄ = ⁵⁴⁄₆₄, which is about 84 percent.

PROBLEM SECTION 2.2

Part A. Continue the tree to four coins, and find out how many of the tosses will be (*a*) four heads; (*b*) three heads and a tail; (*c*) two heads and two tails; (*d*) one head and three tails; and (*e*) four tails.

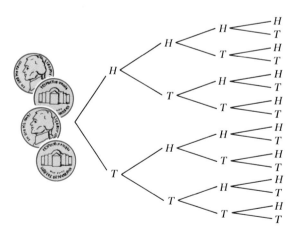

1. What is the probability of getting two heads and two tails?
2. What is the probability of getting all heads?
3. What is the probability of getting at least two tails?
4. What is the probability of getting at least one head?

Part B. Continue the tree to five coins, and make a table of ways. Now find the probability of each of the following:

5. Five heads
7. Three heads, two tails
9. One head, four tails
11. At least three heads

6. Four heads, one tail
8. Two heads, three tails
10. Five tails
12. At least two tails

Part C. We have four slightly loaded coins. Each has been fixed so that it comes up heads 6 out of 10 times. What is the probability of each of the following in one toss of the four unfair coins?

13. Four heads
15. Two heads, two tails
17. Four tails

14. Three heads, one tail
16. One head, three tails
18. At least two heads

2.3 SHUFFLING

You would be very surprised if you shuffled a deck of 52 cards, and someone then guessed their exact order, without looking. Do you know what the probability of this is? It is about 1 in 80,000,000,000,000, 000,000,000,000,000,000,000,000,000,000,000,000,000,000,000,000 (an 8 followed by 67 zeros). This big number represents the total number of ways of shuffling 52 poker cards.

Shuffling Cards

To learn how this was calculated, let us limit ourselves to a small pack of cards.

Suppose we have *two* cards, an ace and a king. Then, after shuffling, we may come up with *AK* or *KA*. Figure 2-8 shows a tree for the two possible results. You will see that there are two shuffles for two cards. (If you guessed the order of the cards, you would be right one-half of the time.)

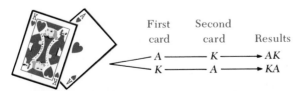

Fig. 2-8 Shuffling two cards.

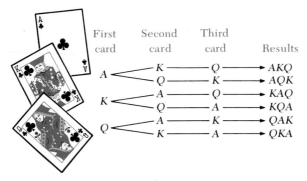

Fig. 2-9   Shuffling three cards.

Suppose we have three cards: *AKQ*. The possibilities are shown in Fig. 2-9. As you can see, there are *six* ways for *three* cards. A guess of the order of the cards would be right one-sixth of the time.

Now, suppose that we have four cards: *AKQJ*. The Kemeny tree is shown in Fig. 2-10. As you can see, there are 24 rearrangements for *four* cards.

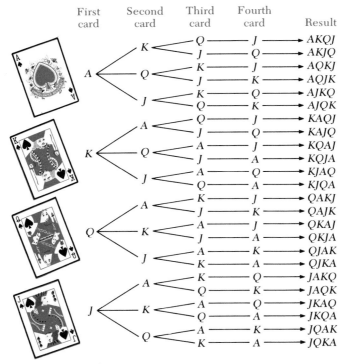

Fig. 2-10   Shuffling four cards.

Notice that for *two* cards, the number of rearrangements by shuffling is 2, which we shall write as 2×1, for reasons which will become apparent presently. For *three* cards, the number of arrangements by shuffling is 6, which we shall write as $3 \times 2 \times 1$. For *four* cards, the number of rearrangements by shuffling is 24, which is $4 \times 3 \times 2 \times 1$. For *five* cards, the number of rearrangements by shuffling would be $5 \times 4 \times 3 \times 2 \times 1 = 120$. Instead of writing the results this way, mathematicians (who deal with large numbers and are inclined to be a little lazy) use *factorial* notation, as follows:

Symbol	Read	Meaning	Result
1!	Factorial 1	1	1
2!	Factorial 2	2×1	2
3!	Factorial 3	$3 \times 2 \times 1$	6
4!	Factorial 4	$4 \times 3 \times 2 \times 1$	24
5!	Factorial 5	$5 \times 4 \times 3 \times 2 \times 1$	120
6!	Factorial 6	$6 \times 5 \times 4 \times 3 \times 2 \times 1$	720

and so on. With this understanding, the number of rearrangements of 52 cards by shuffling is 52!, meaning $52 \times 51 \times \cdots \times 2 \times 1$, yielding the huge number mentioned at the beginning of this section.

illustrative problem 1

What is the probability of guessing the exact arrangement of a set of four shuffled cards?

solution

The total ways of shuffling four different cards is 4!, which equals 24. There is only one favorable outcome (the correct guess). Therefore the probability of a correct guess is ¹⁄₂₄, about 4.2 percent.

Shuffling Roads

You may wonder why this method for finding the number of rearrangements works. Look at Fig. 2-10 again. Doesn't it remind you of the road problem (Fig. 2-1) which started our discussion? For the first card, there is a choice of four "roads," namely, ace, king, queen, or jack. For the second card, there is a choice of only three "roads," because one of the cards has been used. For the third card, there is a choice of only two "roads." For the fourth and last card, there is only one choice left. The situation is like that shown in Fig. 2-11. Using the theorem for successive independent events in Fig. 2-11, we have $4 \times 3 \times 2 \times 1$, or 4! possible selections of roads.

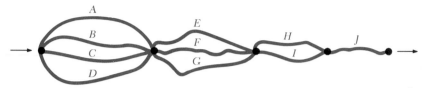

Fig. 2-11   Comparison between card shuffling and road choosing.

The problems are not really the same, but the results are so similar in some ways that we call it to your attention. The following problem is exactly like card shuffling, however.

illustrative problem 2

Three roads, Aberdeen, Brown, and Confoundit, lead from one town to another. In how many ways can one walk along all three roads without going over any road twice?

solution

This merely shuffles the roads, and the answer is 3! = 6 ways. These ways are shown in Fig. 2-12.

Shuffling People

By this time, you may (correctly) suspect that the method for shuffling applies just as well for anything as it does for cards. (Secretly, that is one reason why mathematicians are so interested in this topic.)

illustrative problem 3

How many orders are there of seating Pam, Lance, Eric, and Rita on a straight bench?

solution

We shuffle the four people. The result is 4! or 24 ways.

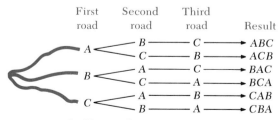

Fig. 2-12   Shuffling roads.

The following problem is a little more difficult.

illustrative problem 4

In Illustrative Problem 3, what is the probability that Pam and Eric will be next to each other?

solution

There are several ways of computing this, but we shall merely list all the possibilities in a Kemeny tree and check the ones that are favorable (Fig. 2-13). There are 12 favorable outcomes out of a total of 24. The probability of the favorable outcome is therefore $^{12}\!/_{24}$, or 50 percent.

Another variation on the shuffling problem is the following.

illustrative problem 5

P, Q, R, S, and T are to be seated on a bench, but P insists upon sitting at one end. How many ways can this be done?

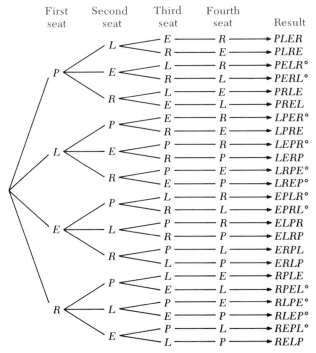

Fig. 2-13 Special seating for Pam and Eric.

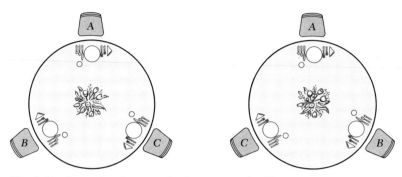

Fig. 2-14 Arranging three people about a round table.

solution

We seat P (there are *two* ways to do this). Now we shuffle the others (there are 4! ways of doing this). Then there are $2 \times 4!$, or 48, ways of accomplishing the rearrangements subject to the condition that P be at one end. (You could draw a Kemeny tree and pick out the favorable outcomes, but that would be harder.)

Round Tables

You might suspect that there are 3! or 6 ways of rearranging three people in seats about a round table, but there are, in fact, only two ways. These two ways are shown in Fig. 2-14.

The reason for the fewer rearrangements is that there are no "ends" at a round table. It is as if the "first seat" had disappeared. Similarly, in rearranging four people about a round table, there are only 3! or 6 ways.

illustrative problem 6

King Arthur and five of his knights are seated at random about his Round Table. How many ways can this be done?

solution

In 5! or 120 ways.

PROBLEM SECTION 2.3

Part A. In how many ways can the following numbers of cards be shuffled, provided they are all different?

1. 5   2. 6   3. 7   4. 8   5. 9   6. 10

Part B

7. A shopkeeper wishes to place five different items in a straight line in his window. How many different ways can this be done ?
8. The chairman of a class committee decides to arrange four posters in a row on the front board before a discussion. How many ways can this be done?
9. An election board is working on the listing of six political parties on a ballot. How many different ways are there of listing them?
10. A player in a word game has seven blocks before him, each one with a different letter. How many different arrangements of the seven letters are there?
11. How many ways are there of arranging eight different beads in a necklace which has no clasp (consider it a round table)?
12. There are six roads between two towns. How many ways are there of going over all the roads, one at a time, without going over any road twice?

Part C

13. How many ways are there of arranging George, Peter, Linda, and Pat on a bench if Pat is to be between George and Peter?
14. If Pat, Mike, Dick, and Jane are arranged on a bench, what is the probability that Jane will be at the left end?
15. P, Q, R, S, and T are to be seated on a bench. What is the probability that P and Q will be at the ends?
16. In Prob. 15, what is the probability that P will be at the left end and Q at the right end?

2.4 EQUAL-SUIT GAMES

The Game of Casino

In some card games, like *Casino,* all suits are the same, so that one king is the same as another, in actual play. How many ways can you shuffle three kings, a queen, and a jack?

You might think that there are $5 \times 4 \times 3 \times 2 \times 1 = 120$ ways, but there are actually only 20 ways, because the three kings are considered the same:

KKKQJ	*KQJKK*	*KKQKJ*	*QKJKK*	*QKKJK*
KKKJQ	*KJQKK*	*KKJKQ*	*JKQKK*	*JKKQK*
KKQJK	*QJKKK*	*KQKJK*	*KQKKJ*	*QKKKJ*
KKJQK	*JQKKK*	*KJKQK*	*KJKKQ*	*JKKKQ*

Note that

$$\frac{5!}{3!} = \frac{5 \times 4 \times \cancel{3} \times \cancel{2} \times \cancel{1}}{\cancel{3} \times \cancel{2} \times \cancel{1}} = 20 \text{ ways}$$

A little experimentation will convince you that, if some of the items are repeated, you have to divide for every repeated item. This *reduces* the number of ways, naturally. If an item appears twice, you divide by 2! which is 2×1. If it appears four times, you divide by 4! which is $4 \times 3 \times 2 \times 1$. Ordinarily, you can simplify the problem by canceling equal factors in the numerator and denominator.

illustrative problem 1

How many ways are there of shuffling three aces, two queens, and a 10, if all the suits are the same?

solution

There are six cards. Using the rule for repetition,

$$\text{Number of ways} = \frac{6!}{3!\,2!} = \frac{6 \times 5 \times \cancel{4} \times \cancel{3} \times \overset{2}{\cancel{2}} \times \cancel{1}}{(\cancel{3} \times \cancel{2} \times 1) \times (2 \times \cancel{1})} = 60 \text{ ways}$$

illustrative problem 2

How many ways are there of shuffling two aces, four queens, three 8s, and a jack, if all suits are the same?

solution

There are 10 cards, in all. Using the rule for repetition,

$$\text{Number of ways} = \frac{10!}{2!\,4!\,3!}$$

$$= \frac{10 \times 9 \times 8 \times 7 \times 6 \times 5 \times 4 \times 3 \times 2 \times 1}{2 \times 1 \times 4 \times 3 \times 2 \times 1 \times 3 \times 2 \times 1}$$

After some careful cancellation, the result is 12,600 ways.

illustrative problem 3

In Illustrative Problem 2, what is the chance that the first card will be a queen?

solution

We are going to do this in two ways: first by applying the rule and then by common sense.

Method 1: We already know that the total number of rearrangements is 12,600. To have a favorable outcome, we must have a queen first. We therefore put a queen on top and shuffle the other nine cards. The possible rearrangements with the queen on top is

$$\frac{9!}{2!\ 3!\ 3!}$$

because there are nine cards to be shuffled, but there are two identical aces, three identical queens (one was removed to be put on top), three 8s, and a jack. The number of favorable outcomes, after the arithmetic is done, is 5,040. Therefore, the probability that the shuffle will end with a queen on top is $5,040/12,600 = \frac{2}{5}$, which is 40 percent.

Method 2: There is another way to look at this problem. We do not care what happens to the cards except for the first one. There are 10 cards, and 4 of them are queens. Therefore, the chances are 4 out of 10 ($= 40\%$) that the first card will be a queen. (As a matter of fact, there are 4 chances out of 10 that *any* card will be a queen.)

If you do the problems in Part C of Problem Section 2.4, try them by both methods, the first one to fix your knowledge of the general rule, and the second to exercise your common sense (and check your answer).

Other Shuffles

The same principle can be applied to other problems, as shown in the following.

illustrative problem 4

How many ways are there to arrange four boys and three girls on a bench, if all girls are the same?

solution

$$\frac{7!}{3!} = 840$$

illustrative problem 5

How many ways are there of rearranging the following letters: Mississippi?

solution

There are 11 letters: one M, four i's, four s's, and two p's. Therefore, the number of ways is

$$\frac{11!}{4!\,4!\,2!} = 34{,}650$$

PROBLEM SECTION 2.4

Part A. In how many ways can the following be shuffled? In each of these problems disregard the suits.

1. Two kings and three queens
2. Three 10s and four 2s
3. One 7 and five jokers
4. Two jacks and four aces

Part B

5. A grocer has ten boxes of cereal, seven of one kind and three of another. How many different arrangements can he make on a shelf?
6. How many different looking ways can a set of twins and a set of triplets be seated, if the twins and triplets are each identical?
7. How many different ways are there of arranging the 10 letters aaeeeiiouu?
8. How many different ways are there of arranging the eight letters mmaaathh?
9. How many ways are there of arranging three identical pennies, and four identical nickels?
10. How many ways are there of arranging two identical roses, five identical lilacs, and two identical gardenias?

Part C

11. In Prob. 1, what is the probability of getting a king first?
12. In Prob. 2, what is the chance of getting a 10 first?
13. In Prob. 3, what is the probability of getting a joker last?
14. In Prob. 4, what is the probability of getting an ace last?
15. In Prob. 3, what is the probability of getting two jokers first?
16. In Prob. 4, what is the probability of getting two aces first?

2.5 PICK A CARD

A magician took a deck of 52 poker cards, shuffled them, and spread them in his hand. "Pick two cards," he said.

illustrative problem 1

What is the probability that the observer will pick two kings?

solution

There are four kings in the deck, and so the chance that the first card will be a king is $\frac{4}{52}$. On the second draw, the first draw being success-ful, there are three kings left in the 51 cards, and so the chance of getting a king is $\frac{3}{51}$. Using the rule for *successive independent events*, the probability of getting two kings is $\frac{4}{52} \times \frac{3}{51} = \frac{12}{2,652}$, which is approximately 45 chances in 10,000.

The following table is for your convenience in doing these problems:

	Product	Approximate Reciprocal
52	52	0.0192
52×51	2,652	0.000,377
$52 \times 51 \times 50$	132,600	0.000,007,54
$52 \times 51 \times 50 \times 49$	6,497,400	0.000,000,154
$52 \times 51 \times 50 \times 49 \times 48$	311,875,200	0.000,000,003,21

Using this table, $\frac{12}{2,652} = 12 \times 0.000,377 = 0.004,52$, or about 45 in 10,000 (which agrees with the previous result).

illustrative problem 2

What is the chance of getting the king of spades followed by the king of clubs when you draw from a full deck?

solution

There is only one way to get the king of spades, and only one way to get the king of clubs, and so the probability is

$$\frac{1}{52} \times \frac{1}{51} = \frac{1}{2,652} = 1 \times 0.000,377 = 0.000,377$$

or about 38 chances out of 100,000.

illustrative problem 3

What is the chance of getting five cards of a red suit, when you draw from a full deck?

solution

There are 26 red cards in the deck of 52 cards.

$$\frac{\overset{1}{\cancel{26}}}{\underset{2}{\cancel{52}}} \times \frac{\overset{1}{\cancel{25}}}{51} \times \frac{\overset{1}{\cancel{24}}}{\underset{2}{\cancel{50}}} \times \frac{23}{49} \times \frac{\overset{11}{\cancel{22}}}{\underset{\underset{1}{2}}{48}} = \frac{253}{9,996} = \text{approx. } 0.025$$

or 25 chances out of 1,000.

PROBLEM SECTION 2.5

Find the probability of the following, assuming that you start with a full poker deck of 52 cards.

1. Drawing three aces.
2. Drawing two jacks.
3. Drawing the 10, jack, and queen of spades.
4. Drawing the 2 of spades and the 10 of diamonds.
5. Drawing four cards of a black suit.
6. Drawing two cards of a red suit followed by three cards of a black suit.
7. Drawing one card of a red suit followed by two cards of a black suit.
8. Drawing one card of a black suit followed by two cards of a red suit.
9. Drawing a five-card flush (all cards in the same suit). (*Hint:* There are 52 ways of drawing the first card, but once this is drawn, there are only 12 ways of matching it on the second draw, 11 ways of matching the third card, and so on.)
10. Drawing any five-card flush, ace high, with the ace first. (*Hint:* There are four ways of picking the ace, but once this is picked, there are only 12 ways of matching the second card, 11 ways of matching the third card, and so on.)

2.6 COMPLICATED GAMES

To end the chapter with a real "bang!", let us investigate a complicated game. Complicated games are more like the ones that turn up in military strategy, in stock maneuvers, and in other "life" games.

illustrative problem

The game is as follows: First, you toss a coin. If the coin turns up heads, you roll a pair of dice. You win if it comes up 6 or 7. If the coin turns up tails, you draw a card from a full poker deck. You win if the card is a picture card. What is your chance of winning this game?

solution

These complicated games are solved by tree diagrams, using the rule of *successive independent events*. The tree is as follows:

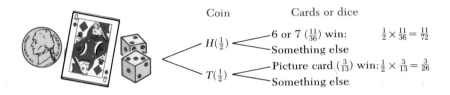

Coin Cards or dice

$H(\frac{1}{2})$ — 6 or 7 ($\frac{11}{36}$) win: $\frac{1}{2} \times \frac{11}{36} = \frac{11}{72}$
Something else

$T(\frac{1}{2})$ — Picture card ($\frac{3}{13}$) win: $\frac{1}{2} \times \frac{3}{13} = \frac{3}{26}$
Something else.

Explanation: For the first branch, the coin (assumed to be fair) has a probability equal to ½ of coming up heads. The probability of getting either a 6 or a 7 with a pair of dice is ^{11}⁄₃₆, as you can see from the table on page 47. The joint probability is ½ × ^{11}⁄₃₆ for the top branch.

For the third branch, the coin has a probability equal to ½ of coming up tails. Also, there are 12 picture cards in a deck of 52 cards, so that the probability of picking a picture card is ^{12}⁄₅₂ or ³⁄₁₃. The joint probability is ½ × ³⁄₁₃ for the third branch.

Adding the winning probabilities, we get ^{11}⁄₇₂ + ³⁄₂₆, which is approximately 0.153 + 0.115 = 0.268. This gives you about a 30 percent chance of winning. To put it another way, you would win 30 games out of 100. For the game to be *fair*, the payoff for a win should be figured out so that 30 wins will balance 70 losses. For example, if the game costs $30 every time you lose, it should pay $70 every time you win. In this way, 30 × $70 = $2,100 = 70 × $30.

PROBLEM SECTION 2.6

Part A

1. In this game, you toss a coin first. If it turns up heads you draw a card from *AAKKK*. You win if you draw an ace. If it turns up tails, you draw a card from *AQQQQ*. You win if you draw an ace. What is your chance of winning?

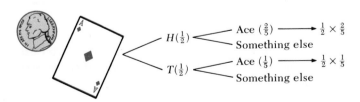

$H(\frac{1}{2})$ — Ace ($\frac{2}{5}$) ⟶ $\frac{1}{2} \times \frac{2}{5}$
Something else

$T(\frac{1}{2})$ — Ace ($\frac{1}{5}$) ⟶ $\frac{1}{2} \times \frac{1}{5}$
Something else

2. In this game, you draw a card from $AKQJ$. If you draw the king, you toss a coin; heads wins. If you do not draw the king, you toss two coins at the same time. Double heads wins. What is your chance of winning?

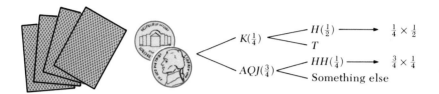

3. In this game, you roll a pair of dice. If you get a 7, you roll the dice again and win on a 5. If you do not get a 7 on the first roll, then you roll the dice again and win on a 4. What is the chance of winning?

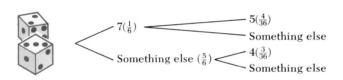

4. In this game, you draw a card from a full poker deck. If it is a 10, you toss a coin; heads wins. If it is not a 10, then you toss two coins at the same time. To win, you must get at least one head. What is your chance of winning?

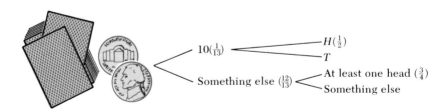

Part B. Make your own tree diagrams, and solve the problems.

5. In this game, you toss a coin. If it turns up heads, you draw one card from JQK; jack wins. If it turns up tails, then you draw two cards from JQK. King and queen (in either order) wins. What is your chance of winning?

6. In this game, first you roll a pair of dice. If it turns up 7, you toss a coin, and heads wins. If it turns up anything but 7, then you toss two coins at the same time. You need at least one tail to win. What are your chances of winning?

7. There are three balls in an opaque jar; one is red, and two are white. You reach in and take a ball. If it is *red,* you reach into a second jar with three red balls and two white balls. A second red ball wins. If the first ball was *white,* you reach into the second jar *twice.* You need *two more white balls* to win. What are your chances of winning?

8. You toss a coin. If it is heads, you draw from a poker deck. Any picture card wins. If it is tails, you draw from a pinochle deck. Any picture card wins. What is the chance of winning? (A pinochle deck has two cards of each suit as follows: 9, 10, *J, Q, K, A.*)

an introduction to matrices

3333333

You already know that a point in two-dimensional space can be represented by a *pair* of numbers, such as $\mathbf{A} = (2,1)$ in Fig. 3-1. $\mathbf{A}$ is called a two-dimensional *row vector*. We shall find it convenient to write the vector vertically, also, as follows:

$$\mathbf{A}^t = \begin{pmatrix} 2 \\ 1 \end{pmatrix} \tag{1}$$

in which case it is called a two-dimensional *column vector*. We indicate that it is vertical by the superscript *t*, which stands for the word *transpose*. (The *t* is *not* an exponent.) We read statement [1] as "$\mathbf{A}$ transpose equals two, one." It is precisely the same vector as $\mathbf{A}$ but is written differently.

In three-dimensional space (Fig. 3-2), a point is represented by a *triple* of numbers, such as $\mathbf{B} = (1,2,3)$. This is, again, a row vector (three-dimensional, in this case). We can write the corresponding column vector as follows:

$$\mathbf{B}^t = \begin{pmatrix} 1 \\ 2 \\ 3 \end{pmatrix} \tag{2}$$

Statement [2] is read, "$\mathbf{B}$ transpose equals one, two, three."

Now we shall consider a table of values, such as Table I. The first column

$$\begin{pmatrix} 80 \\ 90 \\ 70 \\ 80 \end{pmatrix}$$

is a column vector describing the distribution of English marks.

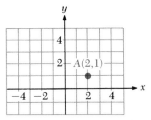

Fig. 3-1   **A** *is represented by a pair of numbers.*

TABLE I.   *GRADES OF FOUR STUDENTS IN THREE SUBJECTS*

	English	Social Science	Math
Peter	80	85	90
Quent	90	85	80
Rob	70	90	80
Sam	80	70	90

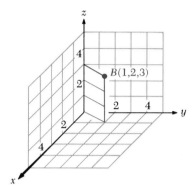

Fig. 3-2 **B** *is represented by a triple of numbers.*

$$\begin{pmatrix} 80 & 85 & 90 \\ 90 & 85 & 80 \\ 70 & 90 & 80 \\ 80 & 70 & 90 \end{pmatrix}$$

Fig. 3-3   A 4×3 *matrix.*

There are two other column vectors in the table. The first *row* (80,85,90) is a row vector describing Peter's marks. There are three other row vectors.

If we remove the top heading and side heading, we have Fig. 3-3 and this is called a *matrix*. As you see, it is the body of a table of values. It is composed of four row vectors and three column vectors; in this case we describe it as a 4×3 ("four by three") matrix, meaning that it has four rows and three columns.

Row vector **A,** which we mentioned before, can be considered a 1×2 matrix, and column vector **B**^{t} can be considered a 3×1 matrix. The plural of *matrix* is *matrices*. In this chapter, we shall discuss an application of matrices (this includes vectors) to problems in business, the sciences, and the social sciences.

3.1   THE SIMPLE EXPLOSION PROBLEM

One of the many things a businessman has to be able to calculate quickly is how much stock he needs to fill an order. Illustrative Problem 1 is a very easy problem, and two methods for doing it are given. The first method is simple arithmetic, perfectly all right for very small problems, but unsatisfactory for more complicated ones. We show it in order to explain the second method.

The process of calculating inventory needs by matrices in order to solve these elementary problems is called *simple explosion*. The word *explosion* comes from the idea that we "explode" an order into its parts. The word *simple* refers to the fact that there is another kind of explosion called *complex,* which we shall not have time to explore.

illustrative problem 1

A small ice cream sundae requires 4 ounces of ice cream and 1 ounce of goo. A large ice cream sundae requires 6 ounces of ice cream and 2 ounces of goo. How much is required for 50 small sundaes and 30 large sundaes?

solution

Method 1: We proceed as in arithmetic. Our ice cream needs are as follows:

Small sundaes	$50 \times 4 =$	200 ounces of ice cream
Large sundaes	$30 \times 6 =$	180 ounces of ice cream
Total		380 ounces of ice cream

Our goo needs are as follows:

Small sundaes	$50 \times 1 =$	50 ounces of goo
Large sundaes	$30 \times 2 =$	60 ounces of goo
Total		110 ounces of goo

Answer: 380 ounces of ice cream and 110 ounces of goo.

Method 2: In the matrix method, we first make a table called an *inventory file*. This is shown in Table II. The matrix associated with Table II is

$$\begin{pmatrix} 4 & 6 \\ 1 & 2 \end{pmatrix} \begin{matrix} \leftarrow \text{ first row vector} \\ \leftarrow \text{ second row vector} \end{matrix}$$

which we shall call **F**, the *inventory-file matrix*. In this case, **F** is a

TABLE II. INVENTORY FILE FOR ILLUSTRATIVE PROBLEM 1

	Small Sundaes	Large Sundaes
Ice cream	4	6
Goo	1	2

2×2 matrix. The *needs* of the businessman are given by a *production vector*,

$$\mathbf{P}^t = \begin{pmatrix} 50 \\ 30 \end{pmatrix} \begin{matrix} \leftarrow \text{ small sundaes} \\ \leftarrow \text{ large sundaes} \end{matrix} \qquad [3]$$

The order of entries in $\mathbf{P}^t$ must be the same as the order in the top heading of the inventory-file table. Now we write the following equation, which we shall explain immediately:

$$\begin{pmatrix} 4 & 6 \\ 1 & 2 \end{pmatrix}\begin{pmatrix} 50 \\ 30 \end{pmatrix} = \begin{pmatrix} 200 + 180 \\ 50 + 60 \end{pmatrix} = \begin{pmatrix} 380 \\ 110 \end{pmatrix} \begin{array}{l} \leftarrow \text{ice cream} \\ \leftarrow \text{goo} \end{array} \qquad [4]$$

$$\;\;\mathbf{F} \qquad\;\; \mathbf{P}^t \qquad\qquad\qquad\qquad\qquad \mathbf{R}^t$$

The *result vector* $\mathbf{R}^t$ gives the number of ounces of ice cream (380) and the number of ounces of goo (110) in precisely the same order as in the inventory file.

Now we shall explain how we arrived at the answer. The first (top) entry in $\mathbf{R}^t$ is obtained by multiplying and adding as follows:

$$(4 \times 50) + (6 \times 30) = 200 + 180 = 380$$

The second (bottom) entry in $\mathbf{R}^t$ is obtained by multiplying and adding as follows:

$$(1 \times 50) + (2 \times 30) = 50 + 60 = 110$$

Notice that we travel along the matrix from left to right, and along the column vector from top to bottom. To get the *first* entry of $\mathbf{R}^t$, we multiply the *first row vector* of $\mathbf{F}$ by the column vector $\mathbf{P}^t$, and to get the *second* entry of $\mathbf{R}^t$, we multiply the *second row vector* of $\mathbf{F}$ by the column vector $\mathbf{P}^t$.

This method of multiplication (involving the multiplication of corresponding entries and then addition) may seem odd. We justify it on the grounds that it gives the right answers. It may seem strange at first, but (after a while) you will get used to it.

The next problem is just another example of multiplication of a matrix by a vector.

illustrative problem 2

If $\mathbf{F} = \begin{pmatrix} 3 & 4 \\ 5 & 6 \end{pmatrix}$, and $\mathbf{P}^t = \begin{pmatrix} 7 \\ 8 \end{pmatrix}$, find the product $\mathbf{F}\mathbf{P}^t$.

solution

$$\begin{pmatrix} 3 & 4 \\ 5 & 6 \end{pmatrix}\begin{pmatrix} 7 \\ 8 \end{pmatrix} = \begin{pmatrix} 21 + 32 \\ 35 + 48 \end{pmatrix} = \begin{pmatrix} 53 \\ 83 \end{pmatrix}$$

$$\;\;\mathbf{F} \qquad \mathbf{P}^t \qquad\qquad\qquad\qquad \mathbf{R}^t$$

It is easy to extend this kind of multiplication to a larger matrix, as in the next problem. See whether you can follow it.

illustrative problem 3

If $\mathbf{F} = \begin{pmatrix} 2 & 3 \\ 5 & 6 \\ 8 & 9 \end{pmatrix}$, and $\mathbf{P}^t = \begin{pmatrix} 4 \\ 7 \end{pmatrix}$, find the product $\mathbf{F}\mathbf{P}^t$.

solution

$$\begin{pmatrix} 2 & 3 \\ 5 & 6 \\ 8 & 9 \end{pmatrix}\begin{pmatrix} 4 \\ 7 \end{pmatrix} = \begin{pmatrix} 8 + 21 \\ 20 + 42 \\ 32 + 63 \end{pmatrix} = \begin{pmatrix} 29 \\ 62 \\ 95 \end{pmatrix}$$

$\quad\quad$ **F** $\quad$ **P**^{t} $\quad\quad\quad\quad\quad\quad\quad\quad$ **R**^{t}

In the next problem, we multiply a 4 × 3 matrix by a 3 × 1 vector, using exactly the same strange rules.

illustrative problem 4

Find the product of the matrix and vector shown below:

$$\begin{pmatrix} 1 & 2 & 3 \\ 6 & 5 & 4 \\ 7 & 8 & 9 \\ 12 & 11 & 10 \end{pmatrix}\begin{pmatrix} 2 \\ 4 \\ 6 \end{pmatrix} = \ ?$$

solution

$$\begin{pmatrix} 2 + 8 + 18 \\ 12 + 20 + 24 \\ 14 + 32 + 54 \\ 24 + 44 + 60 \end{pmatrix} = \begin{pmatrix} 28 \\ 56 \\ 100 \\ 128 \end{pmatrix}$$

Now that (we hope) you know the correct method for multiplying a matrix by a vector, we shall do one more problem involving a simple explosion.

illustrative problem 5

A hardware merchant sells three types of cartons of screws. Type A has one 3-inch screw, six 2-inch screws, seven 1-inch screws and twelve ½-inch screws. Type B has, in the same order, 2, 5, 8, and 11; and type C has, in the same order, 3, 4, 9, and 10. (*a*) Write an inventory file. (*b*) How many of each type of screw would be needed for an order of two type A, four type B, and six type C?

solution

The inventory-file table is shown at the top of page 77 (Table III).

The **F** matrix is, therefore, $\begin{pmatrix} 1 & 2 & 3 \\ 6 & 5 & 4 \\ 7 & 8 & 9 \\ 12 & 11 & 10 \end{pmatrix}$. From the problem, **P**^{t}, the

*TABLE III.   INVENTORY FILE FOR ILLUSTRATIVE
PROBLEM 5*

	Type A	Type B	Type C
3-inch	1	2	3
2-inch	6	5	4
1-inch	7	8	9
½-inch	12	11	10

production vector, is $\begin{pmatrix} 2 \\ 4 \\ 6 \end{pmatrix}$. The product, as shown in Illustrative Problem 4,

is $\begin{pmatrix} 28 \\ 56 \\ 100 \\ 128 \end{pmatrix}$. These are in the same order as the inventory file, so that

the merchant needs 28 3-inch screws, 56 2-inch screws, 100 1-inch
screws, and 128 ½-inch screws.

PROBLEM SECTION 3.1

Part A. (Do these by multiplying matrices by vectors; check by arithmetic.)

1. A company prints fat books and thin books. The fat book requires
   320 pages and a pair of covers. The thin book requires 192 pages
   and a pair of covers. a. Write the inventory file. b. How many pages
   and covers are needed for an order of 100 fat books and 50 thin
   books?
2. A toy company makes two military toy sets, the "Large" (which is
   really small) and the "Super-colossal" (which is medium-sized).
   The Large size has two atom bombs and three tubes of burn ointment, and the Super-colossal size has five atom bombs and seven
   tubes of burn ointment. a. Write the inventory file. b. How many
   atom bombs and tubes of burn ointment are needed for an order of
   25 Large and 20 Super-colossal?
3. A school has commercial and technical classes. Each commercial
   class has 20 women and 5 men, and each technical class has 2 women
   and 18 men. a. Write an inventory file. b. How many men and
   women are there in 10 commercial classes and 12 technical classes?
4. A Swiss manufacturer makes a large knife and a smaller one. The
   large one has 12 blades and 4 bolts, and the smaller one has 8 blades
   and 2 bolts. a. Write an inventory file. b. How many blades and bolts
   would be needed for an order of 100 large knives and 200 smaller
   ones?

Part B

5. A manufacturer makes two sizes of desk lamps. Size 1 has 4 feet of wire, one fluorescent tube, and one switch. Size 2 has 6 feet of wire, two fluorescent tubes, and two switches. a. Write an inventory file. b. How much of each part is needed for an order of 30 size 1 and 20 size 2?

6. A mathematics department is trying to build a file of impossible questions for final tests. The test for the honors classes has 50 short-answer, 10 long-answer, and 5 horribles. The test for the regular classes has 30 short-answer, 5 long-answer, and 2 horribles. a. Write an inventory file. b. How many of each type of question will be needed for 6 honors tests and 8 regular tests?

7. A watch manufacturer makes a cheap watch and an expensive watch. The cheap watch has a steel case, 2 hands, 6 jewels, and 25 gears. The expensive watch has a gold case, 3 hands, 17 jewels, and 30 gears. a. Write an inventory file. b. How many of each part is needed for an order of 500 cheap watches and 300 expensive watches?

8. A hi-fi kit has 12 panels, 2 breadboards, 75 resistors, 60 capacitors, 45 inductances, 8 dials, and 30 feet of wire. A low-fi set has 5 panels, 1 breadboard, 50 resistors, 40 capacitors, 30 inductances, 4 dials, and 20 feet of wire. a. Write an inventory file. b. How many of each part is needed for an order of 10 hi-fi and 20 low-fi sets?

Part C

9. An inexpensive dress takes 3 yards of material, 4 yards of thread, 6 buttons, and 4 pads. A medium-priced dress takes 4 yards of material, 5 yards of thread, 3 buttons, and 2 pads. An expensive dress takes 5 yards of material, 7 yards of thread, and 2 buttons, but no pads. a. Write an inventory file. b. How much of each item is needed to fill an order of 12 inexpensive dresses, 6 medium-priced dresses, and 3 expensive dresses?

10. Type A tool kit has 1 drill, 20 drill points, 4 screwdrivers, 6 pliers, and 5 wrenches. Type B tool kit has 1 drill, 40 drill points, 6 screwdrivers, 8 pliers, and 8 wrenches. Type C tool kit has 2 drills, 60 drill points, 12 screwdrivers, 8 pliers, and 16 wrenches. a. Write an inventory file. b. How many of each part is needed for an order of 20 type A, 10 type B, and 5 type C?

3.2   OPERATIONS WITH MATRICES (PART I)

We have demonstrated one little example of the use of matrices in industry. There are, literally, thousands of examples of the matrix approach in real-life problems. We shall show other applications, one of them (in this chapter) to the problem of *transitions* in the sciences and social sciences. Before doing so, it is necessary that we discuss the arithmetic of matrices. We shall do so in two sections, of which this is the first.

Addition of Matrices

We shall define the *sum* of two matrices as the result when corresponding elements are added, as in the following illustrative problems.

illustrative problem 1

$$\begin{pmatrix} 1 & 2 \\ 3 & 4 \end{pmatrix} + \begin{pmatrix} 5 & 6 \\ 7 & 8 \end{pmatrix} = \begin{pmatrix} 6 & 8 \\ 10 & 12 \end{pmatrix}$$

Explanation: $1 + 5 = 6, 2 + 6 = 8, 3 + 7 = 10, 4 + 8 = 12.$

illustrative problem 2

$$\begin{pmatrix} 1 & 2 \\ 3 & 4 \end{pmatrix} + \begin{pmatrix} -3 & 0 \\ 6 & -7 \end{pmatrix} = \begin{pmatrix} -2 & 2 \\ 9 & -3 \end{pmatrix}$$

illustrative problem 3

$$\begin{pmatrix} 1 & 2 & 3 \\ 4 & 5 & 6 \end{pmatrix} + \begin{pmatrix} -7 & 8 & 9 \\ 10 & 11 & 12 \end{pmatrix} = \begin{pmatrix} -6 & 10 & 12 \\ 14 & 16 & 18 \end{pmatrix}$$

illustrative problem 4

$$\begin{pmatrix} 3 & 5 \\ 7 & 9 \\ 11 & 13 \end{pmatrix} + \begin{pmatrix} 2 & -4 \\ 6 & 8 \\ 10 & 12 \end{pmatrix} = \begin{pmatrix} 5 & 1 \\ 13 & 17 \\ 21 & 25 \end{pmatrix}$$

illustrative problem 5

$$\begin{pmatrix} 1 & 2 \\ 3 & 4 \end{pmatrix} + \begin{pmatrix} 5 \\ 6 \end{pmatrix} = (no\ answer)$$

In Illustrative Problem 5, there is no answer because the elements do not correspond properly. The two matrices in this problem are said to be *not conformable for addition*. If two matrices can be added, as in the other illustrative problems, they are said to be *conformable for addition*.

illustrative problem 6

$$\begin{pmatrix} 8 \\ 9 \end{pmatrix} + \begin{pmatrix} 12 \\ 15 \end{pmatrix} = \begin{pmatrix} 20 \\ 24 \end{pmatrix} \qquad \text{and} \qquad (8,9) + (12,15) = (20,24)$$

Subtraction of Matrices

We shall define the *difference* of two matrices as the result when corresponding elements are subtracted.

illustrative problem 7

$$\begin{pmatrix} 1 & 2 \\ 3 & 4 \end{pmatrix} - \begin{pmatrix} 3 & 5 \\ 7 & 9 \end{pmatrix} = \begin{pmatrix} -2 & -3 \\ -4 & -5 \end{pmatrix}$$

The result can also be written

$$-\begin{pmatrix} 2 & 3 \\ 4 & 5 \end{pmatrix}$$

and it is understood that the negative sign, $-$, applies to *every* element of the matrix that follows.

illustrative problem 8

$$\begin{pmatrix} 1 & 2 & 3 \\ 4 & -5 & 6 \end{pmatrix} - \begin{pmatrix} 3 & 8 & -11 \\ 4 & -6 & 0 \end{pmatrix} = \begin{pmatrix} -2 & -6 & 14 \\ 0 & 1 & 6 \end{pmatrix}$$

illustrative problem 9

$$\begin{pmatrix} 2 \\ 5 \\ -7 \end{pmatrix} - \begin{pmatrix} -8 \\ 3 \\ -6 \end{pmatrix} = \begin{pmatrix} 10 \\ 2 \\ -1 \end{pmatrix}$$

Zero Matrix

A matrix with each element equal to 0 is called a *zero matrix*. Under some conditions, this will arise in an addition, a subtraction, or a multiplication.

illustrative problem 10

$$\begin{pmatrix} 1 & 2 & 3 \\ 4 & 5 & 6 \end{pmatrix} + \begin{pmatrix} -1 & -2 & -3 \\ -4 & -5 & -6 \end{pmatrix} = \begin{pmatrix} 0 & 0 & 0 \\ 0 & 0 & 0 \end{pmatrix}$$

In this problem, if the first matrix is called **A**, the second one will be $-\mathbf{A}$. We can now write

$$\mathbf{A} + (-\mathbf{A}) = \mathbf{O}$$

This is called a *matrix equation.*

illustrative problem 11

$$\begin{pmatrix} 1 & 2 & 3 \\ 4 & 5 & 6 \end{pmatrix} - \begin{pmatrix} 1 & 2 & 3 \\ 4 & 5 & 6 \end{pmatrix} = \begin{pmatrix} 0 & 0 & 0 \\ 0 & 0 & 0 \end{pmatrix}$$

The matrix equation for this is

$$\mathbf{A} - \mathbf{A} = \mathbf{O}$$

Associative Postulate for Addition

For real numbers, we know that

$$(2 + 3) + 7 = 5 + 7 = 12$$
$$2 + (3 + 7) = 2 + 10 = 12$$

so that

$$(2 + 3) + 7 = 2 + (3 + 7)$$

In general, for real numbers,

$$(a + b) + c = a + (b + c)$$

This is called the *associative postulate for addition* (we can "associate" the numbers as we please). As a result of this postulate, when we write

$$2 + 3 + 7$$

we are free to interpret it as $(2 + 3) + 7$ or as $2 + (3 + 7)$. The result is the same. [Note, however, that (Dick + Jane) + John is definitely not the same as Dick + (Jane + John)!]

Fortunately, the same law holds for matrices.

illustrative problem 12

Let $\mathbf{A} = \begin{pmatrix} 2 & 3 \\ 5 & -8 \end{pmatrix}$, $\mathbf{B} = \begin{pmatrix} 3 & -5 \\ 4 & 0 \end{pmatrix}$, $\mathbf{C} = \begin{pmatrix} 1 & -3 \\ 5 & -2 \end{pmatrix}$. Find $\mathbf{A} + \mathbf{B} + \mathbf{C}$.

solution

$\mathbf{A} + \mathbf{B} = \begin{pmatrix} 5 & -2 \\ 9 & -8 \end{pmatrix}$. Adding **C**, we have $\begin{pmatrix} 6 & -5 \\ 14 & -10 \end{pmatrix}$. Instead of this, we may find $\mathbf{B} + \mathbf{C} = \begin{pmatrix} 4 & -8 \\ 9 & -2 \end{pmatrix}$. Adding this to **A**, we have $\begin{pmatrix} 6 & -5 \\ 14 & -10 \end{pmatrix}$, which is (as promised) precisely the same.

Commutative Postulate for Addition

For real numbers, $3 + 5 = 5 + 3$. In general,

$$a + b = b + a$$

This is called the *commutative postulate for addition*. The same law holds for matrices.

illustrative problem 13

Let $\mathbf{A} = \begin{pmatrix} 1 & -2 & 3 \\ -4 & 5 & -6 \end{pmatrix}$ and $\mathbf{B} = \begin{pmatrix} 7 & -8 & 9 \\ -10 & 11 & -12 \end{pmatrix}$. Find $\mathbf{A} + \mathbf{B}$ and $\mathbf{B} + \mathbf{A}$.

solution

Either way, the sum is $\begin{pmatrix} 8 & -10 & 12 \\ -14 & 16 & -18 \end{pmatrix}$.

PROBLEM SECTION 3.2

Part A. In the following, $\mathbf{A} = \begin{pmatrix} 3 & 4 \\ 7 & 9 \end{pmatrix}$, $\mathbf{B} = \begin{pmatrix} 2 & 0 \\ 1 & 8 \end{pmatrix}$, $\mathbf{C} = \begin{pmatrix} 9 & 2 \\ 0 & 4 \end{pmatrix}$.

1. Find $\mathbf{A} + \mathbf{B}$; $\mathbf{A} - \mathbf{B}$.
2. Find $\mathbf{A} + \mathbf{C}$; $\mathbf{A} - \mathbf{C}$.
3. Find $\mathbf{B} + \mathbf{C}$; $\mathbf{B} - \mathbf{C}$.
4. Find $\mathbf{A} + \mathbf{B} + \mathbf{C}$.

Part B. In the following,

$$\mathbf{D} = \begin{pmatrix} 2 & 3 & -5 \\ 4 & -8 & 7 \\ -6 & 0 & -8 \end{pmatrix}, \quad \mathbf{E} = \begin{pmatrix} 1 & -3 & 7 \\ -9 & 5 & 11 \\ 2 & 0 & -4 \end{pmatrix}, \quad \mathbf{F} = \begin{pmatrix} -6 & 8 & 0 \\ 9 & -2 & 3 \\ 4 & 7 & -5 \end{pmatrix}$$

5. Find $\mathbf{D} + \mathbf{E} - \mathbf{F}$.
6. Find $\mathbf{D} - \mathbf{E} + \mathbf{F}$.
7. Find $-\mathbf{D} + \mathbf{E} + \mathbf{F}$.
8. Find $-\mathbf{D} - \mathbf{E} + \mathbf{F}$.

3.3   OPERATIONS WITH MATRICES (PART II)

The Problem of Multiplication

We have already learned a way to multiply a matrix by a vector. We review in the following.

illustrative problem 1

Multiply $\begin{pmatrix} 1 & 2 & 3 \\ 4 & 5 & 6 \end{pmatrix}$ by $\begin{pmatrix} 7 \\ 8 \\ 9 \end{pmatrix}$.

solution

First row →

Second row →

$$\begin{pmatrix} 1 & 2 & 3 \\ 4 & 5 & 6 \end{pmatrix} \begin{pmatrix} 7 \\ 8 \\ 9 \end{pmatrix} = \begin{pmatrix} 7 + 16 + 27 \\ 28 + 40 + 54 \end{pmatrix} = \begin{pmatrix} 50 \\ 122 \end{pmatrix}$$

$$\underset{2 \times ③}{\mathbf{A}} \quad \underset{③ \times 1}{\mathbf{B}^t} \qquad \qquad = \quad \underset{2 \times 1}{\mathbf{C}^t}$$

These
must
agree

The numbers under the letters **A**, **B**^{t} (**B** transpose), and **C**^{t} tell the "shape" of the matrix or vector. In each case, the first numeral tells how many *rows* there are in the matrix, and the second tells how many *columns*. For example, a 5×7 matrix has 5 rows and 7 columns. Notice that the *inside* ones, 3 and 3, agree, and the *outside* ones, 2 and 1, give the "shape" of the product which, in this case, is a column vector.

To multiply a matrix by another matrix (not a vector), we may regard the *second* matrix as a set of column vectors. This is shown in the following illustrative problem, but it is not the method we shall eventually use. We demonstrate it only to show that the other method, in the next section, gives the same result.

illustrative problem 2

First we do the first column:

$$\begin{pmatrix} 1 & 2 & 3 \\ 4 & 5 & 6 \end{pmatrix} \begin{pmatrix} 7 \\ 8 \\ 9 \end{pmatrix} = \begin{pmatrix} 50 \\ 122 \end{pmatrix}$$

First row → $\begin{pmatrix} 1 & 2 & 3 \\ 4 & 5 & 6 \end{pmatrix}$

Second row →

2×3

First column   Second column

$$\begin{pmatrix} 7 & 2 \\ 8 & 5 \\ 9 & 1 \end{pmatrix}$$

3×2

solution

First we do the first column:

$$\begin{pmatrix} 1 & 2 & 3 \\ 4 & 5 & 6 \end{pmatrix} \begin{pmatrix} 7 \\ 8 \\ 9 \end{pmatrix} = \begin{pmatrix} 50 \\ 122 \end{pmatrix}$$

$2 \times 3 \quad 3 \times 1 \quad 2 \times 1$

Then we do the second column:

$$\begin{pmatrix} 1 & 2 & 3 \\ 4 & 5 & 6 \end{pmatrix} \begin{pmatrix} 2 \\ 5 \\ 1 \end{pmatrix} = \begin{pmatrix} 15 \\ 39 \end{pmatrix}$$

$2 \times 3 \quad 3 \times 1 \quad 2 \times 1$

Putting these together in the same order, we have

$$\begin{pmatrix} 50 & 15 \\ 122 & 39 \end{pmatrix}$$

2×2

which is the 2×2 product matrix.

Notice that in both cases the *inner* numbers describing the shapes of the matrices to be multiplied had to be the same, and the *outer* numbers gave the shape of the product matrix. Matrices whose inner numbers are the same can always be multiplied; they are said to be *conformable for multiplication*.

The Inner-product Method for Multiplication

There is another way to do matrix multiplication which is much more practical for large problems. Besides, it is the way that a computer does it.

First, we shall define the *inner product* of two vectors as the sum of the products of corresponding elements.

illustrative problem 3

Find $(2,3,4) \begin{pmatrix} 5 \\ 6 \\ 7 \end{pmatrix}$.

solution

$10 + 18 + 28 = 56$. The result is a 1×1 matrix, 56. We shall follow general practice for a 1×1 matrix and write it without parentheses or brackets. When written this way, mathematicians call it a *scalar.*

Explanation: $2 \times 5 = 10$
$$3 \times 6 = 18$$
$$4 \times 7 = \underline{28}$$
$$56$$

Second, we *locate* the elements of a matrix (Fig. 3-4) by naming its *row* and *column. We always name them in that order: first, row; then, column.*

Third, to find a product matrix, element by element, we merely find the correct inner products, as shown below.

We return to Illustrative Problem 2, where we wish to find

$$\begin{pmatrix} 1 & 2 & 3 \\ 4 & 5 & 6 \end{pmatrix} \begin{pmatrix} 7 & 2 \\ 8 & 5 \\ 9 & 1 \end{pmatrix}$$
$$2 \times 3 \qquad 3 \times 2$$

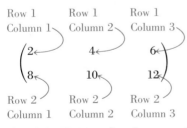

Row 1   Row 1   Row 1
Column 1   Column 2   Column 3

$$\begin{pmatrix} 2 \\ 8 \end{pmatrix} \quad \begin{matrix} 4 \\ 10 \end{matrix} \quad \begin{matrix} 6 \\ 12 \end{matrix}$$

Row 2   Row 2   Row 2
Column 1   Column 2   Column 3

Fig. 3-4 Naming the elements of a matrix.

We know immediately that these are conformable for multiplication (because both inner numbers are 3) and that the product will be a 2×2 matrix. This product matrix will have *four* elements:

First row, first column
First row, second column
Second row, first column
Second row, second column

To find the element in the first row, first column, we find the *inner product* of the first row of the *first* matrix and the first column of the *second* matrix:

$$(1 \quad 2 \quad 3) \begin{pmatrix} 7 \\ 8 \\ 9 \end{pmatrix} = 7 + 16 + 27 = 50$$

To find the element in the first row, second column, we find the *inner product* of the first row of the *first* matrix and the second column of the *second* matrix:

$$(1 \quad 2 \quad 3) \begin{pmatrix} 2 \\ 5 \\ 1 \end{pmatrix} = 2 + 10 + 3 = 15$$

To find the element in the second row, first column, we find the *inner product* of the second row of the *first* matrix and the first column of the *second* matrix:

$$(4 \quad 5 \quad 6) \begin{pmatrix} 7 \\ 8 \\ 9 \end{pmatrix} = 28 + 40 + 54 = 122$$

Finally, to find the element in the second row, second column, we find the *inner product* of the second row of the *first* matrix and the second column of the *second* matrix:

$$(4 \quad 5 \quad 6) \begin{pmatrix} 2 \\ 5 \\ 1 \end{pmatrix} = 8 + 25 + 6 = 39$$

This seems a long way to do it, element by element, but with practice it becomes quite fast. You ask yourself, "Which element am I looking for?" Then you do the multiplications and additions on scrap paper and enter the result in the proper place.

illustrative problem 4

$$\begin{pmatrix} -1 & 5 & 8 \\ 6 & 1 & 9 \end{pmatrix}\begin{pmatrix} 2 & 3 \\ 4 & 5 \\ 6 & 7 \end{pmatrix} = \begin{pmatrix} -2 + 20 + 48 & -3 + 25 + 56 \\ 12 + 4 + 54 & 18 + 5 + 63 \end{pmatrix} = \begin{pmatrix} 66 & 78 \\ 70 & 86 \end{pmatrix}$$

$\quad\; 2 \times 3 \qquad 3 \times 2 \qquad\qquad\qquad\qquad\qquad\qquad\qquad\qquad\qquad\quad 2 \times 2$

illustrative problem 5

$$(-1,5,8)\begin{pmatrix} 2 & 3 \\ 4 & 5 \\ 6 & 7 \end{pmatrix} = (-2 + 20 + 48, \;\; -3 + 25 + 56) = (66,78)$$

$\;\; 1 \times 3 \quad\; 3 \times 2 \qquad\qquad\qquad\qquad\qquad\qquad\qquad\qquad\qquad\quad 1 \times 2$

You may note that a matrix times a column vector (Illustrative Problem 1) yields a *column* vector, and a row vector times a matrix (Illustrative Problem 5) yields a *row* vector. The two situations in Fig. 3-5 are *impossible* because the matrices are not conformable for multiplication.

$$\begin{pmatrix} 7 \\ 8 \\ 9 \end{pmatrix}\begin{pmatrix} 1 & 2 & 3 \\ 4 & 5 & 6 \end{pmatrix} \qquad \begin{pmatrix} 2 & 3 \\ 4 & 5 \\ 6 & 7 \end{pmatrix}(-1,5,8)$$

$\;\; 3 \times 1 \quad\; 2 \times 3 \qquad\qquad 3 \times 2 \quad\; 1 \times 3$

$\qquad\quad (a) \qquad\qquad\qquad\qquad (b)$

Fig. 3-5   *The matrices are not conformable for multiplication.*

illustrative problem 6

$$\begin{pmatrix} 1 \\ 2 \\ 3 \end{pmatrix}(4,5,6) = \begin{pmatrix} 4 & 5 & 6 \\ 8 & 10 & 12 \\ 12 & 15 & 18 \end{pmatrix}$$

$3 \times 1 \;\; 1 \times 3 \qquad\qquad 3 \times 3$

illustrative problem 7

$$(4,5,6)\begin{pmatrix}1\\2\\3\end{pmatrix}= (32) \; = 32 \qquad \textit{This is a scalar.}$$

$1 \times 3 \quad 3 \times 1 \quad 1 \times 1$

illustrative problem 8

If $\mathbf{Q} = \begin{pmatrix} 2 & 0 & 3 \\ 4 & 1 & 5 \\ 1 & 2 & 4 \end{pmatrix}$, find $\mathbf{Q}^2$.

solution

$$\begin{pmatrix} 2 & 0 & 3 \\ 4 & 1 & 5 \\ 1 & 2 & 4 \end{pmatrix}\begin{pmatrix} 2 & 0 & 3 \\ 4 & 1 & 5 \\ 1 & 2 & 4 \end{pmatrix} = \begin{pmatrix} 4+0+3 & 0+0+6 & 6+0+12 \\ 8+4+5 & 0+1+10 & 12+5+20 \\ 2+8+4 & 0+2+8 & 3+10+16 \end{pmatrix}$$

$\qquad 3 \times 3 \qquad\quad 3 \times 3$

$$= \begin{pmatrix} 7 & 6 & 18 \\ 17 & 11 & 37 \\ 14 & 10 & 29 \end{pmatrix}$$

$\qquad\qquad 3 \times 3$

Identity Matrix

The following illustrative problems introduce you to a special kind of matrix.

illustrative problem 9

$$\begin{pmatrix} 1 & 2 & 3 \\ 4 & 5 & 6 \\ 7 & 8 & 9 \end{pmatrix}\begin{pmatrix} 1 & 0 & 0 \\ 0 & 1 & 0 \\ 0 & 0 & 1 \end{pmatrix} = \begin{pmatrix} 1 & 2 & 3 \\ 4 & 5 & 6 \\ 7 & 8 & 9 \end{pmatrix}$$

illustrative problem 10

$$\begin{pmatrix} 1 & 0 & 0 \\ 0 & 1 & 0 \\ 0 & 0 & 1 \end{pmatrix}\begin{pmatrix} 1 & 2 & 3 \\ 4 & 5 & 6 \\ 7 & 8 & 9 \end{pmatrix} = \begin{pmatrix} 1 & 2 & 3 \\ 4 & 5 & 6 \\ 7 & 8 & 9 \end{pmatrix}$$

illustrative problem 11

$$\begin{pmatrix} 1 & 0 \\ 0 & 1 \end{pmatrix}\begin{pmatrix} 3 & 5 \\ 7 & -9 \end{pmatrix} = \begin{pmatrix} 3 & 5 \\ 7 & -9 \end{pmatrix}$$

illustrative problem 12

$$\begin{pmatrix} 3 & 5 \\ 7 & -9 \end{pmatrix}\begin{pmatrix} 1 & 0 \\ 0 & 1 \end{pmatrix} = \begin{pmatrix} 3 & 5 \\ 7 & -9 \end{pmatrix}$$

In Illustrative Problem 9, we may write the matrix equation as

AI = A

where **I** is the matrix with 1s in its *principal diagonal* (the diagonal from top left to bottom right) and 0s everywhere else. Similarly, in Illustrative Problem 10, we may write the matrix equation as

IA = A

from which we may conclude that

AI = IA = A

In Illustrative Problems 11 and 12, we have

BI = IB = B

where **I** is, once again, the matrix with 1s in the principal diagonal and 0s everywhere else. Note that an **I** *matrix,* which we call an *identity matrix,* is not always the same. In one case that we demonstrated, it was 3×3, and in the other it was 2×2. The fact is that there is an entire set of identity matrices with 1s in the principal diagonal and 0s elsewhere, and they all have the property that

MI = IM = M

where **M** is a conformable square matrix. The identity matrix acts like a 1 in ordinary arithmetic, just as the zero matrix acts like a 0 in ordinary arithmetic.

Associative Postulate for Multiplication

In ordinary arithmetic $(2 \times 3) \times 7 = 6 \times 7 = 42$, and $2 \times (3 \times 7) = 2 \times 21 = 42$. Therefore, the expression

$$2 \times 3 \times 7$$

may be interpreted as $(2 \times 3) \times 7$ or as $2 \times (3 \times 7)$. In general,

$$abc = (ab)c = a(bc)$$

This fact is called the *associative postulate for multiplication,* because we can "associate" pairs of numbers in multiplication as we please.

The same thing is true for matrices, fortunately, so that the product of three matrices, **ABC**, can be interpreted as **(AB)C** or as **A(BC)**.

illustrative problem 13

$$\mathbf{A} = \begin{pmatrix} 1 & 2 \\ 3 & 4 \end{pmatrix}, \mathbf{B} = \begin{pmatrix} 0 & 1 \\ 4 & 6 \end{pmatrix}, \mathbf{C} = \begin{pmatrix} 1 & 0 \\ 3 & 5 \end{pmatrix}.$$ Find **ABC**.

solution

Method 1: $\mathbf{AB} = \begin{pmatrix} 8 & 13 \\ 16 & 27 \end{pmatrix}$. Then

$$(\mathbf{AB})\mathbf{C} = \begin{pmatrix} 8 & 13 \\ 16 & 27 \end{pmatrix} \begin{pmatrix} 1 & 0 \\ 3 & 5 \end{pmatrix} = \begin{pmatrix} 47 & 65 \\ 97 & 135 \end{pmatrix}$$

Method 2: $\mathbf{BC} = \begin{pmatrix} 3 & 5 \\ 22 & 30 \end{pmatrix}$

$$\mathbf{A}(\mathbf{BC}) = \begin{pmatrix} 1 & 2 \\ 3 & 4 \end{pmatrix} \begin{pmatrix} 3 & 5 \\ 22 & 30 \end{pmatrix} = \begin{pmatrix} 47 & 65 \\ 97 & 135 \end{pmatrix}$$

No Commutative Postulate for Multiplication

In ordinary arithmetic, $2 \times 3 = 6$, and $3 \times 2 = 6$. This is called the *commutative postulate for multiplication.* We have already noted that, if **M** and **I** are square matrices,

MI = IM

This may lead to a suspicion that **AB = BA**, at least for square matrices. Unfortunately, this is not true, as shown in the following illustration, and therefore it is most important that in doing multiplication problems the *order* of the matrices be kept unchanged.

illustrative problem 14

$$\mathbf{A} = \begin{pmatrix} 2 & 4 \\ 6 & 8 \end{pmatrix}, \mathbf{B} = \begin{pmatrix} 1 & 3 \\ 5 & 7 \end{pmatrix}.$$ Find **AB** and **BA**.

solution

$$\mathbf{AB} = \begin{pmatrix} 2 & 4 \\ 6 & 8 \end{pmatrix} \begin{pmatrix} 1 & 3 \\ 5 & 7 \end{pmatrix} = \begin{pmatrix} 22 & 34 \\ 46 & 74 \end{pmatrix}$$

$$\mathbf{BA} = \begin{pmatrix} 1 & 3 \\ 5 & 7 \end{pmatrix} \begin{pmatrix} 2 & 4 \\ 6 & 8 \end{pmatrix} = \begin{pmatrix} 20 & 28 \\ 52 & 76 \end{pmatrix}$$

illustrative problem 15

Is $\mathbf{QQ}^2$ the same as $\mathbf{Q}^2\mathbf{Q}$?

solution

As a result of Illustrative Problem 14, there is a strong temptation to say, immediately, that they may not be the same. However, $\mathbf{Q}^2$ is just a shorthand symbol for $\mathbf{QQ}$, so that what we are asking here is whether $(\mathbf{Q})(\mathbf{QQ})$ is the same as $(\mathbf{QQ})(\mathbf{Q})$. Of course they are, not because of the commutative postulate (which does *not* hold), but because of the associative postulate (which *does*).

In the Problem Section, we shall deal only with square matrices because these are the ones that will occur in the useful problems we are going to explain. This is probably your introduction to matrix multiplication; we assure you that (1) you have our sympathy and (2) the pain goes away after a while. Besides, the problems that you can do with matrices are absolutely fascinating!

PROBLEM SECTION 3.3

Part A. $\mathbf{A} = \begin{pmatrix} 2 & 0 \\ 3 & 5 \end{pmatrix}$, $\mathbf{B} = \begin{pmatrix} 0 & 1 \\ 3 & 1 \end{pmatrix}$, $\mathbf{C} = \begin{pmatrix} 2 & 3 \\ 1 & 0 \end{pmatrix}$.

  1. Find $\mathbf{AB}$ and $\mathbf{BA}$.
  2. Find $\mathbf{AC}$ and $\mathbf{CA}$.
  3. Find $\mathbf{BC}$ and $\mathbf{CB}$.
  4. Find $(\mathbf{AB})\mathbf{C}$ and $\mathbf{A}(\mathbf{BC})$.

Part B. $\mathbf{D} = \begin{pmatrix} 1 & 0 & 2 \\ 0 & 3 & 4 \\ 5 & 6 & 0 \end{pmatrix}$, $\mathbf{E} = \begin{pmatrix} 0 & 0 & 2 \\ 3 & 1 & 0 \\ 0 & 4 & 0 \end{pmatrix}$, $\mathbf{F} = \begin{pmatrix} 2 & 0 & 0 \\ 4 & 3 & 0 \\ 5 & 6 & 1 \end{pmatrix}$.

  5. Find $\mathbf{DE}$ and $\mathbf{ED}$.
  6. Find $\mathbf{DF}$ and $\mathbf{FD}$.
  7. Find $\mathbf{EF}$ and $\mathbf{FE}$.
  8. Find $(\mathbf{DE})\mathbf{F}$ and $\mathbf{D}(\mathbf{EF})$.

Part C

  9. Find $\mathbf{A}^2$ and $\mathbf{A}^3$.
  10. Find $\mathbf{D}^2$ and $\mathbf{D}^3$.

3.4 TRANSITIONS

A *state* describes the condition in which a thing exists. For example, a chemical may be in one of three states: solid, liquid, or gas. A person may be professional, semiprofessional, skilled, or unskilled. A society may be in one of three states: evolving, static, or disintegrating.

In most cases, things are not as simple as this. A thing usually is one of a set, with some of the things in the set in one state and some in another. Furthermore, they may be changing from one state to another. For example, suppose you have a mixture of ice, liquid water, and steam. There will be a certain percent of each, but you would not expect each molecule to remain in the state in which it happens to be. Some of the liquid water may freeze into ice, and some may become steam. Similarly, some of the steam may condense into liquid water or may even freeze. This changing situation is called a *transition*. (This is not a very careful mathematical description, but we are not trying to be careful right now. We just want to give you the general idea of our topic.)

The study of transitions, whether in the sciences, the social sciences, commerce, or industry is obviously of great importance. In this section, we shall merely show how to *describe* the changes by a diagram, by a table, and by a matrix. In the next section, we shall make use of the matrix to predict the future. As you see, mathematicians use matrices instead of a crystal ball. It is harder, but more nearly accurate, we think.

illustrative problem

A certain chemical can exist in three states: S, L, and G. In a typical transition period, if it is in state S, there is a 50 percent probability that it will go to state G, and a 50 percent probability that it will go to state L. If it is in state L, there is a 100 percent chance that it will go to state G. If it is in state G, there is a 20 percent chance that it will go to state S, a 50 percent chance that it will go to state L, and a 30 percent chance that it will remain in state G. (*a*) Draw a transition diagram, (*b*) make a transition table, and (*c*) form a transition matrix.

solution

(*a*) See Fig. 3-6.

(*b*)

		To		
		S	L	G
	S	0	0.50	0.50
From	L	0	0	1.00
	G	0.20	0.50	0.30

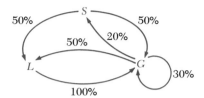

50%   S   50%
        50% 20%
    L
              G
                        30%
        100%

Fig. 3-6   Transition diagram.

As a quick check, notice that the sum of the entries for any row is 100 percent. This means that there is 100 percent probability that *something* will happen to the chemical, no matter in what state it starts.

(c) $\begin{pmatrix} 0 & 0.50 & 0.50 \\ 0 & 0 & 1.00 \\ 0.20 & 0.50 & 0.30 \end{pmatrix}$

This may not seem to be a very useful problem. It is not, yet, but you will see in the next section how much information can be derived from this matrix.

PROBLEM SECTION 3.4

For each of the following, (a) draw a transition diagram; (b) form a transition matrix. *All the probabilities below are strictly fictitious.*

1. A state that votes Democan in a presidential election has an 80 percent chance of voting Democan again, and a 20 percent chance of switching to Republocratic. On the other hand, a state that votes Republocratic has a 90 percent chance of voting the same way in the next election, and only a 10 percent chance of switching.

2. A student who takes math has a 70 percent chance of taking more math next term and a 30 percent chance of switching to the social sciences. A student who takes social science has a 90 percent chance of taking social science again next term and a 10 percent chance of switching to mathematics.

3. Over a 4-year period, people living in the city have a 10 percent chance of moving to the suburbs, and people living in the suburbs have a 5 percent chance of moving to the city.

4. A young man who likes to sleep often gets up late for work. Every time he is late, he resolves to get up early the next day, and 40 percent of the time he does. However, whenever he is early on one day, he oversleeps the next day about 75 percent of the time.

5. A young lady has three dresses: a red one, a green one, and a black one. After wearing the red one, she wears the green one 30 percent of the time, and the black one the rest of the time. After wearing the green one, she wears it again 20 percent of the time, the black one 60 percent of the time, and the red one 20 percent of the time. After wearing the black one, she wears it again 60 percent of the time, switches to the red one 10 percent of the time, and to the green one 30 percent of the time.

6. A manufacturer buys raw materials from companies A, B, and C. If he has just bought from A, then 40 percent of the time he reorders from A, 40 percent from B, and 20 percent from C. If he has just bought from B, then 30 percent of the time he reorders from B, and 70 percent of the time from C. If he has just bought from C, then 80 percent of the time he buys from A, and the rest of the time from B.

3.5 MARKOV CHAINS

In Sec. 3.4, we described a situation in which the hourly transitions were as shown in the following matrix:

$$
\begin{array}{c}
 & & \text{(To)} \\
 & & \text{Solid} \quad \text{Liquid} \quad \text{Gas} \\
\text{(From)} &
\begin{array}{c}
\text{Solid} \\
\text{Liquid} \\
\text{Gas}
\end{array} &
\begin{pmatrix}
0 & 0.50 & 0.50 \\
0 & 0 & 1.00 \\
0.20 & 0.50 & 0.30
\end{pmatrix}
\end{array}
$$

illustrative problem 1

Suppose now that we have a *mixture* of the three states of this chemical: 20 percent solid, 50 percent liquid, and 30 percent gas. (For example, it could be 20 percent ice, 50 percent liquid water, and 30 percent steam. According to the transition matrix, the ice "wants" to become either liquid or steam, the liquid water "wants" to become steam, and the steam "wants" to become ice, to become liquid water, or to remain as steam.) What will the resulting mixture be after 1 hour, if the transition period in the matrix is 1 hour?

solution

Method 1: We can use a Kemeny tree, just as we did in Chap. 2. The result is shown in Fig. 3-7.

According to Fig. 3-7, the *liquid* phase will have $0.10 + 0.15 = 0.25 = 25\%$; the *gas* phase will have $0.10 + 0.50 + 0.09 = 0.69 = 69\%$;

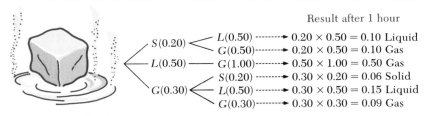

Result after 1 hour

$S(0.20)$ — $L(0.50)$ --------→ $0.20 \times 0.50 = 0.10$ Liquid
$G(0.50)$--------→ $0.20 \times 0.50 = 0.10$ Gas
$L(0.50)$ —— $G(1.00)$--------→ $0.50 \times 1.00 = 0.50$ Gas
$S(0.20)$ --------→ $0.30 \times 0.20 = 0.06$ Solid
$G(0.30)$ — $L(0.50)$ --------→ $0.30 \times 0.50 = 0.15$ Liquid
$G(0.30)$--------→ $0.30 \times 0.30 = 0.09$ Gas

Fig. 3-7   Result after one transition period.

and the solid phase will have $0.06 = 6\%$. In other words, the mixture will be 6% ice, 25% liquid water, and 69% steam, if the beginning mixture was the three states of water.

Method 2: Noting that the result is obtained by a series of multiplications and additions, it may occur to you that this is the sort of thing that happens in matrix multiplication. An investigation does, indeed, show that the same result can be obtained by multiplying the *present situation vector* (0.20, 0.50, 0.30) by the *transition matrix*, which we shall call **Q.**

$$(0.20, 0.50, 0.30) \begin{pmatrix} 0 & 0.50 & 0.50 \\ 0 & 0 & 1.00 \\ 0.20 & 0.50 & 0.30 \end{pmatrix}$$

$1 \times 3 \qquad\qquad 3 \times 3$

$$= (0 + 0 + 0.06, \quad 0.10 + 0 + 0.15, \quad 0.10 + 0.50 + 0.09)$$
$$= (0.06, 0.25, 0.69)$$

1×3

which can also be written as $(6\%, 25\%, 69\%)$. This is much faster than the Kemeny-tree method and gives the same result. Notice that the *order* of items in the result vector is the same as that in the *present situation vector* and in the **Q**-matrix, namely, solid, liquid, gas.

illustrative problem 2

What happens to the mixture after 2 hours?

solution

If we wanted to, we could multiply our 1-hour vector, $(0.06, 0.25, 0.69)$, by the **Q**-matrix again. This would give us the product

$(0.06, 0.25, 0.69)\mathbf{Q}$ [5]

However, the result vector is, itself, $(0.20,0.50,0.30)\mathbf{Q}$. Substituting this in [5], we have

$$(0.20,0.50,0.30)\mathbf{QQ} \tag{6}$$

or, more simply written (meaning the same);

$$(0.20,0.50,0.30)\mathbf{Q}^2 \tag{7}$$

We therefore find $\mathbf{Q}^2$:

$$\begin{pmatrix} 0 & 0.50 & 0.50 \\ 0 & 0 & 1 \\ 0.20 & 0.50 & 0.30 \end{pmatrix}\begin{pmatrix} 0 & 0.50 & 0.50 \\ 0 & 0 & 1 \\ 0.20 & 0.50 & 0.30 \end{pmatrix} = \begin{pmatrix} 0.10 & 0.25 & 0.65 \\ 0.20 & 0.50 & 0.30 \\ 0.06 & 0.25 & 0.69 \end{pmatrix}$$

Now we multiply the present situation vector by $\mathbf{Q}^2$ to give the result after *two* transition periods:

$$(0.20,0.50,0.30)\begin{pmatrix} 0.10 & 0.25 & 0.65 \\ 0.20 & 0.50 & 0.30 \\ 0.06 & 0.25 & 0.69 \end{pmatrix} = (0.138,0.375,0.487)$$

This means that after *two* transition periods the mixture will be 13.8 percent solid, 37.5 percent liquid, and 48.7 percent gas. Of course, the same answer could have been gotten by taking the result of Illustrative Problem 1 and multiplying by the $\mathbf{Q}$-matrix.

We shall not burden you with a lot of arithmetic in the Problem Section, but we should like to demonstrate one more, just for the general idea, and with the promise that we shall not ask you to do the same unless you happen to have a computer handy.

illustrative problem 3

Find the nature of the mixture after three transition periods (in this case, 3 hours).

solution

We shall use the fact that

$$\mathbf{Q}^3 = \mathbf{Q}^2\mathbf{Q} = \begin{pmatrix} 0.10 & 0.25 & 0.65 \\ 0.20 & 0.50 & 0.30 \\ 0.06 & 0.25 & 0.69 \end{pmatrix}\begin{pmatrix} 0.00 & 0.50 & 0.50 \\ 0.00 & 0.00 & 1.00 \\ 0.20 & 0.50 & 0.30 \end{pmatrix}$$

$$Q^3 = \begin{pmatrix} 0.130 & 0.375 & 0.495 \\ 0.060 & 0.250 & 0.690 \\ 0.138 & 0.375 & 0.487 \end{pmatrix}$$

Now we multiply the *present situation vector* by Q^3:

$$(0.20, 0.50, 0.30) \begin{pmatrix} 0.130 & 0.375 & 0.495 \\ 0.060 & 0.250 & 0.690 \\ 0.138 & 0.375 & 0.487 \end{pmatrix} = (0.0974, 0.3125, 0.5901)$$

In plain English, this means that after three transition periods (3 hours, in this problem) the resulting mixture will be 9.74 percent solid, 31.25 percent liquid, and 59.01 percent gas. Of course, the same result could be obtained by taking the result of Illustrative Problem 2 and multiplying by the **Q**-matrix:

$$(0.138, 0.375, 0.487) \begin{pmatrix} 0 & 0.50 & 0.50 \\ 0 & 0 & 1 \\ 0.20 & 0.50 & 0.30 \end{pmatrix} = (0.0974, 0.3125, 0.5901)$$

You may think it is easier to do the multiplications one by one instead of calculating Q^2, Q^3, and so on. This may very well be true, but from a practical standpoint the one-by-one method is not as useful. For example, an engineer might want to know the result only after 25 hours, 50 hours, 75 hours, etc. The procedure is to "throw" **Q** into a computer and ask, very politely, for Q^{25}, Q^{50}, etc. As a matter of fact, the computer could probably type out Q^2, Q^3, ..., Q^{100} faster than you could do Illustrative Problem 1. That is why we showed you the method which may be harder by hand.

The system illustrated is a demonstration of a so-called *Markov process*. This is a system of transitions where the result depends upon the initial state (as given by the present situation vector) and a transition matrix, and on nothing else. It is named in honor of a great Russian mathematician of the twentieth century who studied dynamic changes based upon probabilities.

PROBLEM SECTION 3.5

For each of the transitions in Problem Section 3.4, (a) find the result after *one* transition, (b) find Q^2, (c) find the result after *two* transitions. Interpret your answers. The following information is the present situation vector. (They are not real.)

1. 80 percent Democan, 20 percent Republocrat.
2. 30 percent of the students are taking mathematics, 70 percent social sciences.
3. There are 60 percent in the cities, 40 percent in the suburbs.
4. 20 percent of the time he is on time, 80 percent late.
5. She is at present wearing a red dress 30 percent of the time, a green dress 20 percent of the time, and a black dress 50 percent of the time.
6. He is buying 70 percent from company A, 30 percent from company B, and nothing from company C.

an
introduction
to the
theory
of
games

4444444

4

A game which has been played in Italy for hundreds of years is *Two-finger Morra*. This game is played by two people. Each of the two people has a choice of showing *one* finger or *two*. They show their fingers at a signal and, at the same time, each calls out his guess as to how many fingers his opponent is going to show. (It sounds more complicated than it is.)

If only one player guesses correctly, he wins an amount equal to the *sum* of the numbers of fingers shown. This sum can be 2, 3, or 4. Otherwise, it is a draw.

For example, Enrico shows one finger and yells, "Due," which is "Two" in Italian. Giuseppe shows two fingers and yells, "Due." Enrico has guessed right, but Giuseppe has not. Enrico wins 3, because three fingers were shown by the two players, and Giuseppe has to give him three pizzas, or three coins in the fountain, or something.

Our problem is this. Is there an especially clever way to play this and other games? The Two-finger Morra game was one of the first worked out when mathematicians started to work on the theory of games, but the solution is too difficult to show in this book. However, we shall show you many other games in Chaps. 4 and 5, and you will learn the general principles upon which the theory of games rests.

4.1 THE GAME MATRIX

We shall limit ourselves to *two-person games,* for example, us against the enemy. The enemy may, in fact, be Nature or may be a group of people (such as the faculty). We want to win as much as possible against any maneuvers of the enemy, or, if we have to lose, we want to lose as little as possible. Our foul enemies unfortunately have opposing interests (they never cooperate!) so that there is a conflict between us. We shall investigate plans to come out on top. Of the plans we investigate, one or more of these plans will be best. These we shall call *optimal strategies.* (*Optimal* means *best.*)

A *strategy* may be *pure,* such as: always stick out one finger and yell "*Two,*" or may be *mixed,* such as: half the time stick out one finger and yell "*Two*" and the rest of the time stick out two fingers and yell "*One.*" Of course, our enemy also has optimal strategies. If he is not as smart as we are, he is likely to lose much more than necessary.

In this section, we shall merely explain how to set up the games. In the later sections and in Chap. 5, we shall explain how to solve all of them except Two-finger Morra.

illustrative problem 1

Our enemy says, "Let's match pennies. If we match *heads*, we break even. If we match *tails*, I'll give you 3¢. If we don't match, you give me 3¢." We say, "That sounds all right, but I don't have any small change. All my money is tied up in very large bills." The enemy says, "O.K., then, let's just call them off at the same time. It's the same as flipping them."

Actually, it is not the same. Write the *game matrix*.

solution

The *game matrix* is a table which tells how much *we* shall win or lose. It is customary to write the game matrix as a table with lines and headings (unlike matrices in other branches of mathematics). The following is the solution; we shall explain it directly.

		Enemy	
		H	*T*
We	*H*	0¢	−3¢
	T	−3¢	3¢

Explanation: The numbers in the matrix are *payoffs* to *us*. We read from left to right as follows. *In row* 1, the combination *HH* pays us 0¢, and *HT* pays us −3¢, which means we lose 3¢. *In row* 2, *TH* pays us −3¢, meaning that we lose 3¢, and *TT* pays us 3¢.

From the enemy's point of view, the *positive* entries are *losses*, and the *negative* entries are *wins*. From our point of view, as you can see, the reverse is the case. It should be obvious that we always want to make the numbers as large as possible, and the enemy wants to make them as small as possible; in fact, he prefers to have them negative.

We shall follow the usual convention and always play the rows, and the enemy will always play the columns. The game illustrated is called a 2 × 2 (*two-by-two*) game.

illustrative problem 2

"I have a weird game for you," says Frank H., the enemy. "Let's pretend there is a horse race and I decide whether the horse wins, places (comes in second), or shows (comes in third). If it wins, I get $5. If it places, I get $3. If it shows, I get $1." "When do I get to win?" I ask. "Well," he says, "you can decide whether or not to enter the horse. If I decide on *win* and the horse is scratched (withdrawn), I pay you $2.

If I decide on *place,* and the horse is scratched, I pay you $4. If I decide on *show,* and the horse is scratched, I pay you $6." "That *is* a weird game," I say, "but I will be happy to play it." Write the game matrix. Do you see a strategy by which I can always win?

solution

		Frank H.		
		Win	Place	Show
Me	Run	−5	−3	−1
	Scratch	2	4	6

This is a 2×3 (two rows by three columns) game.

illustrative problem 3

Your friendly enemy, the teacher, sometimes gives a quiz at the beginning of the period and sometimes does not. Every quiz *failure* costs you 1 point on your end-of-term grade. A *pass* mark does not change your grade (you are expected to study without reward). When a quiz is given, the teacher does not collect the homework.

You have a choice of (1) not studying each day, (2) giving the material a quick glance, or (3) doing a thorough job of studying. If you do not study at all, then about 40 percent of the time you come out all right anyhow even if a quiz is given; if no quiz is given, you have lost nothing. If you just refresh your memory by glancing at the material, then about 70 percent of the time you come out all right if a quiz is given; but if no quiz is given, you lose ½ point because you have not completed your homework. (You spent the extra time refreshing your memory. How unfair life is!) If you study hard, you will always pass the quiz if it is given; but if no quiz is given, the teacher collects the homework (which you have not had time to do) and you lose 1 point for that.

Write the game matrix.

solution

In the table, the entries are net points won or lost.

		Teacher	
		Quiz	No quiz
You	No study	−0.6	0
	Glance	−0.3	−0.5
	Study hard	0	−1.0

This is a 3×2 game.

illustrative problem 4

Write a game matrix for the game of Two-finger Morra described at the beginning of this chapter.

solution

			Enemy			
		Shows	1	1	2	2
Shows	Guesses	Guesses	1	2	1	2
1	1		0	2	−3	0
1	2		−2	0	0	3
2	1		3	0	0	−4
2	2		0	−3	4	0

(We)

illustrative problem 5

A and B are playing a game. Each of them announces a number at the same time. The payoff depends upon whether they match for *even* or *odd* or do not match at all. Explain the following payoffs.

	B	
	Even	Odd
A Even	4¢	−2¢
A Odd	−5¢	3¢

solution

If they match *even*, B pays A 4¢. If they match *odd*, B pays A 3¢. If A calls *even* and B calls *odd*, A pays B 2¢. If A calls *odd* and B calls *even*, A pays B 5¢.

PROBLEM SECTION 4.1

Part A. In each of the following, explain the payoffs.

1. George and Pete are matching pennies; H = heads, T = tails.

	Pete	
	H	T
George H	−2¢	3¢
George T	3¢	−2¢

2. Pam and Susan are playing for points. They select red and black cards simultaneously.

		Susan	
		Red	Black
Pam	Red	3	−1
	Black	−5	3

3. Lance and Eric are playing Paper-Scissors-Stone, a game for which *stone* breaks *scissors*, *scissors* cuts *paper*, and *paper* covers *stone*. Each one chooses one of the possibilities and these are announced simultaneously.

		Eric		
		Paper	Scissors	Stone
Lance	Paper	0	−1	1
	Scissors	1	0	−1
	Stone	−1	1	0

4. Mr. Buyer has a concession at Soldiers' Field. He can sell candy, sunglasses, and umbrellas, but he must naturally choose different amounts depending upon the weather. Whatever he does not sell is a total loss because it is spoiled and he has to throw it away. (Don't ask us why.) In this case, he loses the cost of the item.

		Nature (Actual weather)		
		Rain	Cloudy	Sunny
Mr. Buyer (guess)	Rain	200	50	−100
	Cloudy	100	300	−100
	Sunny	−250	−100	500

Part B. For each of the following, write a game matrix.

5. *X* and *Y* are matching fingers. Each one sticks out an odd or an even number of fingers. If the sum is even, *X* wins 1 point, and if it is odd, *X* loses 1 point.

6. Steve and Jerry are going on a double blind date. Jerry asks Steve to pick his girl in advance. "Well," says Steve, "how can I do that? I don't even know what they look like." Jerry says, "I haven't met the

girls yet, but I've heard from Milton what they look like. Here's what good old Milt says." He proceeds to tell Steve. On the basis of the description, Steve calculates that the pleasure of picking the right girl is worth 5 points. However, Milt is a well-known liar (sometimes) and what he said may or may not be the truth. If Milt told the truth and Steve believes him, then Steve gets his 5 points. If Milt told the truth but Steve does not believe him, then Steve will pick the wrong girl; the disappointment in the girl and his shame at not believing what Milt told Jerry will lose him 4 points. If Steve believes what Milt said, but Milt was lying, then Steve will not only be disappointed but also be quite irritated. This represents a loss of 5 points. Finally, if what Milt said was a lie, and Steve did not believe it, then Steve will get the right girl, but under the wrong circumstances. This is worth only 3 points. (Consider Milt as the enemy.)

7. Richard and Charles invent the following game. Each one writes a 2, 3, or 4. If the sum is even, Richard gets that many points. If the sum is odd, Charles gets it. (Consider Charles as the enemy.)

8. Ernie does not remember whether Helen's birthday is today, tomorrow, or next month. If he brings the gift on the right date, the big smile from Helen has a joy-value of 5. If he is a little early, he can always get by with some fast talking, but the joy-value is only 2. If he is very early (more than two weeks), he has a lot of quick talking to do, and the joy-value is −2. If Ernie is a little late, the roof falls partly in and the joy-value is −5. If he is more than two weeks late, the present has to be sent to Helen's new address, and the joy-value is −10. (Consider the actual birthdate as the enemy.)

4.2 SADDLE-POINT GAMES (2 × 2)

From one point of view, there are only two types of two-person games: (1) the type in which a "simple" command to each player describes his optimal strategy and (2) the type in which each player must sometimes do one thing and sometimes another. The first of these is called a *pure strategy*, and the second a *mixed strategy*.

The first type is, by far, the easiest to deal with. We shall dispose of it completely within this chapter. In the following, we propose a very simple game and explore it.

illustrative problem 1

We and the enemy are playing a simplified version of matching. Each of us puts out one finger or two. The payoffs are as follows:

	Enemy	
	1	2
We 1	2¢	6¢
2	1¢	7¢

How should we play to win as much as possible? In other words, what is our optimal strategy?

Discussion: We have a clear choice: one finger or two. If we put out *one* finger, we may win 2¢ or 6¢, depending upon the enemy's play. If we put out *two* fingers, we may win 1¢ or 7¢. Of course, if we knew what the enemy was going to do, there would be no problem (no game, either). If we knew the enemy was going to put out one finger, we would put out one and win 2¢. On the other hand, if we knew the enemy was going to put out two fingers, we would also put out two fingers and win 7¢. Unfortunately, the enemy has no intention of telling us what he intends to do. (That is how enemies are.)

Under the circumstances, let us investigate further. The *least* we can win (the *minimum*) in each row is as follows:

Pure Strategy	Row Minimum
Row 1 (one finger)	2¢
Row 2 (two fingers)	1¢

and we can be *sure* of winning 2¢ by putting out one finger at every play of this game. If we are stupid enough to put out *two* fingers, the enemy may put out only *one,* and we will win only 1¢.

Now, let us look at the situation from the enemy's point of view. The *most* he can lose (the *maximum*) in each column is

Pure Strategy	Column Maximum
Column 1 (one finger)	2¢
Column 2 (two fingers)	7¢

If the enemy plays column 1, he will lose 2¢, but if he plays column 2, he may lose 7¢. He cuts down his possible maximum loss by playing column 1.

We are interested in a *sure* win of as much as possible, and the enemy is interested in a *sure* loss of as little as possible. If our choice happens to turn out the same as his, as it does in this game (both were

2¢ in row 1, column 1), we say we have a *saddle-point game*. The saddle point is the place where the common value exists. In this case, the saddle point is (1,1), meaning *row* 1, *column* 1. The common value, in this case 2¢, is called the *value of the game*. It is, of course, the value to us.

The formal method for solving a saddle-point game is explained in the following.

solution

In the following, the *row minima* and *column maxima* appear in color in the appropriate places. The *largest minimum* and the *smallest maximum* are encircled.

		Enemy		
		1	2	Row minima
We	1	2¢✱	6¢	②
	2	1¢	7¢	1
Column maxima		②	7	

As you see, the largest row minimum is equal to the smallest column maximum. Under these circumstances, 2¢ is the value of the game, and the saddle point is where the 2¢ was, namely, at row 1, column 1.

This game is called an *unfair game* because the enemy has to lose every time. In this case, he must lose at least 2¢ if we play correctly, more if we play correctly and he does not.

It may occur to you that the theory of games is not quite heroic. We are afraid to play row 2 (two fingers) because we might not win all we feel we are entitled to. In fact, our optimal strategy is row 1, and the enemy's optimal strategy is column 1. We win more if the enemy plays incorrectly, and the enemy loses less if we play incorrectly.

illustrative problem 2

Having lost his shirt, so to speak, the enemy says, "This game is unfair!" Being of noble character, as everyone knows, we agree to change the game matrix to the following one, by subtracting 2 from each "box."

		Enemy	
		1	2
We	1	0	4
	2	−1	5

What is the optimal strategy for each player, and what is the value of the game?

		Enemy		
		1	2	Row minima
We	1	0*	4	⓪
	2	−1	5	−1
Column maxima		⓪	5	

Using the same method as before, we find that the largest minimum is 0, the smallest maximum is 0, and therefore there is a saddle point at (1,1) as before, but the value of the game is now 0.

A game with a value of *zero* is called a *fair game* or (this is clever!) a *zero-sum game*. It is fair because, if the players play correctly, they will always break even. Notice that if the enemy plays correctly (column 1) and we play incorrectly (row 2), we will lose 1¢. If we play correctly (row 1) and the enemy plays incorrectly (column 2), we will win 4¢. It is not likely that both players will play incorrectly, and the theory of games does not consider this possibility. We play only with intelligent people.

We shall not go into the proof of the following theorem in this book, but it is fairly easy to prove by using matrix arithmetic.

theorem for adding to games

If the same number is added to every element of a game matrix, the strategy is unchanged, but the value of the game is increased by that amount.

In Illustrative Problem 2, the strategy is the same as that of Illustrative Problem 1 (we merely added 2 to each entry), but the value has been increased by 2.

illustrative problem 3

Feeling his oats, the enemy now says, "Let's triple the stakes!" Being, as we remarked previously, of very noble character, we agree. Of course, the enemy meant that we should double the *new* game, but we shall lean heavily on a legal technicality and assume that the *original* game was meant. Consider the strategy and the value of the new game formed by tripling the payoffs in Illustrative Problem 1.

solution

The game matrix is as follows:

		Enemy		
		1	2	Row minima
We	1	6✱	18	⑥
	2	3	21	3
Column maxima		⑥	21	

According to this, the strategy (we play row 1, the enemy plays column 1) is still the same as in the previous two problems, but the value of the game has been multiplied by 3.

As you might have guessed, this illustrates (but does not prove) the following theorem:

theorem for multiplying games

If each element of a game matrix is multiplied by the same positive number, the strategy is unchanged, but the value of the game is multiplied by the same number.

illustrative problem 4

Find the saddle point and the value of the following game.

		Enemy	
		1	2
We	1	$-2\frac{1}{7}$	$-4\frac{2}{7}$
	2	5	$-6\frac{2}{7}$

solution

It is not really necessary but, being allergic to fractions, we shudder and multiply each entry by 7. This gives us

	1	2
1	-15	-30
2	35	-44

We just discovered a slight allergy to negative numbers, too. We add 44 to each entry, leading to

	1	2	Row minima
1	29	*14	⑭
2	79	0	0
Column maxima	79	⑭	

There is a saddle point at (row 1, column 2). Meddling with the entries has not changed the *position* of the saddle point but has changed its value. There are two ways of getting the correct value of the game. *First,* we can "unwind" what we did by *reversing the order,* as follows:

1. We added 44. Now we subtract 44.

$$14 - 44 = -30$$

2. We multiplied by 7. Now we divide by 7.

$$-{}^{30}\!/_{7} = -4{}^{2}\!/_{7}$$

The value of the game is $-4{}^{2}\!/_{7}$. *Second,* we can just look into the proper "box" in the original game. We find, at row 1, column 2, the same value, namely, $-4{}^{2}\!/_{7}$. All is well.

In this specific game, it would have been almost as easy to work with the original matrix, but we wanted to demonstrate the use of the theorems for later work. In general, we shall always multiply entries to avoid fractions and add to avoid negative numbers. It is worth the trouble.

PROBLEM SECTION 4.2

Part A. Find the saddle point, the optimal strategies, and the value of each game.

1.

	1	2
1	2	4
2	3	5

2.

	1	2
1	6	1
2	15	8

3.

	1	2
1	7	14
2	9	13

4.

	1	2
1	52	75
2	35	18

Part B. In each, multiply and add before finding the saddle point and optimal strategies; then correct the apparent value by subtraction and division to find the actual value of the game.

5.

	1	2
1	−¾	0
2	−3¾	−4

6.

	1	2
1	−1⅔	4
2	15	8

7.

	1	2
1	−⅕	−⅖
2	⅕	1

8.

	1	2
1	3	4
2	2½	−3½

Part C. Solve each game. Decide whether it is "fair" or "unfair." If it is "unfair," to whom is it "unfair"?

9. We choose a letter and the enemy chooses a letter. If they are both consonants, we pay 3¢ to the enemy. If they are both vowels, he pays us 3¢. If we choose a consonant and he chooses a vowel, he pays us 2¢; if the reverse, we break even.

10. We choose a number and the enemy chooses a number. If they are both odd, we lose 2¢. If they are both even, we have a "draw" (no payment). If we choose odd and he chooses even, we lose 1¢; if the reverse, we win 1¢.

11. We have a concession at the beach. We may buy either for rain or for sunny weather. (We are playing against Nature.) If we buy for sunny weather and it is sunny, we make $50. If we buy for sunny weather and it rains, we make only $30. If we buy for rain and it is sunny, we break even. If we buy for rain and it does rain, we make $20.

12. Our family has been bothering us to speak to the boss about a raise and we have decided to do so. In fact, we have made an appointment with him, and he knows we are going to ask for a raise. The only trouble is that we do not know how much to ask for. If we ask for $3 and he is in a foul mood, he will give us nothing. If he is in a good mood, he will give us a raise of $2. If we ask for $5 and he is in a foul mood, he will reduce our salary by $2, but if he is in a good mood he will give us a raise of $4.

4.3 LARGER SADDLE-POINT GAMES

Saddle-point games may be of any size and are always fairly easy to solve.

illustrative problem 1

Solve the game

	1	2	3
1	−2	−1⅓	−⅔
2	−⅔	0	1⅓
3	3⅓	2⅔	2

solution

For convenience, we first multiply the game by 3 in order to remove fractions.

	1	2	3
1	−6	−4	−2
2	−2	0	4
3	10	8	6

Then, again for convenience, we add 6 to the game.

	1	2	3	Row minima
1	0	2	4	0
2	4	6	10	4
3	16	14	*12	(12)
Column maxima	16	14	(12)	

The saddle point is at row 3 and column 3. The value of the *altered* matrix is 12. We subtract 6 and then divide by 3. The value of the original game is 2. (Alternatively, we may look in row 3, column 3 of the original game. The way we did it provides a check.)

PROBLEM SECTION 4.3

Part A. Find the saddle point and the value of the game.

1.

	1	2	3
1	−2	−3	3
2	−1	0	1
3	−4	1	−1

2.

	1	2	3
1	4	−1	−4
2	−9	−5	−2
3	2	0	6

3.

	1	2	3	4
1	0	−4	−6	−2
2	−2	−6	−4	−8
3	6	0	2	4
4	−2	−1	0	1

4.

	1	2	3	4
1	2	4	0	−2
2	4	8	2	6
3	−2	0	−4	2
4	−4	−2	−2	0

Part B. Find the saddle point. What is the value of the game?

5.

	1	2
1	−4	−3
2	0	1
3	−2	3

6.

	1	2
1	1	−3
2	9	3
3	7	6

7.

	1	2	3
1	4	2.5	3
2	1	2	1.5

8.

	1	2	3
1	0	1	4
2	−2	2	−1

Part C. Solve the following saddle-point games.

9. We have a date with our favorite girl, Dorothy. We are supposed to meet at the corner of Walk and Don't Walk Streets. Our problem (and hers) is whether to come early, on time, or late. If we come early and she does, too, the joy-value to us is 5. If we come early and she comes on time, we shrug it off. The joy-value is 0. If we come early and she comes late, we are annoyed—but making up is such fun! The joy-value is 9, as a matter of fact. If we come on time and she comes early, we are in some trouble (-5). If we both come on time, it is very pleasant; the joy-value is 5. If we come on time and she comes late we shrug it off (0). If we come late and she comes early, we are in a lot of trouble (-15). If we come late and she comes on time, we are still in trouble (-10). If we both come late, it is a relief to both of us and the joy-value is 10. What are the optimal strategy and the joy-value of the game?

10. Lee's wife, Mildred, knows that he likes meat and bread but is not so happy about spinach. Lee knows that he should eat spinach for lunch but does not want to eat it twice in one day. On the other hand, if he stuffs himself with meat at lunch, he is unable to eat his dinner and Mildred becomes rather annoyed. The bread situation is as follows. Lee is, unfortunately, developing a paunch. It is all right for him to eat bread once a day, but not twice. Mildred's problem is what to serve for dinner. Her rating scheme is as follows. (1) Suppose she serves meat and bread. If Lee has already had meat and bread, -5, because he should not have bread twice. If Lee has had bread and spinach, 0; he should not have bread twice, but it is good that he had spinach. If he has had meat and spinach, 5. He will just have to eat the meat. (2) Suppose she serves bread and spinach. If Lee had meat and bread, -5, because of the bread. If Lee had bread and spinach, 5, because of the spinach. (He is annoyed by the lack of meat.) If Lee had meat and spinach, 10. (Actually, Lee is not too happy about doubles in spinach.) (3) Suppose Mildred serves meat and spinach. If Lee has had meat and bread, 5. If Lee has had bread and spinach, 10. Finally, if Lee has had meat and spinach, 0, because of the lack of bread.

What should she serve and what should Lee have for lunch? What is the joy-value of the game?

4.4 DOMINANCE

Sometimes a game appears to have more (intelligent) choices than it really does. We shall illustrate. For convenience, we shall use matrices whose entries are neither negative nor fractional, since we know that every game can be converted, by multiplication and addition, into this form without changing the strategy. (*Remember that the value of the game may change, however, and we must correct for our alterations.*)

illustrative problem 1

Solve the game

		Enemy			
		1	2	3	Row minima
	1	2¢	6¢	1¢	1
We	2	4¢	7¢	2¢	②
	3	1¢	8¢	3¢	1
Column maxima		4	8	③	

solution

A glance will show you that this game has no saddle point. However, all is not lost. Look at the rows. In every column, the payoff for row 2 is more than that for row 1. There will never be any sense in playing row 1 because we can, for every possible response from the enemy, do better by playing row 2. We say that row 2 *dominates* row 1 and we *delete* (remove) the dominated row.

row principle

Keep dominant rows; delete dominated rows.

The result is a 2 × 3 game called a *subgame* of the original game.

		1	2	3	Row minima
	2	4	7	2	②
	3	1	8	3	1
Column maxima		4	8	③	

This has no saddle point, either. (*Always* check for a saddle point at each stage of the solution. It is possible to get wrong answers by missing a saddle point.)

Now, examine the subgame from the point of view of the enemy. So far as he is concerned, he hates column 2. With those high payoffs, he will never play it. In fact, just as we deleted row 1 because it was too low, he will delete column 2 because it is too high. Note that each entry in column 2 is larger than each entry in column 1. Column 2 dominates column 1. As a matter of fact, column 2 also dominates column 3. We delete column 2.

column principle

If a column dominates any other column of a game or subgame, delete it.

The resulting subgame is

	1	3	Row minima
2	4	2	(2)
3	1	3	1
Column maxima	4	(3)	

This game has no saddle point, nor is there any dominance for rows or columns. At this point, we leave it. We shall discuss how to finish it in Chap. 5. It requires a mixed strategy.

illustrative problem 2

Solve the 5 × 2 game

	1	2	Row minima
1	4	8	4
2	5	2	2
3	7*	9	(7)
4	2	10	2
5	1	8	1
Column maxima	(7)	10	

solution

A straightforward consideration of row minima and column maxima shows that (row 3, column 1) is a saddle point and the game is unfair to the enemy, with a value of 7 (to us). This is the easiest way to solve the problem, but we wish to demonstrate the dominance argument. (As it turns out, it is all right to investigate dominance before saddle points. You get the right answer either way. We are doing this for practice.)

It is obvious that row 3 dominates rows 1, 2, and 5. We delete the dominated rows and obtain

	1	2	Row minima
3	*7	9	⑦
4	2	10	2
Column maxima	⑦	10	

This game also has a saddle point (at the same place, of course, as the original) but, once again, we are going to continue for purposes of illustration. The enemy sees that column 2 dominates column 1. He deletes column 2 and we have the subgame

	1	Row minima
3	*7	⑦
4	2	2
Column maximum	⑦	

This has the same saddle point, but we continue. We see that row 3 dominates row 4, and so we delete row 4. This leaves

	1
3	7*

The resulting strategy is (row 3, column 1) as before. The value of the game is 7.

Remember that we did this just for explanatory purposes. The best time to finish a problem is if and when you reach a saddle point.

illustrative problem 3

Solve the 2 × 4 game

	1	2	3	4
1	1	−3	−2	2
2	0	−4	−1	1

solution

First, we alter the game by adding 4 to each entry.

	1	2	3	4	Row minima
1	5	1✳	2	6	①)
2	4	0	3	5	0
Column maxima	5	①	3	6	

By straightforward methods, we see that there is a saddle point at (row 1, column 2). The value of the original game is -3, showing that it is unfair (to us).

From the standpoint of dominance, we note that row 1 does not dominate row 2, and row 2 does not dominate row 1. What about the enemy? Column 4 dominates column 1, column 1 dominates column 3, and column 3 dominates column 2. The enemy detests dominant columns, and so all of them are eliminated. This leaves column 2.

	2
1	1✳
2	0

Now, *we* look again. We want the dominant row, namely, row 1. This leaves us with the same answer as the one we obtained quickly by a saddle-point argument: row 1, column 2. Looking in the *original* game, we see that the entry in (row 1, column 2) is -3, which checks.

You may think that dominance is a rather long way to search for saddle points. Its real use is to make smaller subgames. We have already demonstrated one of these simplifying processes (in Illustrative Problem 1). Here is another one.

illustrative problem 4

Solve the following 5×2 game. (The solution will be incomplete at this point.)

	1	2	Row minima
1	3	6	3
2	5	4	4
3	4	7	4
4	6	5	(5)
5	5	5	(5)
Column maxima	6	7	

solution

There is no saddle point, as you can see. However, row 5 dominates row 2 (delete row 2), row 3 dominates row 1 (delete row 1), row 4 dominates row 5 (delete row 5). This leaves

	1	2	Row minima
3	4	7	4
4	6	5	(5)
Column maxima	(6)	7	

There is no saddle point. Furthermore, there is no more dominance (if there were, there would be a saddle point). We are left with a 2×2 subgame which will be solved in Chap. 5. Anyhow, it is a smaller problem than the original. Besides, just by looking at the subgame, you can see that the value is somewhere between 4 and 7, probably between 5 and 6.

PROBLEM SECTION 4.4

The following games may or may not have saddle points. Simplify them as much as possible by dominance. Solve if you can. Otherwise, your smallest subgame is the answer for the time being.

1.

	1	2	3	4
1	20	5	10	15
2	9	8	7	12
3	13	3	4	8

2.

	1	2	3
1	1	7	2
2	2	8	3
3	3	4	6
4	4	5	7
5	3	7	5

3.

	1	2	3	4
1	31	29	21	26
2	1	19	5	7
3	15	13	27	9
4	37	3	21	25

4.

	1	2	3	4
1	5	8	11	10
2	20	15	13	14
3	15	20	16	12
4	10	14	9	7

5.

	1	2	3	4	5	6
1	0	2	4	−1	0	3
2	4	2	2	2	2	2
3	1	3	5	0	1	4
4	2	−3	0	1	1	−1
5	4	−1	−1	0	2	0
6	3	0	1	2	3	2

6.

	1	2	3	4	5
1	11	8	6	5	12
2	15	2	16	7	16
3	4	3	3	5	19
4	9	2	12	5	7
5	14	1	10	3	6

4.5 EVALUATING DETERMINANTS

We have already practiced on multiplication of row vector by a matrix, and matrix by a column vector. We shall need this in Chap. 5 for more advanced game theory. Before discussing determinants, we take this opportunity to review matrix multiplication.

Row Vector Times Matrix (Review)

illustrative problem 1

$$(1,2)\begin{pmatrix} 3 & 4 & 5 \\ 6 & 7 & 8 \end{pmatrix} = (3+12,\ 4+14,\ 5+16) = (15,18,21)$$

$$1 \times 2 \quad 2 \times 3 \qquad\qquad\qquad\qquad\qquad 1 \times 3$$

illustrative problem 2

In the following, we *factor* the vector. This is often very useful.

$$(\tfrac{1}{7},\tfrac{2}{7})\begin{pmatrix} 3 & 4 & 5 \\ 6 & 7 & 8 \end{pmatrix} = \tfrac{1}{7}(1,2)\begin{pmatrix} 3 & 4 & 5 \\ 6 & 7 & 8 \end{pmatrix} = \tfrac{1}{7}(15,18,21)$$

$$1 \times 2 \quad 2 \times 3$$

$$= (\tfrac{15}{7},\tfrac{18}{7},\tfrac{21}{7}) = (2\tfrac{1}{7},2\tfrac{4}{7},3)$$

$$1 \times 3$$

illustrative problem 3

$$(\tfrac{1}{7},\tfrac{2}{7},\tfrac{4}{7})\begin{pmatrix} 0 & 1 & 2 \\ 3 & 4 & 5 \\ 6 & 7 & 8 \end{pmatrix} = \tfrac{1}{7}(1,2,4)\begin{pmatrix} 0 & 1 & 2 \\ 3 & 4 & 5 \\ 6 & 7 & 8 \end{pmatrix}$$

$$1 \times 3 \qquad 3 \times 3$$

$$= \tfrac{1}{7}(0+6+24,\ 1+8+28,\ 2+10+32)$$
$$= \tfrac{1}{7}(30,37,44)$$

$$= (\tfrac{30}{7},\tfrac{37}{7},\tfrac{44}{7}) = (4\tfrac{2}{7},5\tfrac{2}{7},6\tfrac{2}{7})$$

$$1 \times 3$$

Matrix Times Column Vector (Review)

illustrative problem 4

$$\begin{pmatrix} 1 & 2 & 3 \\ 4 & 5 & 6 \end{pmatrix} \begin{pmatrix} 7 \\ 8 \\ 9 \end{pmatrix} = \begin{pmatrix} 7 + 16 + 27 \\ 28 + 40 + 54 \end{pmatrix} = \begin{pmatrix} 50 \\ 122 \end{pmatrix}$$

$$2 \times 3 \quad 3 \times 1 \qquad\qquad\qquad\qquad 2 \times 1$$

illustrative problem 5

$$\begin{pmatrix} 1 & 2 & 3 \\ 4 & 5 & 6 \end{pmatrix} \begin{pmatrix} \frac{1}{7} \\ \frac{2}{7} \\ \frac{4}{7} \end{pmatrix} = \frac{1}{7}\begin{pmatrix} 1 & 2 & 3 \\ 4 & 5 & 6 \end{pmatrix} \begin{pmatrix} 1 \\ 2 \\ 4 \end{pmatrix} = \frac{1}{7}\begin{pmatrix} 1 + 4 + 12 \\ 4 + 10 + 24 \end{pmatrix}$$

$$2 \times 3 \quad 3 \times 1$$

$$= \frac{1}{7}\begin{pmatrix} 17 \\ 38 \end{pmatrix} = \begin{pmatrix} 1\frac{7}{7} \\ 3\frac{8}{7} \end{pmatrix} = \begin{pmatrix} 2\frac{3}{7} \\ 5\frac{3}{7} \end{pmatrix}$$

$$2 \times 1$$

2×2 Determinants

As you know, part of the reason for the "tricky" rules in multiplying vectors and matrices is *convenience*. (Just think how hard it would be to keep track of the multiplications and additions if mathematicians had not hit upon this automatic checking device.) For the same reason, we now define a new symbol:

$$\begin{vmatrix} a & b \\ c & d \end{vmatrix}$$

as a 2×2 *determinant* with the single numerical value (by definition) of

$$(a \times d) - (b \times c)$$

where a, b, c, and d are any numbers. This can, of course, also be written as

$$ad - bc$$

meaning the same thing.

illustrative problem 6

$$\begin{vmatrix} 1 & 2 \\ 3 & 4 \end{vmatrix} = (1)(4) - (2)(3) = (4) - (6) = -2$$

illustrative problem 7

$$\begin{vmatrix} -3 & 5 \\ -8 & 2 \end{vmatrix} = (-3)(2) - (5)(-8) = (-6) - (-40) = -6 + 40 = 34$$

illustrative problem 8

$$\begin{vmatrix} \frac{1}{3} & \frac{1}{3} \\ -\frac{1}{3} & \frac{2}{3} \end{vmatrix} = (\frac{1}{3})(\frac{2}{3}) - (\frac{1}{3})(-\frac{1}{3}) = (\frac{2}{9}) - (-\frac{1}{9}) = \frac{2}{9} + \frac{1}{9} = \frac{3}{9} = \frac{1}{3}$$

Notice that this is *not* the same as

$$\frac{1}{3} \begin{vmatrix} 1 & 1 \\ -1 & 2 \end{vmatrix} = \frac{1}{3}[(1)(2) - (1)(-1)] = \frac{1}{3}[2 + 1] = \frac{3}{3} = 1$$

Determinants can be factored, but not in the same way as matrices. We mention this here in order to avoid a misunderstanding.

3 × 3 Determinants

For convenience, we also define a 3 × 3 determinant, represented by the symbol

$$\begin{vmatrix} a & b & c \\ d & e & f \\ g & h & i \end{vmatrix}$$

where, once again, the letters stand for any numbers. The value of this determinant is a single number and is calculated in a rather strange manner. (Remember that the method described below was chosen purely for convenience in keeping track of additions and multiplications in certain types of problems.)

illustrative problem 9

As in the case of the 2 × 2 determinant, there are two sums of products, one of which is subtracted from the other. For the purpose of explanation, we shall do it in two parts. You will probably find it easy to do it all at once. The extra columns shown outside the determinant sign are merely an aid to the memory; they do not really belong there. They are columns 1 and 2, repeated.

$$\begin{vmatrix} 1 & 2 & 3 \\ 4 & -5 & 6 \\ -7 & 0 & 9 \end{vmatrix} \begin{matrix} 1 & 2 \\ 4 & -5 \\ -7 & 0 \end{matrix} \rightarrow \begin{matrix} (1)(-5)(9) + (2)(6)(-7) + (3)(4)(0) \\ = (-45) + (-84) + (0) = -129 \end{matrix}$$

$$\begin{vmatrix} 1 & 2 & 3 \\ 4 & -5 & 6 \\ -7 & 0 & 9 \end{vmatrix} \begin{matrix} 1 & 2 \\ 4 & -5 \\ -7 & 0 \end{matrix} \rightarrow \begin{matrix} (3)(-5)(-7) + (1)(6)(0) + (2)(4)(9) \\ = (105) + (0) + (72) = 177 \end{matrix}$$

$$\begin{vmatrix} 1 & 2 & 3 \\ 4 & -5 & 6 \\ -7 & 0 & 9 \end{vmatrix} = (-129) - (177) = -306$$

illustrative problem 10

$$\begin{vmatrix} 1 & -1 & 23 \\ 1 & 0 & -1 \\ 1 & 1 & 0 \end{vmatrix} = \begin{vmatrix} 1 & -1 & 23 \\ 1 & 0 & -1 \\ 1 & 1 & 0 \end{vmatrix} \begin{matrix} 1 & -1 \\ 1 & 0 \\ 1 & 1 \end{matrix} =$$

$$= [(1)(0)(0) + (-1)(-1)(1) + (23)(1)(1)] - [(23)(0)(1) + (1)(-1)(1) + (-1)(1)(0)]$$
$$= (0 + 1 + 23) - (0 - 1 + 0) = (24) - (-1) = 25$$

illustrative problem 11

$$\begin{vmatrix} 0 & 1 & 23 \\ 1 & 1 & -1 \\ -23 & 1 & 0 \end{vmatrix} = \begin{vmatrix} 0 & 1 & 23 \\ 1 & 1 & -1 \\ -23 & 1 & 0 \end{vmatrix} \begin{matrix} 0 & 1 \\ 1 & 1 \\ -23 & 1 \end{matrix}$$

$$= [(0)(1)(0) + (1)(-1)(-23) + (23)(1)(1)] - [(23)(1)(-23) + (0)(-1)(1) + (1)(1)(0)]$$
$$= (0 + 23 + 23) - (-529 + 0 + 0) = 46 + 529$$
$$= 575$$

PROBLEM SECTION 4.5

Part A (review). Multiply as indicated.

1. $(0.2, 0.8)\begin{pmatrix} 2 & 5 \\ 3 & 1 \end{pmatrix}$

2. $(0.3, 0.7)\begin{pmatrix} 2 & 5 \\ 3 & 1 \end{pmatrix}$

3. $(0.8, 0.2)\begin{pmatrix} 2 & 5 \\ 3 & 1 \end{pmatrix}$

4. $(0.4, 0.6)\begin{pmatrix} 2 & 5 \\ 3 & 1 \end{pmatrix}$

5. $(\frac{1}{2}, \frac{1}{2})\begin{pmatrix} 2 & 5 \\ 3 & 1 \end{pmatrix}$

6. $(\frac{1}{4}, \frac{3}{4})\begin{pmatrix} 0 & -3 \\ -3 & 3 \end{pmatrix}$

7. $\begin{pmatrix} 2 & 5 \\ 3 & 1 \end{pmatrix}\begin{pmatrix} 0.3 \\ 0.7 \end{pmatrix}$

8. $\begin{pmatrix} 2 & 5 \\ 3 & 1 \end{pmatrix}\begin{pmatrix} 0.1 \\ 0.9 \end{pmatrix}$

9. $\begin{pmatrix} 2 & 5 \\ 3 & 1 \end{pmatrix}\begin{pmatrix} 0.5 \\ 0.5 \end{pmatrix}$

10. $\begin{pmatrix} 2 & 5 \\ 3 & 1 \end{pmatrix}\begin{pmatrix} 0.8 \\ 0.2 \end{pmatrix}$

11. $\begin{pmatrix} 0 & -3 \\ -3 & 3 \end{pmatrix}\begin{pmatrix} \frac{2}{3} \\ \frac{1}{3} \end{pmatrix}$

12. $\begin{pmatrix} 0 & -3 \\ -3 & 3 \end{pmatrix}\begin{pmatrix} \frac{1}{2} \\ \frac{1}{2} \end{pmatrix}$

Part B. 2×2 determinants to be evaluated.

13. $\begin{vmatrix} 2 & 4 \\ 1 & 0 \end{vmatrix}$

14. $\begin{vmatrix} 1 & 3 \\ 0 & 5 \end{vmatrix}$

15. $\begin{vmatrix} 2 & -8 \\ 5 & -3 \end{vmatrix}$

16. $\begin{vmatrix} -5 & 3 \\ -2 & -1 \end{vmatrix}$

17. $\begin{vmatrix} -7 & -9 \\ -3 & 4 \end{vmatrix}$

18. $\begin{vmatrix} 3 & 5 \\ 3 & 5 \end{vmatrix}$

Part C. 3×3 determinants to be evaluated.

19. $\begin{vmatrix} 0 & -1 & 1 \\ 1 & 0 & 1 \\ -23 & 1 & 1 \end{vmatrix}$

20. $\begin{vmatrix} 5 & 2 & 1 \\ 7 & 3 & 4 \\ -3 & 6 & 2 \end{vmatrix}$

21. $\begin{vmatrix} -3 & 1 & 2 \\ 1 & 2 & 4 \\ 1 & -2 & 5 \end{vmatrix}$ 22. $\begin{vmatrix} 0 & -1 & 3 \\ 2 & 3 & 4 \\ 1 & 5 & -1 \end{vmatrix}$

23. $\begin{vmatrix} 3 & -1 & 1 \\ 1 & -1 & 3 \\ 1 & -3 & 1 \end{vmatrix}$ 24. $\begin{vmatrix} 3 & 1 & 1 \\ 14 & -10 & 16 \\ -1 & -3 & -1 \end{vmatrix}$

the
theory of
games;
mixed
strategy

5555555555

It would be very easy (and very boring) if all games had saddle points, so that one player played the same row all the time and the other played the same column all the time. Alas, even simple games rarely come out this way.

Suppose, for example, that a batter can hit low, slow curves for a 0.200 batting average (this means *one* hit for every *five* times at bat). His average is up to 0.300 for a high, fast ball. There is a man on first, and a possible winning strategy is to bunt. For bunting, his batting average is 0.600 against the low curve and only 0.100 against the fast ball (the bunted ball may lead to a double play). What is the optimal strategy?

The game matrix is

		Pitcher	
		Low, slow curve	High, fast ball
Batter	Swing	0.200	0.300
	Bunt	0.600	0.100

A glance will assure you that there is no saddle point, and no dominance argument seems to help. This is an example of a game in which there is no saddle point. You will find that it is fairly easy to solve. The answer is that the *batter* should swing *five* out of *six* times, unpredictably, and the *pitcher* should throw curves *one* out of *three* times, unpredictably. Under these optimal strategies, there will be a hit about 27 percent of the time. (You will soon learn to do this calculation yourself.)

We digress to discuss briefly what is meant by *unpredictable* or *at random*. (1) Suppose you decide to choose every third name in the telephone book. Is this "random" or "unpredictable"? The answer is *no*. Once you have established a rule which excludes certain elements of a set and includes others, the result is perfectly predictable and therefore not random. (2) Suppose the pitcher, in the example just given, decides to throw a curve the first, fourth, seventh, . . . time and a fast ball the other times. Is this random? Of course not. It is predictable by a rule, therefore not random.

In random actions, every action in a set of actions must be equally probable. One way for the pitcher to accomplish an unpredictable "pattern" would be to toss a coin twice, disregard the toss whenever two tails appeared, throw a curve when two heads appeared, and a fast ball otherwise. (If you draw a Kemeny tree, you will see that this yields a 1:3 ratio.) We know that no pitcher is going to do this but perhaps it illustrates what unpredictability is. On page 138, we explore some other ways of making random patterns.

Just remember that in a game with an opponent who is acting at random *neither* of you knows what is coming next.

5.1 MIXED STRATEGY (PART I)

Pure-strategy Vectors

We have already discussed the value of games like those in Fig. 5-1. In (a), the saddle point is (1,1), and the value of the game is 4; the game is unfair to the column player. In (b), the saddle point is (1,2), the value of the game is 0, and it is a fair game. In (c), the saddle point is (2,1), the value of the game is -3, and the game is unfair to the row player.

Let us examine one of these games again. According to our investigation, *we* should play row 2 all the time (100 percent) and row 1 never (0 percent) in game (c). We shall say that the *strategy vector for rows,* **r**, is (0,1), which means (0%,100%). The *enemy*, in the same game, should play column 1 all the time and column 2 never. The *strategy vector for columns,* **c**, is $\begin{pmatrix} 1 \\ 0 \end{pmatrix}$ which means $\begin{pmatrix} 100\% \\ 0\% \end{pmatrix}$. Because the strategy vector for columns, **c**, is always a column vector, we shall not bother to write $\mathbf{c}^t$.

illustrative problem 1

What are the strategy vectors for games (a) and (b)?

solution

For game (a), $\mathbf{r} = (1,0)$, $\mathbf{c} = \begin{pmatrix} 1 \\ 0 \end{pmatrix}$. For game (b), $\mathbf{r} = (1,0)$, $\mathbf{c} = \begin{pmatrix} 0 \\ 1 \end{pmatrix}$.

The strategies for rows and columns illustrated in these three games are called *pure strategies*, because only one row or column is to be played. The vector for a pure strategy has a 1 as one component and all the other components are 0's.

	1	2
1	4✱	6
2	-5	9

(a)

	1	2
1	2	0✱
2	5	-5

(b)

	1	2
1	-4	2
2	-3✱	0

(c)

Fig. 5-1   *Three saddle-point games.*

Mixed-strategy Vectors

In most games, there is no immediate saddle-point solution. Consider the following game:

		Columns	
		1	2
Rows	1	2¢	5¢
	2	3¢	1¢

The row player has two possible pure strategies, namely, (1,0) and (0,1). For his play of row 1, he may win 2¢ or may win 5¢, depending upon how the columns are played. For his play of row 2, he may win 3¢ or 1¢, depending upon how the columns are played. However, because there is no saddle point, none of these expectations is very firm. All we can say, at the moment, is that the value of the game is somewhere between 1 and 5¢, probably not as low as 1¢ (unless the row player is very stupid) or as high as 5¢ (if the column player is equally stupid).

In games like this one, the proper strategy for the row player is to "change off," sometimes playing row 1 and sometimes row 2. Suppose he plays row 1, at random, for 20 percent of the time, and row 2 the rest of the time. Then we shall say that the row strategy vector is

$$\mathbf{r} = (0.2, 0.8)$$

Suppose the column player plays column 1, at random, 30 percent of the time, and column 2 the rest of the time. Then we shall say that the column strategy vector is

$$\mathbf{c} = \begin{pmatrix} 0.3 \\ 0.7 \end{pmatrix}$$

In both cases, we say that the strategies are *mixed strategies*.

Row Expectation (E_r)

We have already discussed the winnings if the row player plays a pure strategy, i.e., (1,0) or (0,1). But suppose $\mathbf{r} = (0.2, 0.8)$. What are the winnings then? Obviously, this depends upon whether the enemy plays column 1 or column 2.

Against column 1: We win 2¢ 20 percent of the time so that our *expectation* is $0.2 \times 2¢ = 0.4¢$. We win 3¢ 80 percent of the time, so that our expectation is $0.8 \times 3¢ = 2.4¢$. Our total expectation, if the enemy plays column 1, is $0.4¢ + 2.4¢ = 2.8¢$.

Against column 2: We win 5¢ 20 percent of the time, so that our expectation is $0.2 \times 5¢ = 1.0¢$. We win 1¢ 80 percent of the time, so that our expectation, if the enemy plays column 2, is $1.0¢ + 0.8¢ = 1.8¢$.

Notice that with the strategy (0.2,0.8) we have narrowed the value of the game to something between 1.8 and 2.8¢.

Our real problem is that we want to be *sure* of our winnings *against any play of the enemy*. The theory of games has nothing to do with speculation or gambling. It deals with "a sure thing." We would like to develop a mixed strategy which *guarantees* us the same payoff regardless of the strategy of the enemy.

Before proceeding, we note with interest that we could have obtained the same pair of results with less struggle by merely using

$$\mathbf{E}_r = \mathbf{rG}$$

where $\mathbf{E}_r$ is a row vector of expectation for the row player, $\mathbf{r}$ is the row strategy, and $\mathbf{G}$ is the game matrix.

$$\mathbf{E}_r = (0.2,0.8)\begin{pmatrix} 2¢ & 5¢ \\ 3¢ & 1¢ \end{pmatrix} = (0.4 + 2.4,\ 1.0 + 0.8) = (2.8,1.8)$$

Using this faster method, we shall calculate the results for a few other selected mixed strategies.

illustrative problem 2

In the same game, calculate the expectation for a row strategy of (0.3,0.7), and explain.

solution

$$\mathbf{E}_r = (0.3,0.7)\begin{pmatrix} 2¢ & 5¢ \\ 3¢ & 1¢ \end{pmatrix} = (0.6 + 2.1,\ 1.5 + 0.7) = (2.7,2.2)$$

The expectation is 2.7¢ if the enemy plays column 1 and 2.2¢ if the enemy plays column 2.

Table I, which we invite you to verify, shows the results of various mixed strategies on the part of the row player.

The crucial row strategy is the one in which the column player is helpless. We win the same no matter what he does. As you can see from Table I, this happens if we play row 1 40 percent of the time, and row 2 the other 60 percent. If we do this, then we win 2.6¢ for any play of the columns, including a mixture. We say that the *value* of the game, to us, is 2.6¢.

TABLE I

| Row Strategy | Expectation Against | |
	Column 1, ¢	Column 2, ¢
(0.0,1.0)	3.0	1.0
(0.1,0.9)	2.9	1.4
(0.2,0.8)	2.8	1.8
(0.3,0.7)	2.7	2.2
(0.4,0.6)	2.6✱	2.6✱
(0.5,0.5)	2.5	3.0
(0.6,0.4)	2.4	3.4
(0.7,0.3)	2.3	3.8
(0.8,0.2)	2.2	4.2
(0.9,0.1)	2.1	4.6
(1.0,0.0)	2.0	5.0

Column Expectation (E_c)

How about the column player? How can he make *sure* of a fixed pay-off regardless of the row player's strategy? We shall omit the full discussion, which is the same as that for the row player, and state that the expectation for the column player is

$$\mathbf{E}_c = \mathbf{Gc}$$

where $\mathbf{E}_c$ is a column vector of expectation for the column player, $\mathbf{G}$ is the game matrix, and $\mathbf{c}$ is a column vector for column strategy. (Remember that we are writing $\mathbf{c}$ instead of $\mathbf{c}^t$ throughout this chapter.)

illustrative problem 3

In the same game, calculate the expectation for a column strategy of $\begin{pmatrix} 0.3 \\ 0.7 \end{pmatrix}$ and explain.

solution

$$\mathbf{E}_c = \begin{pmatrix} 2¢ & 5¢ \\ 3¢ & 1¢ \end{pmatrix} \begin{pmatrix} 0.3 \\ 0.7 \end{pmatrix} = \begin{pmatrix} 0.6 + 3.5 \\ 0.9 + 0.7 \end{pmatrix} = \begin{pmatrix} 4.1 \\ 1.6 \end{pmatrix}$$

This means that the column player has an expectation of (losing) 4.1¢ if row 1 is played and 1.6¢ if row 2 is played. Notice that $\mathbf{E}_r$ represents payoff to the row player, and so does $\mathbf{E}_c$.

Using the formula for $\mathbf{E}_c$, we calculate the payoffs for different, selected mixed strategies for the column player in Table II. According to this table, the strategy that leaves the row player helpless is $\begin{pmatrix} 0.8 \\ 0.2 \end{pmatrix}$, meaning that the column player should play column 1 80 percent of the time, at random, and column 2 the other 20 percent of the time. Under these circumstances, he will lose only 2.6¢. (This game is unfair to the enemy, but this is the best he can do against intelligent play.) The value of the game, from the point of view of the column player, is 2.6¢, *exactly the same as it was for the row player.*

TABLE II

Column Strategy	Expectation Against	
	Row 1, ¢	Row 2, ¢
$\begin{pmatrix} 0.0 \\ 1.0 \end{pmatrix}$	5.0	1.0
$\begin{pmatrix} 0.1 \\ 0.9 \end{pmatrix}$	4.7	1.2
$\begin{pmatrix} 0.2 \\ 0.8 \end{pmatrix}$	4.4	1.4
$\begin{pmatrix} 0.3 \\ 0.7 \end{pmatrix}$	4.1	1.6
$\begin{pmatrix} 0.4 \\ 0.6 \end{pmatrix}$	3.8	1.8
$\begin{pmatrix} 0.5 \\ 0.5 \end{pmatrix}$	3.5	2.0
$\begin{pmatrix} 0.6 \\ 0.4 \end{pmatrix}$	3.2	2.2
$\begin{pmatrix} 0.7 \\ 0.3 \end{pmatrix}$	2.9	2.4
$\begin{pmatrix} 0.8 \\ 0.2 \end{pmatrix}$	2.6✱	2.6✱
$\begin{pmatrix} 0.9 \\ 0.1 \end{pmatrix}$	2.3	2.8
$\begin{pmatrix} 1.0 \\ 0.0 \end{pmatrix}$	2.0	3.0

The fact that the value to the row player and the value to the column player are the same is important. It is a theorem which was proved by the great John von Neumann in 1928.

minimax theorem

With the best play on both sides, the expectation of winning for the row player is the same as the expectation of losing for the column player. This expectation is defined as the *value*, *v*, of the game.

An Example

We illustrate with an example which completes Illustrative Problem 4 on pages 118 to 119 of Chap. 4. In that problem, we started with a 5×2 game and, using the ideas of dominance, reduced the problem to

	1	2
3	4¢	7¢
4	6¢	5¢

Unfortunately, this is not a saddle-point game.

illustrative problem 4

In the above game, find (*a*) optimal row strategy, (*b*) optimal column strategy, and (*c*) the value of the game.

solution

(*a*) Table III shows the results of some selected row strategies. In the table, we look in vain for a row strategy that yields exactly the same return against any play of the columns. There is none. This is not surprising; we tested only a few out of an infinity of possible row strategies. For example, perhaps the optimal row strategy is (0.225,0.775). It might be. However, in this case, the problem is not so serious. From the results for (0.2,0.8) and (0.3,0.7), it looks as if the optimal row strategy might possibly be midway between them. We test (0.25,0.75):

$$(0.25,0.75)\begin{pmatrix} 4¢ & 7¢ \\ 6¢ & 5¢ \end{pmatrix} = (1 + 4.5, 1.75 + 3.75) = (5.5¢,5.5¢)$$

As you see, this strategy leaves the column player helpless. Therefore it is the optimal row strategy. Against any play by the column player, including mixtures of column 1 and column 2, we win 5.5¢ on an aver-

TABLE III

Row Strategy	Expectation Against	
	Column 1	Column 2
(0.0,1.0)	6.0	5.0
(0.1,0.9)	5.8	5.2
(0.2,0.8)	5.6	5.4
(0.3,0.7)	5.4	5.6
(0.4,0.6)	5.2	5.8
(0.5,0.5)	5.0	6.0
(0.6,0.4)	4.8	6.2
(0.7,0.3)	4.6	6.4
(0.8,0.2)	4.4	6.6
(0.9,0.1)	4.2	6.8
(1.0,0.0)	4.0	7.0

age. This is the value of the game to us. The complete row strategy for the original 5×2 game is, therefore,

$$\mathbf{r} = (0,0,0.25,0.75,0)$$

where the zeros indicate that the row player should never play rows 1, 2, or 5. He should play row 3 one-quarter of the time, at random, and row 4 the other three-quarters of the time.

We are, of course, not too happy about the fact that we had to guess at the optimal row strategy. You probably have guessed that there are better methods. For the moment, notice that if we *plot* the payoffs for row strategies (Fig. 5-2) the meeting point of the two lines is directly above (0.25,0.75).

The calculations for column strategy are shown in Table IV. From the table, the optimal column strategy is $\begin{pmatrix} 0.5 \\ 0.5 \end{pmatrix}$. Notice that the value of the game to the column player is also 5.5¢ (lost).

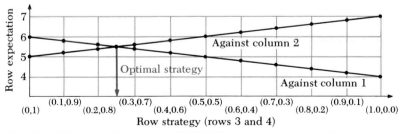

Fig. 5-2   The optimal strategy is (0.25,0.75).

TABLE IV

Column Strategy	Expectation Against	
	Row 1	Row 2
$\begin{pmatrix} 0.0 \\ 1.0 \end{pmatrix}$	7.0	5.0
$\begin{pmatrix} 0.1 \\ 0.9 \end{pmatrix}$	6.7	5.1
$\begin{pmatrix} 0.2 \\ 0.8 \end{pmatrix}$	6.4	5.2
$\begin{pmatrix} 0.3 \\ 0.7 \end{pmatrix}$	6.1	5.3
$\begin{pmatrix} 0.4 \\ 0.6 \end{pmatrix}$	5.8	5.4
$\begin{pmatrix} 0.5 \\ 0.5 \end{pmatrix}$	5.5 *	5.5 *
$\begin{pmatrix} 0.6 \\ 0.4 \end{pmatrix}$	5.2	5.6
$\begin{pmatrix} 0.7 \\ 0.3 \end{pmatrix}$	4.9	5.7
$\begin{pmatrix} 0.8 \\ 0.2 \end{pmatrix}$	4.6	5.8
$\begin{pmatrix} 0.9 \\ 0.1 \end{pmatrix}$	4.3	5.9
$\begin{pmatrix} 1.0 \\ 0.0 \end{pmatrix}$	4.0	6.0

A Graphical Shortcut

You may have noticed that, as expectation increases in one set, it decreases in the other. Furthermore, from Fig. 5-2, you may suspect that these form straight lines. Your suspicion is well founded; they do, indeed, form straight lines. Under those circumstances, we can save ourselves a great deal of arithmetic; only two points are needed to draw a straight line. This is illustrated in the following.

illustrative problem 5

Complete the first illustrative problem in Chap. 4 which had the game matrix

	Heads	Tails
Heads	0¢	−3¢
Tails	−3¢	3¢

solution

First, we check for a saddle point. *This must always be done immediately, regardless of the size or shape of the matrix.* There is none. Then we calculate *two* row strategies:

	Expectation Against	
Row Strategy	Column 1	Column 2
(0,1)	−3	3
(1,0)	0	−3

Now we plot, as shown in Fig. 5-3. From the graph, it appears that the optimal row strategy is between 60 and 70 percent for row 1, and the rest for row 2. Another method, which we shall explain later, shows that it is actually $(\frac{2}{3},\frac{1}{3})$ meaning that we should call *heads* two out of three times, at random, and *tails* the rest of the time. We shall check our correct value by calculating the value of the game:

$$(\tfrac{2}{3},\tfrac{1}{3})\begin{pmatrix} 0 & -3 \\ -3 & 3 \end{pmatrix} = (-1,-1)$$

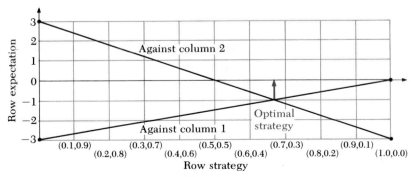

Fig. 5-3   *Graph for Illustrative Problem 5.*

The game is unfair to us; we average a loss of 1¢ at each play, but that is the best we can do (except refuse to play).

A similar analysis for the enemy, with a similar graph, shows that his best strategy is also $\begin{pmatrix} 2/3 \\ 1/3 \end{pmatrix}$. Checking again, we have

$$\begin{pmatrix} 0 & -3 \\ -3 & 3 \end{pmatrix}\begin{pmatrix} 2/3 \\ 1/3 \end{pmatrix} = \begin{pmatrix} -1 \\ -1 \end{pmatrix}$$

In Problem Section 5.1, we have the exact answers (obtained by the method you will learn next). Count yourself correct if your graphical solution is near the exact answer.

Random Sequences

Suppose that in the game we just investigated (with *heads* and *tails*) we have arranged to play 12 times. (We chose that figure to make the explanation easy.) Then, according to our calculations, our best bet is to call *heads* eight times and *tails* four times. If we call *heads* the first eight times and *tails* the last four times, the cunning enemy may see what we are doing. He will call *tails* the first eight times and *heads* the last four times. This will cost us 3¢ each play, instead of 1¢. We have a right to be unhappy about that way of playing. It is most unsatisfactory.

What we must do is mix our choices *unpredictably*, so that the enemy cannot guess reliably what we are going to do next. We call this unpredictable arrangement a *random sequence*.

There are many excellent ways of getting a random sequence. (See Dodes and Greitzer, "Numerical Analysis," pp. 135–137, Hayden, 1964.) We shall be satisfied with the following approximate system. All you need is a watch with a second hand.

Now, suppose the desired strategy is (⅔,⅓), at random. You multiply by 60 (you will see why in a moment) and get (40,20). Before each

Fig. 5-4   Play row 1.

Fig. 5-5   Play row 2.

play, you look quickly at the second hand of your watch. If, at that precise instant, the second hand is between 0 and 40 (counting 0 but not 40), you play row 1 (Fig. 5-4).

 If the second hand is between 40 and 60 (counting 40, but not 60 which is the same as 0), you play row 2 (Fig. 5-5).

illustrative problem 6

Suppose row strategy is (0.25,0.75). How do you obtain a random sequence by using your watch?

solution

Multiplying by 60, you get (15,45). If the second hand is between 0 and 15 (not including 15), play row 1. Otherwise, play row 2.

 We repeat that this is not a perfect method, but it will be good enough for our present purposes.

PROBLEM SECTION 5.1

Part A. How would you divide your seconds dial to obtain the following strategies?

1. (0.1,0.9)   2. (0.2,0.8)
3. ($\frac{1}{3}$,$\frac{2}{3}$)   4. ($\frac{2}{5}$,$\frac{3}{5}$)
5. ($\frac{4}{15}$,$\frac{11}{15}$)   6. ($\frac{7}{12}$,$\frac{5}{12}$)

Part B. These problems refer to the ones in Problem Section 4.1 (beginning on page 103). For each of the problems find the optimal strategies and the value of the game.

7. Problem Section 4.1, Prob. 1.
8. Problem Section 4.1, Prob. 2.
9. Problem Section 4.1, Prob. 5.
10. Problem Section 4.1, Prob. 6.

Part C. Find the optimal strategies and the value of the game for each of the following. Remember to reduce the original games by dominance in order to obtain a 2×2 subgame.

11. Problem Section 4.3, Prob. 5, page 113.
12. Problem Section 4.3, Prob. 8, page 113.

5.2   MIXED STRATEGY (PART II)

Payoff for Any Play

We have been assuming throughout that the game is played correctly, at least by one of the opponents. For example, in the preceding section, we investigated the game matrix

		⅔	⅓
		1	2
⅔	1	0	−3
⅓	2	−3	3

Inserted, in color, is the correct strategy for each row and column. The value of the game was -1, showing that it was unfair to the row player.

Now, suppose that the players play incorrectly, as follows:

		⅓	⅔
		1	2
¼	1	0	−3
¾	2	−3	3

In other words, the row player plays (¼,¾) and the column player plays $\begin{pmatrix} ⅓ \\ ⅔ \end{pmatrix}$. Let us see what the result will be.

To simplify the explanation, suppose we consider a set of 24 plays. (We chose 24 because it is convenient to divide into.) For 6 plays, we play row 1. Against this, the enemy chooses column 1 one-third of the time (in other words, *twice*) and column 2 the rest of the time (in other words, *four times*). For our other 18 plays, we play row 2. Against this, the enemy plays column 1 one-third of the time (6 times) and column 2 the rest of the time (12 times). The following is a summary for the 24 plays:

$$\begin{pmatrix} 0 \text{ (twice)} & -3 \text{ (four times)} \\ -3 \text{ (six times)} & 3 \text{ (12 times)} \end{pmatrix}$$

The payoff, for the 24 games, is

$$2(0) + 4(-3) + 6(-3) + 12(3) = 0 - 12 - 18 + 36 = 6$$

The payoff per play (played incorrectly) is $\tfrac{6}{24} = 0.25$ instead of -1. When the game is played incorrectly, the payoff may be more than or less than, or equal to, the actual value of the game.

As you may suspect by this time, there is a faster way to obtain the payoff for any play. The faster way uses the formula

$$P = \mathbf{r}\mathbf{G}\mathbf{c}$$

where P is the payoff, $\mathbf{r}$ is the row strategy, $\mathbf{G}$ is the game matrix, and $\mathbf{c}$ is the column strategy.

$$P = (\tfrac{1}{4},\tfrac{3}{4})\begin{pmatrix} 0 & -3 \\ -3 & 3 \end{pmatrix}\begin{pmatrix} \tfrac{1}{3} \\ \tfrac{2}{3} \end{pmatrix} = (-\tfrac{9}{4},\tfrac{6}{4})\begin{pmatrix} \tfrac{1}{3} \\ \tfrac{2}{3} \end{pmatrix}$$

$$= (-\tfrac{9}{4})(\tfrac{1}{3}) + (\tfrac{6}{4})(\tfrac{2}{3}) = -\tfrac{3}{4} + 1 = 0.25$$

illustrative problem 1

Find the payoff for the following game played incorrectly.

		$\tfrac{1}{5}$	$\tfrac{4}{5}$
		1	2
$\tfrac{1}{2}$	1	2¢	5¢
$\tfrac{1}{2}$	2	3¢	1¢

solution

$$P = \quad \mathbf{r} \quad\quad \mathbf{G} \quad\quad \mathbf{c}$$

$$= (\tfrac{1}{2},\tfrac{1}{2})\begin{pmatrix} 2 & 5 \\ 3 & 1 \end{pmatrix}\begin{pmatrix} \tfrac{1}{5} \\ \tfrac{4}{5} \end{pmatrix}$$

$$= (\tfrac{5}{2},\tfrac{6}{2})\begin{pmatrix} \tfrac{1}{5} \\ \tfrac{4}{5} \end{pmatrix} = (\tfrac{5}{2})(\tfrac{1}{5}) + (\tfrac{6}{2})(\tfrac{4}{5})$$

$$= 0.5 + 2.4 = 2.9¢$$

If played *correctly* by at least one of the players, the payoff is the value of the game, 2.6¢.

A Little Theory (Optional)

You can skip this if you must. Our purpose is to explain a quick method for solving 2×2 games. This method is given in the following subsection. We want you to know where the quick method came from.

Let the 2×2 game be

	1	2
1	a	b
2	c	d

where a, b, c, and d represent payoffs to the row player. Now suppose that x fraction of the time we play row 1. For example, x may be ¼. Then we must play row 2 for $1 - x$ fraction of the time. If x is ¼, then $1 - x$ will be ¾. Similarly, if the enemy plays column 1 for y fraction of the time, he must play column 2 for $1 - y$ fraction of the time. In the following illustration, we have taken x as ¼ and y as ⅓.

		$y = ⅓$	$1 - y = ⅔$
		1	2
$x = ¼$	1	a	b
$1 - x = ¾$	2	c	d

Then the payoff is calculated by formula as shown:

$$P = \quad \mathbf{r} \qquad \mathbf{G} \qquad \mathbf{c}$$

$$= (x, 1 - x)\begin{pmatrix} a & b \\ c & d \end{pmatrix}\begin{pmatrix} y \\ 1 - y \end{pmatrix}$$

$$= (a - b - c + d)xy + (b - d)x + (c - d)y + d$$

This is not very informative. It can be rearranged somewhat as follows:

$$P = (a - b - c + d)\left(x + \frac{c - d}{a - b - c + d}\right)\left(y + \frac{b - d}{a - b - c + d}\right)$$
$$- \frac{(c - d)(b - d)}{a - b - c + d} + d$$

Now, let us examine this payoff formula. First, we must assume that $a - b - c + d$ does not equal zero. (Otherwise, the formula makes no sense, because we cannot divide by zero.) We shall call this denominator D (for "denominator"). Note that the last two terms of the formula do not depend on row strategy or column strategy (this is obvious because there is no x or y in them). We collect them and call them k (mathematicians frequently use k for "constant"). Then the formula becomes

$$P = D\left(x + \frac{c - d}{D}\right)\left(y + \frac{b - d}{D}\right) + k \qquad\qquad\text{I}$$

Now, suppose the row player chooses x in such a way that

$$x + \frac{c - d}{D} = 0 \qquad\qquad\text{II}$$

or, in other words,

$$x = -\frac{c - d}{D} \qquad\qquad\text{III}$$

Then, formula I becomes

$$P = D(0)\left(y + \frac{b - d}{D}\right) + k \qquad\qquad\text{IV}$$

and this means that

$$P = k \qquad\qquad\text{V}$$

regardless of the strategy of the column player. He is absolutely helpless and cannot influence the payoff. This must be the best strategy for the row player.

   Similarly, suppose that the enemy chooses a strategy such that

$$y = -\frac{b - d}{D} \qquad\qquad\text{VI}$$

Then we have, by substituting in formula I,

$$P = D\left(x + \frac{c - d}{D}\right)(0) + k \qquad\qquad\text{VII}$$

and, once again, we find that $P = k$, regardless of the strategy of the column player. Now the row player is helpless. Obviously, formula VI is the optimal strategy for the column player.

   Continuing the arithmetic (we omit the gory details), we find that the optimal strategy for the row player is given by

$$x = -\frac{c - d}{D} = \frac{d - c}{D}$$

$$1 - x = \frac{a - b}{D}$$

and the optimal strategy for the column player is

$$y = -\frac{b - d}{D} = \frac{d - b}{D}$$

$$1 - y = \frac{a - c}{D}$$

The short method, to be given in the next subsection, uses the fact that the ratio of x to $1 - x$ is $(d - c)/(a - b)$, and the ratio of y to $1 - y$ is $(d - b)/(a - c)$.

A Quick Method for the 2 × 2 Game

In the preceding (optional) subsection, we examined the mathematical basis for a mixed strategy for either rows or columns. Suppose the game is

		½	½
		1	2
¼	1	4¢	7¢
¾	2	6¢	5¢

then the row strategy is (¼,¾) and the row *odds* are ¼:¾, or 1:3. We shall call each "part" of the odds an *oddment*. (This word is borrowed from a hilarious book, "The Compleat Strategyst," by J. D. Williams.[1] We urge you to read it.) In this problem, 1 is a row oddment, and 3 is a row oddment. Also, 1 and 1 are the column oddments. The oddments are simply the numerators of the strategy when the denominators are all the same. To find the denominators, knowing the oddments, we merely add the oddments, as shown in the following.

illustrative problem 2

The oddments for a certain game are 2 and 5. What is the strategy?

solution

If these are row oddments, the strategy is (²⁄₇,⁵⁄₇). If these are column oddments, the strategy is $\begin{pmatrix} ²⁄₇ \\ ⁵⁄₇ \end{pmatrix}$.

illustrative problem 3

The column oddments for a certain game are 0, 7, 10, and 2. What is the column strategy?

---

[1] McGraw-Hill, New York, rev. ed., 1965.

solution

$$\begin{pmatrix} 0 \\ \frac{7}{19} \\ \frac{10}{19} \\ \frac{2}{19} \end{pmatrix}$$

Now we return to our main problem. We wish to find the oddments for games in which there is no saddle point. According to the explanation in the preceding subsection, the row strategy for the game

	1	2
1	a	b
2	c	d

has oddments $d - c$ and $a - b$. This means that the oddment for row 1 is the determinant

$$\begin{vmatrix} 1 & 1 \\ c & d \end{vmatrix} = d - c$$

and the oddment for row 2 is the determinant

$$\begin{vmatrix} a & b \\ 1 & 1 \end{vmatrix} = a - b$$

Similarly, the oddment for column 1 is the determinant

$$\begin{vmatrix} 1 & b \\ 1 & d \end{vmatrix} = d - b$$

and the oddment for column 2 is the determinant

$$\begin{vmatrix} a & 1 \\ c & 1 \end{vmatrix} = a - c$$

oddment theorem

To find the oddment for any row or column of a game without saddle points, replace the row or column by 1s and calculate the determinant.

illustrative problem 4

Find the optimal strategies and the value of the following game.

	1	2
1	-0.6	2.4
2	0.4	-1.6

solution

First, we add 1.6 to each entry in order to avoid negative entries. Remember that this changes the value but not the strategies. This results in

	1	2
1	1	4
2	2	0

Second, we check for a saddle point. There is none. *Third,* we calculate the oddments.

$$\begin{vmatrix} 1 & 1 \\ 2 & 0 \end{vmatrix} = (0) - (2) = -2 \qquad \text{oddment for row 1}$$

$$\begin{vmatrix} 1 & 4 \\ 1 & 1 \end{vmatrix} = (1) - (4) = -3 \qquad \text{oddment for row 2}$$

The sum of the oddments is -5, so that the strategy is $\left(\dfrac{-2}{-5}, \dfrac{-3}{-5}\right)$ which is the same as $(\frac{2}{5}, \frac{3}{5})$ or $(0.4, 0.6)$. *Notice that the entries for a strategy cannot be negative.* Also, as you already know, the sum of the parts of a strategy is 1, which means 100 percent. *Fourth,* we calculate the column oddments.

$$\begin{vmatrix} 1 & 4 \\ 1 & 0 \end{vmatrix} = (0) - (4) = -4 \qquad \text{oddment for column 1}$$

$$\begin{vmatrix} 1 & 1 \\ 2 & 1 \end{vmatrix} = (1) - (2) = -1 \qquad \text{oddment for column 2}$$

The sum of the column oddments is -5, so that the column strategy is $\begin{pmatrix} \frac{4}{5} \\ \frac{1}{5} \end{pmatrix}$ or $\begin{pmatrix} 0.8 \\ 0.2 \end{pmatrix}$. *Fifth,* we find the value of the game. Remember that we altered the game by adding 1.6 to each entry. We shall have to subtract it later. We can find the value of the (altered) game either by

$$E = rG$$

or

$$E = Gc$$

and they should be the same. We shall do both, for practice.

$$E = rG = (\tfrac{2}{5},\tfrac{3}{5})\begin{pmatrix} 1 & 4 \\ 2 & 0 \end{pmatrix} = \tfrac{1}{5}(2,3)\begin{pmatrix} 1 & 4 \\ 2 & 0 \end{pmatrix} = \tfrac{1}{5}(8,8) = (\tfrac{8}{5},\tfrac{8}{5}) = (1\tfrac{3}{5},1\tfrac{3}{5})$$

$$E = Gc = \begin{pmatrix} 1 & 4 \\ 2 & 0 \end{pmatrix}\begin{pmatrix} \tfrac{4}{5} \\ \tfrac{1}{5} \end{pmatrix} = \tfrac{1}{5}\begin{pmatrix} 1 & 4 \\ 2 & 0 \end{pmatrix}\begin{pmatrix} 4 \\ 1 \end{pmatrix} = \tfrac{1}{5}\begin{pmatrix} 8 \\ 8 \end{pmatrix} = \begin{pmatrix} \tfrac{8}{5} \\ \tfrac{8}{5} \end{pmatrix} = \begin{pmatrix} 1\tfrac{3}{5} \\ 1\tfrac{3}{5} \end{pmatrix}$$

The value of the altered game is 1.6. The value of the original game is, therefore, 0. It is a fair game.

illustrative problem 5

Find the oddments for

	1	2
1	1	3
2	4	5

solution

$$\begin{vmatrix} 1 & 1 \\ 4 & 5 \end{vmatrix} = (5) - (4) = 1$$

$$\begin{vmatrix} 1 & 3 \\ 1 & 1 \end{vmatrix} = (1) - (3) = -2$$

According to this, the strategy is $\left(\dfrac{1}{-1},\dfrac{-2}{-1}\right)$ or $(-1,2)$. This is completely meaningless! It would seem that row 1 should be played -100 percent of the time, and row 2 should be played 200 percent of the time. Why did the results turn out that way? That is simple: we forgot to check for a saddle point. In fact, this is a saddle-point game with the saddle point at (row 2, column 1), so that the optimal strategy really is

$$r = (0,1) \qquad c = \begin{pmatrix} 1 \\ 0 \end{pmatrix}$$

and the value of the game is 4. *Always check for a saddle point before doing anything else.*

PROBLEM SECTION 5.2

Part A. For each of the games below, (a) find the optimal row strategy, (b) find the optimal column strategy, (c) find the value of the game, and (d) find the payoff for the incorrect strategies given in the problem.

1.

	1	2
1	4	7
2	1	2

Incorrect strategy: $(\frac{1}{2},\frac{1}{2})$; $\begin{pmatrix} \frac{1}{3} \\ \frac{2}{3} \end{pmatrix}$

2.

	1	2
1	2	6
2	9	7

Incorrect strategy: $(\frac{1}{3},\frac{2}{3})$; $\begin{pmatrix} \frac{7}{8} \\ \frac{1}{8} \end{pmatrix}$

3.

	1	2
1	5	3
2	0	8

Incorrect strategy: $(\frac{2}{5},\frac{3}{5})$; $\begin{pmatrix} \frac{3}{5} \\ \frac{2}{5} \end{pmatrix}$

4.

	1	2
1	8	5
2	1	10

Incorrect strategy: $(\frac{4}{5},\frac{1}{5})$; $\begin{pmatrix} \frac{1}{3} \\ \frac{2}{3} \end{pmatrix}$

Part B. In the following, it is suggested that the games be altered by addition and/or multiplication to simplify the arithmetic.

5.

	1	2
1	-2	6
2	3	1

Incorrect strategy: $(\frac{1}{2},\frac{1}{2})$; $\begin{pmatrix} \frac{2}{3} \\ \frac{1}{3} \end{pmatrix}$

6.

	1	2
1	2	-3
2	-2	7

Incorrect strategy: $(\frac{9}{14},\frac{5}{14})$; $\begin{pmatrix} \frac{5}{7} \\ \frac{2}{7} \end{pmatrix}$

7.

	1	2
1	4	-1
2	-3	2

Incorrect strategy: $(\frac{1}{2},\frac{1}{2})$; $\begin{pmatrix} \frac{3}{10} \\ \frac{7}{10} \end{pmatrix}$

8.

	1	2
1	4	-1
2	-4	1

Incorrect strategy: $(\frac{1}{2},\frac{1}{2})$ $\begin{pmatrix} \frac{1}{5} \\ \frac{4}{5} \end{pmatrix}$

Part C. In the following, it is suggested that the games be altered to simplify the arithmetic.

9.

	1	2
1	-1.6	0.4
2	2.4	-0.6

Incorrect strategy: $(\frac{1}{2}, \frac{1}{2})$; $\begin{pmatrix} \frac{3}{4} \\ \frac{1}{4} \end{pmatrix}$

10.

	1	2
1	$-1\frac{1}{3}$	$-\frac{1}{3}$
2	$1\frac{2}{3}$	$-6\frac{1}{3}$

Incorrect strategy: $(0, 1)$; $\begin{pmatrix} \frac{2}{3} \\ \frac{1}{3} \end{pmatrix}$

5.3   2 × m and m × 2 GAMES; TRIAL-AND-ERROR METHOD

In previous sections, we have investigated $2 \times m$ games and $m \times 2$ games which either reduced to saddle-point games or into 2×2 games which could be solved by oddments. However, there are games which do not seem to have either saddle points or dominance, at least of the kind we have discussed. In this section, we shall discuss trial-and-error methods for these games.

2 × m Games

Consider the following game:

	1	2	3
1	0	2	7
2	10	9	4

This game has no saddle point, nor can we reduce it further by dominance. (There are other kinds of dominance which can be used but we shall not need to discuss them.) What shall we do?

We proceed by dividing the 2×3 game into three 2×2 *subgames* which are in it.

Subgame a

	1	2
1	0	2
2	10	9

Subgame b

	1	3
1	0	7
2	10	4

Subgame c

	2	3
1	2	7
2	9	4

Subgame a has a saddle point at $(2,2)$ with a value of 9. The other subgames have mixed strategies calculated by the oddments method already explained. The row strategies for the three subgames are

Subgame a: $(0,1)$

Subgame b: $(\frac{6}{13},\frac{7}{13})$

Subgame c: $(\frac{1}{2},\frac{1}{2})$

We try each strategy against columns 1, 2, and 3, using the formula $\mathbf{E} = \mathbf{rG}$. This is shown in the following, for subgame b:

$$\mathbf{E} = \mathbf{rG} = (\tfrac{6}{13},\tfrac{7}{13})\begin{pmatrix} 0 & 2 & 7 \\ 10 & 9 & 4 \end{pmatrix} = \tfrac{1}{13}(6,7)\begin{pmatrix} 0 & 2 & 7 \\ 10 & 9 & 4 \end{pmatrix}$$
$$= \tfrac{1}{13}(70,75,70) = (5\tfrac{5}{13},5\tfrac{10}{13},5\tfrac{5}{13})$$

The following table lists the payoffs for each subgame and its strategy. In the second column are listed the columns which we want the column player to play. (He may or may not.) In the last three columns are the actual payoffs to the row player. The one in parentheses is the payoff if the column player does *not* play the column that is in the subgame, i.e., if he plays the column we did *not* choose.

Subgame	Columns	Row Strategy	Expectation Against		
			Column 1	Column 2	Column 3
a	1, 2	$(0,1)$	10	9	(4)
b	1, 3	$(\frac{6}{13},\frac{7}{13})$	$5\frac{5}{13}$	$(5\frac{10}{13})$	$5\frac{5}{13}$
c	2, 3	$(\frac{1}{2},\frac{1}{2})$	(5)	$5\frac{1}{2}$	$5\frac{1}{2}$

In subgame a, we would do well if the enemy played the columns we chose, namely, columns 1 and 2 (these are the columns in subgame a). However, he would be crazy to do so. He does better by playing column 3, in which case he loses only 4. Subgame a cannot possibly contain an optimal strategy, because the enemy is not going to have to play it the way we want it played.

In subgame c, we get $5\frac{1}{2}$ if the enemy plays the columns we have chosen, namely, columns 2 and 3, but he is undoubtedly mean enough to play column 1. Then we win only 5. Subgame c cannot contain an optimal strategy, because the enemy is not forced to play it the way we want it played.

Now, look at subgame b. This subgame contains columns 1 and 3, and if the enemy plays them, we win $5\frac{5}{13}$. Suppose he chooses to be stubborn and play column 2. Then we win even more. *The enemy is forced to play our game.* Subgame *b*, then, has the optimal strategy.

The conclusion of our thinking is that our optimal (row) strategy is $(\%_{13}, \%_{13})$. The optimal column strategy is the one for subgame *b* with 0

for the missing column, i.e., $\begin{pmatrix} \frac{3}{13} \\ 0 \\ \frac{10}{13} \end{pmatrix}$. The value of the game is $5\%_{13}$,

the expectation if both opponents play a perfect game.

We emphasize the main idea which underlies the theory of games:

penalty principle

If either player does not play the optimal strategy, he may be penalized. There can be no advantage in not playing the optimal strategy.

illustrative problem 1

We have settled on a game with the enemy. The enemy may show one, two, or three fingers and we, at the same time, yell "Right" or "Left." Our payoff matrix is as follows:

		Enemy		
		One finger	Two fingers	Three fingers
We	Right	− $0.50	$1.50	− $1.50
	Left	$0.50	− $1.50	$4.50

What are the optimal strategies? Find the value of the game.

solution

We add $1.50 to each entry. The game matrix is now

	1	2	3
1	1	3	0
2	2	0	6

There is, alas, no saddle point. The three possible subgames are

Subgame *a*

	1	2
1	1	3
2	2	0

Subgame *b*

	1	3
1	1	0
2	2*	6

Subgame *c*

	2	3
1	3	0
2	0	6

Subgame b has a saddle point at (row 2, column 1) with a value of 2. The strategies against each of the three columns are shown in the table which follows. Again, the payoffs in parentheses are the ones if the enemy does *not* choose to play the columns in the subgame which we are considering at the moment.

| Subgame | Columns | Row Strategy | Expectation Against | | |
			Column 1	Column 2	Column 3
a	1, 2	(½,½)	1½	1½	(3)
b	1, 3	(0,1)	2	(0)	6
c	2, 3	(⅔,⅓)	(1⅓)	2	2

It should be fairly clear that our best strategy is contained in subgame a, because if the enemy does not choose to play our game according to the columns we have chosen, he will lose 3 instead of just 1½.

With the oddments method, our best strategy is (½,½), the enemy's best strategy is $\begin{pmatrix} ¾ \\ ¼ \\ 0 \end{pmatrix}$ (meaning that he had better not play column 3), and the value of the altered game is 1½. The value of the original game is 0, showing that it is a fair game.

illustrative problem 2

Find the optimal strategies and the value of the following game.

	1	2	3	4
1	1	5	8	16
2	14	8	6	4

solution

There is no saddle point, and no (simple) dominance. There are six possible subgames to be considered: (a) columns 1, 2; (b) columns 1, 3; (c) columns 1, 4; (d) columns 2, 3; (e) columns 2, 4; (f) columns 3, 4. After we consider each game, it turns out that the optimal strategy is in subgame d. The row strategy is (0.4,0.6), the column strategy is $\begin{pmatrix} 0 \\ 0.4 \\ 0.6 \\ 0 \end{pmatrix}$, and the value of the game is 6.8.

m $\times$ 2 Games

In 2 $\times$ m games, we start with two *rows,* and we choose two (out of m) *columns* for our optimal game. In m $\times$ 2 games, we start with two *columns,* and we choose two (out of m) *rows* for the optimal game. The technique is exactly as it was before.

illustrative problem 3

The manufacturer of a small transistor radio has to decide on his quality-control procedure. This is a procedure designed to find defects in the radios before they are sent to distributors. A full check is rather expensive, but there is a less expensive quick check. The quick check does not discover all possible defects, but it does detect the most common ones. Of course, he may decide not to test at all and take a chance.

   If he sends a radio for sale and it is defective, he is in trouble with the distributor (and the customer). Also, it is costly to pay for remailing and replacement.

   What is his best strategy if the following matrix is an estimate of payoffs in dollars? (Nature is the enemy, in this case.)

	Not Defective	Defective
No test	10	-25
Quick check	-4	10
Full test	-11	17

solution

There are no saddle points and no (simple) dominance. First, let us add 25 to each entry. This yields

	1	2
1	35	0
2	21	35
3	14	42

The possible 2 $\times$ 2 subgames are

Subgame a

	1	2
1	35	0
2	21	35

Subgame b

	1	2
1	35	0
3	14	42

Subgame c

	1	2
2	21*	35
3	14	42

Subgame c has a saddle point at (row 2, column 1) with a value of 21. We must now compute *column* strategies and the resulting payoffs, using $\mathbf{E} = \mathbf{Gc}$. To refresh your memory, the calculations are

$$a:\begin{pmatrix} 35 & 0 \\ 21 & 35 \\ 14 & 42 \end{pmatrix} \begin{pmatrix} 5/7 \\ 2/7 \end{pmatrix} = \begin{pmatrix} 25 \\ 25 \\ 22 \end{pmatrix}$$

$$b:\begin{pmatrix} 35 & 0 \\ 21 & 35 \\ 14 & 42 \end{pmatrix} \begin{pmatrix} 2/3 \\ 1/3 \end{pmatrix} = \begin{pmatrix} 70/3 \\ 77/3 \\ 70/3 \end{pmatrix} = \begin{pmatrix} 23\frac{1}{3} \\ 25\frac{2}{3} \\ 23\frac{1}{3} \end{pmatrix}$$

This results in the following table.

Subgame	Rows	Column Strategy	Expectation Against		
			Row 1	Row 2	Row 3
a	1, 2	$\begin{pmatrix} 5/7 \\ 2/7 \end{pmatrix}$	25	25	(22)
b	1, 3	$\begin{pmatrix} 2/3 \\ 1/3 \end{pmatrix}$	23⅓	(25⅔)	23⅓
c	2, 3	$\begin{pmatrix} 1 \\ 0 \end{pmatrix}$	(35)	21	14

If the enemy (Nature, in this case) chooses subgame a, the manufacturer wins 25 if he agrees. (Remember, we added 25 to the original game, and so this means he breaks even). If he chooses to play row 3, he wins only 22. In other words, there is a penalty for not playing subgame a the way it was selected. It would seem that an optimal procedure would be to agree on subgame a.

Before making up our minds, let us examine games b and c. In subgame b, if the manufacturer agrees, he wins 23⅓ and is *not* penalized by placing the wrong row (row 2). Therefore, subgame b cannot be an optimal game, because the manufacturer does better (25⅔) by playing it "wrong." In game c, the manufacturer wins 21 in the saddle point and is *not* penalized by playing the "wrong" row, row 1. Therefore, subgame c cannot be an optimal game.

This settles the question. By the penalty principle, the manufacturer must play subgame *a*. His correct strategy (for the original game) is ($\frac{2}{7}$,$\frac{5}{7}$,0). This means that he should do a quick check on five out of every seven radios, at random, and no test on the others. The value of the altered game is 25, and so (since we added 25) the value of the original game is 0. It is a fair game. Who said Nature was unfair?

PROBLEM SECTION 5.3

Part A. Find the optimal strategies and the value of each game.

1.

	1	2	3
1	3	8	6
2	10	2	3

2.

	1	2	3
1	1	3	5
2	8	4	3

3.

	1	2	3
1	0	3	5
2	2	−1	−3

4.

	1	2	3
1	−4	1	8
2	4	−3	−2

Part B. Find the optimal strategies and the value of each game.

5.

	1	2
1	1	4
2	8	0
3	6	1

6.

	1	2
1	17	0
2	4	7
3	3	10

5.4 2 × m and m × 2 GAMES; GRAPHICAL METHOD

We used the trial-and-error method in the preceding section so that you would learn to appreciate the penalty principle which forces the players to play a certain way. With many apologies, we now offer a short method without explanation. We shall do the same problems as we did in the preceding section, but we shall be able to select the correct 2 × 2 subgame immediately, instead of testing each one. We wish we could explain it, but the explanation is too lengthy. Briefly, let us say that the graph does exactly what we did by arithmetic, but faster.

$2 \times m$ **Games**

illustrative problem 1

Solve the following game.

	1	2	3
1	0	2	7
2	10	9	4

solution

We lay off an unlabeled horizontal axis (which really has to do with row strategy) and two vertical axes, one for each row, as shown in Fig. 5-6. The column 1 chord goes from 0 to 10. The column 2 chord goes from 2 to 9. The column 3 chord goes from 7 to 4. The *lower* boundary is darkened in the figure, and we search for the *highest* point on the *lower* boundary. This is at A, and the point is at the intersection of column 1 and column 3. Therefore, the subgame to be investigated is the one involving columns 1 and 3. This game is

	1	3
1	0	7
2	10	4

The resulting strategy is $(\frac{6}{13}, \frac{7}{13})$ and $\begin{pmatrix} \frac{2}{13} \\ 0 \\ \frac{10}{13} \end{pmatrix}$. The value of the game is $5\frac{5}{13}$.

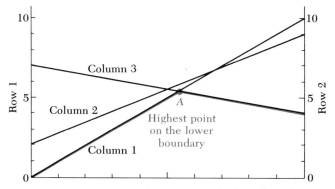

Fig. 5-6   *Point A is the highest point on the lower boundary.*

We note, with no surprise, that the answer is the same one we had in the previous section when using the trial-and-error method.

illustrative problem 2

Solve the following game.

	1	2	3
1	− $0.50	$1.50	− $1.50
2	$0.50	− $1.50	$4.50

solution

We add $1.50 to each entry and obtain

	1	2	3
1	1	3	0
2	2	0	6

The graph, with the lower boundary darkened, is shown in Fig. 5-7. Note that there are *two* intersections (*A* and *B*). We choose the *larger*, *B*. This point is the intersection of the column 1 and column 2 chords. The optimal subgame is, therefore,

	1	2
1	1	3
2	2	0

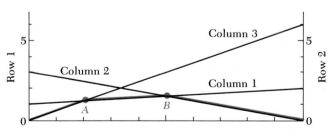

Fig. 5-7   *Point B is the highest point on the lower boundary.*

The resulting strategy is $(\frac{1}{2},\frac{1}{2})$ and $\begin{pmatrix} \frac{3}{4} \\ \frac{1}{4} \\ 0 \end{pmatrix}$. The value of the altered game

is $1\frac{1}{2}$. The value of the original game is, therefore, 0. It is a fair game.

illustrative problem 3

Solve the game

	1	2	3	4
1	1	5	8	16
2	14	8	6	4

solution (Fig. 5-8)

The optimal strategy involves columns 2 and 3 because the highest low point, B, is formed by the chords associated with those columns. The optimal subgame is

	2	3
1	5	8
2	8	6

The resulting strategy is $(\frac{2}{5},\frac{3}{5})$ and $\begin{pmatrix} 0 \\ \frac{2}{5} \\ \frac{3}{5} \\ 0 \end{pmatrix}$. The value of the game is $6\frac{4}{5}$.

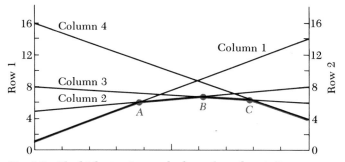

Fig. 5-8   The highest point on the lower boundary is B.

m $\times$ 2 Games

The graphical procédure for m $\times$ 2 games is similar except that, since we are working with columns, we choose the *smallest high point* instead of the largest low point.

illustrative problem 4

Solve the game

	1	2
1	10	−25
2	−4	10
3	−11	17

solution

First, we add 25 to each entry, obtaining

	1	2
1	35	0
2	21	35
3	14	42

Now, we draw the graph by joining pairs of points, one on each column axis. This is shown in Fig. 5-9. The lowest high point is at A, at the intersection of the chords associated with rows 1 and 2. The optimal subgame is, then,

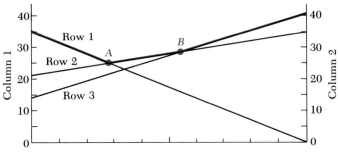

Fig. 5-9 The lowest point on the upper boundary is at A.

	1	2
1	35	0
2	21	35

The strategies are $(\frac{2}{7},\frac{5}{7},0)$ and $\begin{pmatrix}\frac{5}{7}\\\frac{2}{7}\end{pmatrix}$. The value of the original game is 0. It is a fair game.

PROBLEM SECTION 5.4

Solve the problems in Problem Section 5.3, using graphs to select the optimal subgame.

5.5   3 × 3 GAMES

We shall not go beyond 3 × 3 games because the arithmetic becomes more and more involved as the game gets larger. Mathematicians use a method called the *simplex method* for practical problems leading to these larger games. Interestingly enough, the simplex method is also used for practical problems in linear programming where the graphical method cannot be used. In both cases, there is considerable arithmetic (by any method) but a computer can be programmed to do the arithmetic.

   The basic ideas are the same for any size game, and these were all we wanted to tell you about.

The Procedure for 3 × 3 Games

The steps are as follows:

Step 1. Check for a saddle point. This is very important! This leads to a *pure strategy* such as $(1,0,0)$; $\begin{pmatrix}0\\0\\1\end{pmatrix}$, meaning that the row player should always play row 1 and the column player should always play column 3. The value of the game is at the saddle point.

Step 2. Check for dominance. If there is dominance of the simple kind which we have studied, the result may be a 2 × m game, an m × 2 game, or a 2 × 2 game. In these cases, the result is usually a *mixed double strategy* such as $(\frac{1}{3},\frac{2}{3},0)$; $\begin{pmatrix}\frac{4}{7}\\0\\\frac{3}{7}\end{pmatrix}$. The value of the game is found by

$E = rG$ or $E = Gc$ (the result will be the same, of course). Remember that r is the row strategy (a row vector) and c is the column strategy (a column vector); G is the game matrix.

Step 3. If neither of these works (they *must* be tried first!), attempt to find a *mixed triple strategy* such as $(\frac{1}{3},\frac{2}{3},\frac{4}{3})$; $\begin{pmatrix} \frac{1}{3} \\ \frac{1}{3} \\ \frac{1}{3} \end{pmatrix}$. The method for finding this will be described in the subsection Triple-strategy Method below. The value of the game is, again, found by $E = rG$ or $E = Gc$.

Step 4. Finally, if this does not work, assume there is a 2 × 2 game hidden in the 3 × 3 game and that this 2 × 2 game has the optimal strategy. Try every possible 2 × 2 game. We shall describe this in the subsection Double-strategy Method (page 165). This is the hardest procedure because there are so many subgames to try.

Step 5. If none of these works, you have made a mistake. Start all over again and be more careful.

The procedure we are going to describe discovers *an* optimal strategy. Sometimes there are others just as good (but not better) which are not found by our procedure.

Triple-strategy Theory (Optional)

Consider the game

		x	y	$1 - x - y$
		1	2	3
u	1	a	b	c
v	2	d	e	f
$1 - u - v$	3	g	h	i

where the letters and numbers in color represent the fraction of the time that a row or column is to be played. For example, x may be $\frac{2}{9}$ and y may be $\frac{3}{9}$. Then $1 - x - y$, the fraction for column 3, would have to be $1 - \frac{2}{9} - \frac{3}{9} = \frac{4}{9}$. The column strategy would be $\begin{pmatrix} \frac{2}{9} \\ \frac{3}{9} \\ \frac{4}{9} \end{pmatrix}$.

Using $P = rGc$, where P is the payoff, as in the first subsection in Sec. 5.2, we obtain

$$P = u(ax + by + c - cx - cy - gx - hy - i + ix + iy)$$
$$+ v(dx + ey + f - fx - fy - gx - hy - i + ix + iy)$$
$$+ (gx + hy + i - ix - iy) \quad [1]$$

Our plan is the same as the one in Sec. 5.2, namely, to leave the opponent helpless. In this case, we are going to calculate a method to leave the row player helpless. (It does not make any difference.) To do this, we must arrange to have

$$ax + by + c - cx - cy - gx - hy - i + ix + iy = 0$$
$$dx + ey + f - fx - fy - gx - hy - i + ix + iy = 0 \quad [2]$$

Then, if we can do this, Eq. [1] will become

$$P = u(0) + v(0) + gx + hy + i - ix - iy \quad [3]$$

and it does not matter what u and v are. (These represent the strategies of the row player.)

Rearranging Eqs. [2], we have

$$mx + ny = i - c$$
$$px + qy = i - f \quad [4]$$

where

$$m = a - c - g + i$$
$$n = b - c - h + i$$
$$p = d - f - g + i$$
$$q = e - f - h + i \quad [5]$$

The solution of Eqs. [4] is fairly easy, as a matter of fact, and we get

$$x = \frac{(i - c)q - (i - f)n}{D} \quad [6]$$

$$y = \frac{(i - f)m - (i - c)p}{D} \quad [7]$$

where D is a denominator. (We shall, once again, work with oddments, and so we shall not have to worry about the denominator as long as it is not 0.)

Replacing the values of m, n, p, and q from Eqs. [5] into Eqs. [6] and [7], we have

$$x = \frac{1}{D}(ei - fh - bi + ch + bf - ce)$$

$$y = \frac{1}{D}(-di + fg + ai - cg - af + cd) \quad [8]$$

$$1 - x - y = \frac{1}{D}(dh - eg - ah + bg + ae - bd)$$

In the next subsection, we shall make some sense out of this. The numerator is the oddment, in each case, and turns out to be a rather simple 3 × 3 determinant. How fortunate!

Triple-strategy Method

In the preceding (optional) subsection, we sketched a method for finding the column oddments whenever there is a triple mixed strategy. (We assume that saddle points and dominance have been taken care of properly.) The method is as follows:

triple-strategy theorem

To find the oddment for any row or column, replace the row or column by 1s and calculate the determinant.

illustrative problem 1

Solve the game

	1	2	3
1	3	5	2
2	0	6	8
3	4	1	3

solution

First, we check for a saddle point. In the following, the row minima and column maxima are indicated in color:

	1	2	3	Row minima
1	3	5	2	② → largest minimum
2	0	6	8	0
3	4	1	3	1
Column maxima	④	6	8	

↑ smallest maximum

Since the largest minimum and smallest maximum are different, there is no saddle point. *Second,* we check for (simple) dominance. There is none. *Third,* we try for a triple strategy. The oddments for rows are calculated as follows:

Row 1 $\quad\begin{vmatrix} 1 & 1 & 1 & 1 & 1 \\ 0 & 6 & 8 & 0 & 6 \\ 4 & 1 & 3 & 4 & 1 \end{vmatrix}$ $= 18 + 32 + 0 - 24 - 8 - 0 = 18$

Row 2 $\quad\begin{vmatrix} 3 & 5 & 2 & 3 & 5 \\ 1 & 1 & 1 & 1 & 1 \\ 4 & 1 & 3 & 4 & 1 \end{vmatrix}$ $= 9 + 20 + 2 - 8 - 3 - 15 = 5$

Row 3 $\quad\begin{vmatrix} 3 & 5 & 2 & 3 & 5 \\ 0 & 6 & 8 & 0 & 6 \\ 1 & 1 & 1 & 1 & 1 \end{vmatrix}$ $= 18 + 40 + 0 - 12 - 24 - 0 = 22$

The denominator is found by adding the oddments: $18 + 5 + 22 = 45$, so that the triple strategy for rows is $(^{18}/_{45}, ^{5}/_{45}, ^{22}/_{45})$.

The oddments for columns are calculated as follows:

Column 1 $\quad\begin{vmatrix} 1 & 5 & 2 & 1 & 5 \\ 1 & 6 & 8 & 1 & 6 \\ 1 & 1 & 3 & 1 & 1 \end{vmatrix}$ $= 18 + 40 + 2 - 12 - 8 - 15 = 25$

Column 2 $\quad\begin{vmatrix} 3 & 1 & 2 & 3 & 1 \\ 0 & 1 & 8 & 0 & 1 \\ 4 & 1 & 3 & 4 & 1 \end{vmatrix}$ $= 9 + 32 + 0 - 8 - 24 - 0 = 9$

Column 3 $\quad\begin{vmatrix} 3 & 5 & 1 & 3 & 5 \\ 0 & 6 & 1 & 0 & 6 \\ 4 & 1 & 1 & 4 & 1 \end{vmatrix}$ $= 18 + 20 + 0 - 24 - 3 - 0 = 11$

The denominator is $25 + 9 + 11 = 45$, so that the triple strategy for columns is

$$\begin{pmatrix} ^{25}/_{45} \\ ^{9}/_{45} \\ ^{11}/_{45} \end{pmatrix}$$

The value of the game can be calculated from $\mathbf{E} = \mathbf{rG}$ or $\mathbf{E} = \mathbf{Gc}$. We do both, to check.

$$\mathbf{E} = (^{18}/_{45},^{5}/_{45},^{22}/_{45}) \begin{pmatrix} 3 & 5 & 2 \\ 0 & 6 & 8 \\ 4 & 1 & 3 \end{pmatrix} = \tfrac{1}{45}(18,5,22) \begin{pmatrix} 3 & 5 & 2 \\ 0 & 6 & 8 \\ 4 & 1 & 3 \end{pmatrix}$$

$$= \tfrac{1}{45}(54 + 0 + 88,\ 90 + 30 + 22,\ 36 + 40 + 66)$$

$$= \tfrac{1}{45}(142,142,142)$$

$$= (3^{7}/_{45},3^{7}/_{45},3^{7}/_{45})$$

$$\mathbf{E} = \begin{pmatrix} 3 & 5 & 2 \\ 0 & 6 & 8 \\ 4 & 1 & 3 \end{pmatrix} \begin{pmatrix} ^{25}/_{45} \\ ^{9}/_{45} \\ ^{11}/_{45} \end{pmatrix} = \tfrac{1}{45} \begin{pmatrix} 3 & 5 & 2 \\ 0 & 6 & 8 \\ 4 & 1 & 3 \end{pmatrix} \begin{pmatrix} 25 \\ 9 \\ 11 \end{pmatrix}$$

$$= \tfrac{1}{45} \begin{pmatrix} 75 + 45 + 22 \\ 0 + 54 + 88 \\ 100 + 9 + 33 \end{pmatrix} = \tfrac{1}{45} \begin{pmatrix} 142 \\ 142 \\ 142 \end{pmatrix} = \begin{pmatrix} 3^{7}/_{45} \\ 3^{7}/_{45} \\ 3^{7}/_{45} \end{pmatrix}$$

By this time, you should be convinced that the value of the game is $3^{7}/_{45}$.

Double-strategy Method

Sometimes the preceding methods do not work, simply because those answers do not exist. The real reason behind this is that there are some complicated forms of dominance besides the simple kind we have mentioned, dominance caused by *combinations* of rows or columns. We unearth the correct strategy by a rather lengthy procedure demonstrated in the following illustrative problems.

illustrative problem 2

Solve the game

	1	2	3
1	49	50	52
2	200	80	0
3	40	90	140

solution

We test, as usual, for saddle points and simple dominance, but without finding any. Now we try for a triple strategy. The oddments for rows are calculated in the usual way:

$$
\text{Row 1} \quad \begin{vmatrix} 1 & 1 & 1 \\ 200 & 80 & 0 \\ 40 & 90 & 140 \end{vmatrix} = -2,000
$$

$$
\text{Row 2} \quad \begin{vmatrix} 49 & 50 & 52 \\ 1 & 1 & 1 \\ 40 & 90 & 140 \end{vmatrix} = 50
$$

We need go no further. Obviously, the oddments must be *all positive* or *all negative*. Otherwise, at least one of the strategies will have a negative component, and this makes no sense.

We now realize that there is no triple mixed strategy. We try to find an optimal 2×2 game by investigating the three 2×3 subgames in the original matrix. (We might just as well have investigated the three 3×2 games. It makes no difference.)

Subgame a

	1	2	3
1	49	50	52
2	200	80	0

Subgame b

	1	2	3
1	49*	50	52
3	40	90	140

Subgame c

	1	2	3
2	200	80	0
3	40	90	140

Subgame b has a saddle point at (row 1, column 1) with a value of 49 and requires no further investigation. Games a and c are graphed in Figs. 5-10 and 5-11.

According to the graphs, we need consider only the following 2×2 subgames:

Subgame a

	2	3	
1	50	52	40
2	80	0	1
	26	15	

Subgame c

	1	2	
2	200	80	5
3	40	90	12
	1	16	

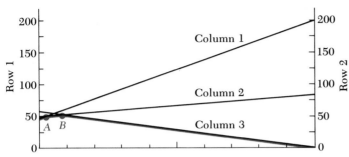

Fig. 5-10 *Graph for subgame a. B is the highest low point.*

The numbers in color are the row and column oddments. The resulting strategies are:

Subgame	Row Strategy	Column Strategy
a	$(^{40}\!/_{41}, ^{1}\!/_{41}, 0)$	$\begin{pmatrix} 0 \\ ^{26}\!/_{41} \\ ^{15}\!/_{41} \end{pmatrix}$
b	$(1, 0, 0)$	$\begin{pmatrix} 1 \\ 0 \\ 0 \end{pmatrix}$
c	$(0, ^{5}\!/_{17}, ^{12}\!/_{17})$	$\begin{pmatrix} ^{1}\!/_{17} \\ ^{16}\!/_{17} \\ 0 \end{pmatrix}$

Using $\mathbf{E} = \mathbf{rG}$, we shall now calculate the payoffs to the row player for the various strategies. For subgame a, the calculation is

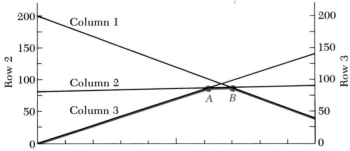

Fig. 5-11 *Graph for subgame c. B is the highest low point.*

$$(^{40}\!/_{41},^{1}\!/_{41},0)\begin{pmatrix} 49 & 50 & 52 \\ 200 & 80 & 0 \\ 40 & 90 & 140 \end{pmatrix} = {}^{1}\!/_{41}(40,1,0)\begin{pmatrix} 49 & 50 & 52 \\ 200 & 80 & 0 \\ 40 & 90 & 140 \end{pmatrix}$$

$$= {}^{1}\!/_{41}(2160,2080,2080)$$

$$= (52^{28}\!/_{41},50^{30}\!/_{41},50^{30}\!/_{41})$$

The payoff table is shown below.

Subgame	Columns	Row Strategy	Expectation Against		
			Column 1	Column 2	Column 3
a	2, 3	$(^{40}\!/_{41},^{1}\!/_{41},0)$	$(52^{28}\!/_{41})$	$50^{30}\!/_{41}$	$50^{30}\!/_{41}$
b	1	$(1,0,0)$	49	(200)	(40)
c	1, 2	$(0,^{5}\!/_{17},^{12}\!/_{17})$	$87^{1}\!/_{17}$	$87^{1}\!/_{17}$	$(98^{14}\!/_{17})$

Subgame a is satisfactory in one respect: The enemy is penalized if he plays the "wrong" column. However, it is not as good as subgame c. In subgame c, we must win at least $87^{1}\!/_{17}$. If the enemy plays the column he should not, namely, column 3, he will lose more ($98^{14}\!/_{17}$).

Actually, we have a complete answer now: the optimal row strategy is $(0,^{5}\!/_{17},^{12}\!/_{17})$; the optimal column strategy is $\begin{pmatrix} ^{1}\!/_{17} \\ ^{16}\!/_{17} \\ 0 \end{pmatrix}$; and the value of the game is $87^{1}\!/_{17}$. However, as a cross check, let us calculate the payoff for the column player, using $\mathbf{E} = \mathbf{Gc}$. The payoff table is given below.

Subgame	Rows	Column Strategy	Expectation Against		
			Row 1	Row 2	Row 3
a	1, 2	$\begin{pmatrix} 0 \\ ^{26}\!/_{41} \\ ^{15}\!/_{41} \end{pmatrix}$	$50^{30}\!/_{41}$	$50^{30}\!/_{41}$	$(108^{12}\!/_{41})$
b	1	$\begin{pmatrix} 1 \\ 0 \\ 0 \end{pmatrix}$	49	(50)	(52)
c	2, 3	$\begin{pmatrix} ^{1}\!/_{17} \\ ^{16}\!/_{17} \\ 0 \end{pmatrix}$	$(48^{13}\!/_{17})$	$87^{10}\!/_{17}$	$87^{10}\!/_{17}$

From the table, it should be obvious that the column player would like to play subgame a, with the row player playing row 1 or row 2. However, we are not that crazy. If we agreed to play subgame a, we would certainly play row 3, where the winnings are more than twice as large. Subgame a cannot be an optimal game, because of the penalty principle. Now look at subgame c. Here the row player is penalized if he plays the "wrong" row, namely, row 1. As we discovered previously, subgame c is the optimal subgame.

The next illustrative problem has the odd feature that the column player has an infinite number of optimal strategies.

illustrative problem 3

Solve the game

	1	2	3
1	8	2	5
2	10	0	5
3	6	8	7

solution

We test for saddle points and (simple) dominance hopefully, but in vain. Now we try for a triple strategy. The oddments for rows turn out to be 0, 0, and 0. It appears that the row player does not wish to play this game at all! However, this strange result merely means that there is no optimal triple mixed strategy.

We now try our last resort, a search for a hidden double mixed strategy. We examine the following three games:

Subgame a

	1	2	3
1	8	2*	5
2	10	0	5

Subgame b

	1	2	3
2	10	0	5
3	6	8	7

Subgame c

	1	2	3
1	8	2	5
3	6	8	7

Subgame a has a saddle point at (row 1, column 2) with a value of 2. When we draw the graphs for subgames b and c, we find that they do not help us much. (See Figs. 5-12 and 5-13.) Because the graphs do not eliminate any of the 2 × 2 subgames, we shall have to try all of them. This is done in the following, with the row and column oddments shown in color.

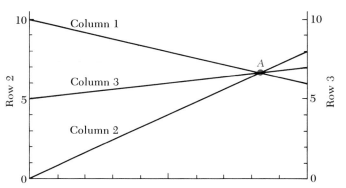

Fig. 5-12   In subgame b, the three column strategies meet at point A.

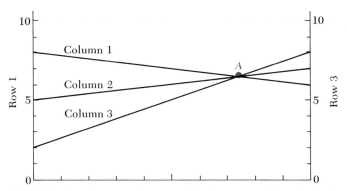

Fig. 5-13   In subgame c, the same thing happens as in subgame b.

	Subgame 1		
	1	2	
2	10	0	1
3	6	8	5
	2	1	

	Subgame 2		
	1	3	
2	10	5	1
3	6	7	5
	1	2	

	Subgame 3	
	2	3
2	0	5
3	8	*7

Saddle point (3,3)

	Subgame 4		
	1	2	
1	8	2	1
3	6	8	3
	3	1	

	Subgame 5		
	1	3	
1	8	5	1
3	6	7	3
	1	1	

	Subgame 6	
	2	3
1	2	5
3	8	*7

Saddle point (3,3)

The game strategies to be tried are, therefore, those listed in Table V.

TABLE V

Subgame	Row Strategy	Column Strategy
a	$(1,0,0)$	$\begin{pmatrix} 0 \\ 1 \\ 0 \end{pmatrix}$
1	$(0,\frac{1}{6},\frac{5}{6})$	$\begin{pmatrix} \frac{2}{3} \\ \frac{1}{3} \\ 0 \end{pmatrix}$
2	$(0,\frac{1}{6},\frac{5}{6})$	$\begin{pmatrix} \frac{1}{3} \\ 0 \\ \frac{2}{3} \end{pmatrix}$
3	$(0,0,1)$	$\begin{pmatrix} 0 \\ 0 \\ 1 \end{pmatrix}$
4	$(\frac{1}{4},0,\frac{3}{4})$	$\begin{pmatrix} \frac{3}{4} \\ \frac{1}{4} \\ 0 \end{pmatrix}$
5	$(\frac{1}{4},0,\frac{3}{4})$	$\begin{pmatrix} \frac{1}{2} \\ 0 \\ \frac{1}{2} \end{pmatrix}$
6	$(0,0,1)$	$\begin{pmatrix} 0 \\ 0 \\ 1 \end{pmatrix}$

We must now calculate the payoff to the row player for each sub-game. This is a rather lengthy procedure. We illustrate for subgame 1, using $\mathbf{E} = \mathbf{rG}$.

$$(0,\tfrac{1}{6},\tfrac{5}{6})\begin{pmatrix} 8 & 2 & 5 \\ 10 & 0 & 5 \\ 6 & 8 & 7 \end{pmatrix} = \tfrac{1}{6}(0,1,5)\begin{pmatrix} 8 & 2 & 5 \\ 10 & 0 & 5 \\ 6 & 8 & 7 \end{pmatrix}$$

$$= \tfrac{1}{6},(40,40,40) = (6\tfrac{2}{3},6\tfrac{2}{3},6\tfrac{2}{3})$$

In this particular case, the expectation is the same for all columns. The complete table for row strategies is Table VI.

TABLE VI

Subgame	Columns	Row Strategy	Expectation Against		
			Column 1	Column 2	Column 3
a	2	(1,0,0)	(8)	2	(5)
1	1, 2	(0,⅙,⅚)	6⅔	6⅔	(6⅔)
2	1, 3	(0,⅙,⅚)	6⅔	(6⅔)	6⅔
3	2, 3	(0,0,1)	(6)	(8)	7
4	1, 2	(¼,0,¾)	6½	6½	(6½)
5	1, 3	(¼,0,¾)	6½	(6½)	6½
6	2, 3	(0,0,1)	(6)	(8)	7

The calculation was less difficult than it looks; there were actually only four different strategies; since only two of them were mixed, it went rather quickly.

Looking over Table VI, we see that subgames 1 or 2 are equally good for us. Our best row strategy is (0,⅙,⅚) with an expectation of 6⅔ regardless of the column player's strategy. *Reminder:* If we chose subgame a, we might win only 2. If we chose game 3 or 6, we might win only 6. If we chose subgame 4 or 5, we are sure to win 6½, but this is less than 6⅔.

Actually, we need test only subgames 1 and 2 to find the optimal strategy for the column player, but we shall produce the entire table for review purposes. As a reminder, we now calculate the column player's expectation for subgame 1, using $\mathbf{E} = \mathbf{Gc}$.

$$\begin{pmatrix} 8 & 2 & 5 \\ 10 & 0 & 5 \\ 6 & 8 & 7 \end{pmatrix} \begin{pmatrix} ⅔ \\ ⅓ \\ 0 \end{pmatrix} = ⅓ \begin{pmatrix} 8 & 2 & 5 \\ 10 & 0 & 5 \\ 6 & 8 & 7 \end{pmatrix} \begin{pmatrix} 2 \\ 1 \\ 0 \end{pmatrix} = ⅓ \begin{pmatrix} 18 \\ 20 \\ 20 \end{pmatrix} = \begin{pmatrix} 6 \\ 6⅔ \\ 6⅔ \end{pmatrix}$$

The table for column strategies is Table VII. From this table, the column player is also satisfied with either subgame 1 or subgame 2. In subgame a, he might lose 8. In subgames 3 and 6, he might lose 7. In game 4, he might lose 7½. In subgame 5, he might lose 9. He is as safe as he can be, under the circumstances, by playing the column strategy of subgame 1 or subgame 2 *or any combination of the two.*

TABLE VII

Subgame	Rows	Column Strategy	Expectation Against		
			Row 1	Row 2	Row 3
a	1	$\begin{pmatrix} 0 \\ 1 \\ 0 \end{pmatrix}$	2	(0)	(8)
1	2, 3	$\begin{pmatrix} 2/3 \\ 1/3 \\ 0 \end{pmatrix}$	(6)	6⅔	6⅔
2	2, 3	$\begin{pmatrix} 1/3 \\ 0 \\ 2/3 \end{pmatrix}$	(6)	6⅔	6⅔
3	3	$\begin{pmatrix} 0 \\ 0 \\ 1 \end{pmatrix}$	(5)	(5)	7
4	1, 3	$\begin{pmatrix} 3/4 \\ 1/4 \\ 0 \end{pmatrix}$	6½	(7½)	6½
5	1, 3	$\begin{pmatrix} 1/2 \\ 0 \\ 1/2 \end{pmatrix}$	6½	(9)	6½
6	3	$\begin{pmatrix} 0 \\ 0 \\ 1 \end{pmatrix}$	(5)	(5)	7

For example, suppose he plays strategy 1 half the time and strategy 2 the other half. Thus his overall strategy is

$$\frac{1}{2}\begin{pmatrix} 2/3 \\ 1/3 \\ 0 \end{pmatrix} + \frac{1}{2}\begin{pmatrix} 1/3 \\ 0 \\ 2/3 \end{pmatrix} = \frac{1}{2}\begin{pmatrix} 2/3 + 1/3 \\ 1/3 + 0 \\ 0 + 2/3 \end{pmatrix} = \begin{pmatrix} 1/2 \\ 1/6 \\ 1/3 \end{pmatrix}$$

Let us test this "new" column strategy and see whether it is better or worse than those in subgames 1 and 2:

$$\begin{pmatrix} 8 & 2 & 5 \\ 10 & 0 & 5 \\ 6 & 8 & 7 \end{pmatrix}\begin{pmatrix} \frac{1}{2} \\ \frac{1}{6} \\ \frac{1}{3} \end{pmatrix} = \frac{1}{6}\begin{pmatrix} 8 & 2 & 5 \\ 10 & 0 & 5 \\ 6 & 8 & 7 \end{pmatrix}\begin{pmatrix} 3 \\ 1 \\ 2 \end{pmatrix} = \frac{1}{6}\begin{pmatrix} 40 \\ 40 \\ 40 \end{pmatrix} = \begin{pmatrix} 6\frac{2}{3} \\ 6\frac{2}{3} \\ 6\frac{2}{3} \end{pmatrix}$$

exactly as before.

PROBLEM SECTION 5.5

Solve the following games completely.

Part A

1.

	1	2	3
1	10	-14	-10
2	-2	-9	-7
3	-15	-1	-8

2.

	1	2	3
1	-3	-4	5
2	-2	-3	-2
3	0	1	3

3.

	1	2	3
1	-175	-75	225
2	-25	25	-25
3	75	-75	125

4.

	1	2	3
1	\$2	\$3	\$4
2	\$3	\$5	\$0
3	\$0	$-\$2$	\$1

Part B

5.

	1	2	3
1	11	6	0
2	7	9	8
3	8	6	7

6.

	1	2	3
1	-2	0	-2
2	-2	-1	0
3	0	-1	-1

7.

	1	2	3
1	-1	1	0
2	0	-1	1
3	1	0	-1

8.

	1	2	3
1	-1	2	2
2	-2	3	1
3	4	-1	-1

Part C

9.

	1	2	3
1	0	2	−2
2	2	3	−1
3	−1	−3	0

10.

	1	2	3
1	2	1	−1
2	1	3	−2
3	0	5	6

the
slide
rule

6666666666

John Napier, the Baron of Merchiston, sat gloomily in front of the fire in his castle on the outskirts of Edinburgh in Scotland. It was 1594; the Baron was working on some problems in trigonometry, possibly having to do with the new-fangled ideas about the Earth and other planets going around the Sun. (Anyone can *see* that the Sun goes around the Earth!)

"Where is my slide rule or my table of logarithms?" he grumbled. "I hate doing messy arithmetic." He thought a moment and said to himself, "Oh, yes. I haven't invented logarithms yet—and slide rules won't be invented for about 28 more years."

Perhaps this story is not quite accurate. However, it is true that many mathematicians do not like arithmetic any more than you do. Ever since the beginning of mathematical problems, people have tried to avoid arithmetic by using piles of pebbles (Fig. 6-1), bone rods (Fig. 6-2), knots (Fig. 6-3), and tally sticks and palm leaves (Fig. 6-4), or by using instruments like the abacus (Fig. 6-5), the slide rule (Fig. 6-6), and other devices, of which the most powerful today is the electronic computer (Fig. 6-7).

In 1620, Edmund Gunter invented *Gunter's chain*, an instrument for solving problems in navigation. This instrument led directly to the slide rule. About 1622, William Oughtred invented the first real slide rule for multiplication and division. The first commercial model arrived about 1654. These slide rules were not used very much for a good many years, probably because they were expensive, and also because they were not very accurate and were too limited in their uses.

The first slide rule that can be called "modern" was designed by Amédée Mannheim (1837–1906) probably when he was a very young man. The modern slide rule is often called a *Mannheim slide rule* and, as you know, it has become very important and popular in this century.

Although the slide rule is more than 300 years old, the Mannheim

Fig. 6-1   In the beginning, man used pebbles.

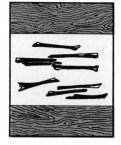

Fig. 6-2   The Koreans used bone rods.

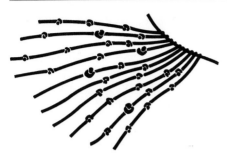

Fig. 6-3   In ancient Peru the quipu was used to record results. A small knot was 1; a big knot, 10.

Fig. 6-4   Tally sticks are almost as old as the notched, split palm leaf, which gave both parties a record.

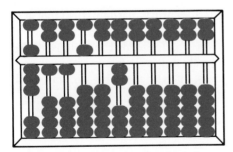

Fig. 6-5   There were many kinds of abacus. The one in the diagram is the Chinese abacus, probably invented in the twelfth century.

Fig. 6-6   A modern slide rule. The first one was invented by William Oughtred in 1622.

Fig. 6-7 The IBM 360, a modern high-speed computer. (IBM Corporation.)

slide rule can truly be called a twentieth-century mathematical tool and, at least for that reason, deserves our attention.

We shall limit ourselves to only a small part of the slide rule. For our purposes, a very inexpensive 10-inch slide rule is adequate.

Warning: For learning purposes, it is inadvisable to start with a short (6-inch) rule or a circular slide rule.

6.1 ARITHMETIC BY SLIDE RULE

The Real-number Line

In Fig. 6-8 part of a line is drawn; on it are identified certain *equally spaced* points representing the integers, such as -2, 0, and 4. Between these points there are other points which represent other numbers, for example 3½ and $\sqrt{2}$ (Fig. 6-9). The set of *all* the points on a line corresponds to a set of numbers. These numbers are called the *real num-*

Fig. 6-8 The real-number line.

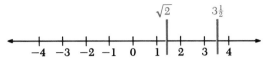

Fig. 6-9 *Some real numbers which are not integers.*

bers. (The term *real* is historical in source and does not suggest that there are other numbers which are not "real" in the everyday sense.)

We shall introduce our topic by discussing, briefly, a real-number *scale* such as the one on Fig. 6-10. Without going into the matter too deeply, we remark that on this scale the integers are *equally spaced.* This means that the distance from 4 to 5 is the same as that from 5 to 6, or 8 to 9, or 0 to 1, etc.

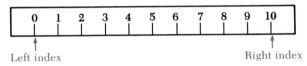

Left index   Right index

Fig. 6-10 *A real-number scale.*

To find the *sum* of two real numbers, say 3 + 5, we may proceed as follows.

Step 1. Place two scales face to face as shown in Fig. 6-11. The leftmost number on each scale is called a *left index* and the rightmost number a *right index*. In the position shown, the two scales are said to be *in home position*. For our own purposes, we shall call one of the scales the *C scale* and the other the *D scale*. (These are not the initials of names. They merely refer to two of the four elementary scales on a Mannheim-type slide rule, namely, A, B, C, and D.) The C and D scales are identical except that they are printed differently. We shall call the *pair* of scales a *slide rule.*

Left index   Right index

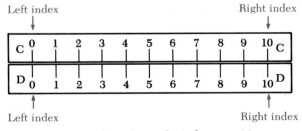

Left index   Right index

Fig. 6-11 *Two real-number scales in home position.*

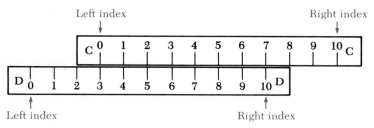

Fig. 6-12 *Place the left index of C over the 3.*

Step 2 (Fig. 6-12). Slide the left index of the C scale until it is over the 3 on the D scale (because we are going to add 5 to 3).

Step 3. Now, move your eye along the C scale to 5 and read, below the 5, the answer, 8, on the D scale. The procedure is summarized in Fig. 6-13.

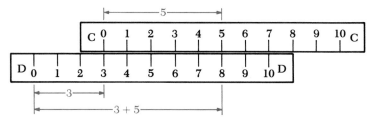

Fig. 6-13 *Adding by using two equally spaced scales.*

In a real slide rule, a transparent runner is mounted on the slide rule (Fig. 6-14). This runner, or *cursor,* has a hairline which assists in reading the scales. (*Cursor* is Latin for *runner.*)

Other Scales

We showed you the procedure for *adding* two numbers by sliding scales because we wanted to point out that sliding one scale over another and then moving your eye (or a cursor) correspond to addition. We call to your attention that in each of the scales used for addition (refer to Fig. 6-14), the following conditions apply:

a. The left index is 0.
b. The scales match, except that (for convenience in reading) one scale is printed on the lower edge (the C scale) and one on the upper (the D scale).
c. The numbers on each scale are equally spaced.

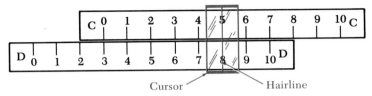

Cursor   Hairline

Fig. 6-14   The answer is on the D scale under the hairline.

In order to emphasize the importance of these three conditions, let us examine Fig. 6-15, where conditions *a* and *c* are satisfied, but not *b*.

In Fig. 6-15*a*, note that 3 (on the D scale) is under the index. Now read across, on the C scale, to 2 and you find that 3 ? 2 = 7 ("Three something two equals seven.").

In Fig. 6-15*b*, you see that 4 ? 2 = 8.

By moving the hairline to various positions, we can develop the following table:

Fig. 6-15*a*	Fig. 6-15*b*
3 ? 0 = 3	4 ? 0 = 4
3 ? 1 = 5	4 ? 1 = 6
3 ? 2 = 7	4 ? 2 = 8
3 ? 3 = 9	4 ? 3 = 10
$\vdots$	$\vdots$

It is not easy to see, but what this slide rule does is called *dabbling*. (To *dabble* is to *double* a number and *add* it to another.) This strange operation is actually used by computer programmers to convert a number from the binary form to the decimal form. In Fig. 6-15*a*, note that 3

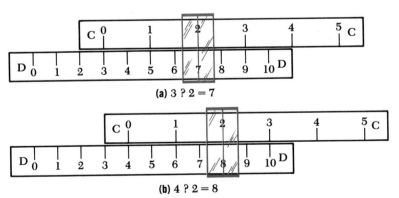

(a) 3 ? 2 = 7

(b) 4 ? 2 = 8

Fig. 6-15   Operating with nonmatching scales.

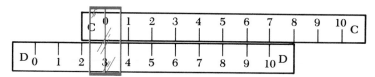

Fig. 6-16 Here 3 + 0 = 3.

(under the C index) added to *double* 2 (on the C scale) is 7 (on the D scale).

By changing the spacing, the matching, and the index, it is possible to make slide rules that perform different operations and serve different purposes. If you have a flashgun for your camera, you may have a special circular slide rule on it which tells you how to adjust the camera for various camera-to-subject positions. You will note that this slide rule satisfies *none* of the three conditions mentioned above.

Multiplication Slide Rules

Our main interest is not to avoid the easy operation of addition but to devise some scheme for avoiding the harder operations of multiplication and division. We shall start with multiplication.

We know, by this time, that if *all* the three conditions in the previous section are met, then we shall always get an ordinary arithmetic addition. Let us consider what a multiplication slide rule must look like. To do this, we reconsider each of the three conditions.

Condition a: left index = 0. In *addition,* the left index must be 0 because it is the no-change condition. To clarify this, look at Fig. 6-16. In this situation, $3 + 0 = 3$. If the index were 1, as in Fig. 6-17, the slide rule would certainly not add 3 and 1 properly.

However, in *multiplication,* we want the left index to be 1, because multiplication by 1 causes no change. In Fig. 6-18, we see that 2 (on the D scale) $\times$ 1 (under the hairline on the C scale) = 2 (under the hairline on the D scale). We conclude that for a multiplication slide rule the left index must be 1.

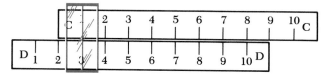

Fig. 6-17 We do not want 3 + 1 = 3.

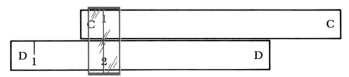

Fig. 6-18 *We do not know what the remainder of the scale looks like, but the left index must be 1 in a multiplication slide rule, because* $2 \times 1 = 2$.

Condition b: matching scales. Having the C and D scales match each other in addition merely means that we should get the same answer whether we add $3 + 2$ or $2 + 3$. In multiplication, it means that we should get the same answer whether we multiply 2×3 or 3×2. In other words, the scales should match if

$$2 + 3 = 3 + 2 \qquad\qquad\qquad [1]$$
$$2 \times 3 = 3 \times 2 \qquad\qquad\qquad [2]$$

However, there are laws of arithmetic for real numbers, called the *commutative postulates*, which assume that Eqs. [1] and [2] are true. We conclude that the slide rule, whether for addition or multiplication, should have matching scales.

Condition c: Equally spaced numbers. To help decide this, we have drawn a slide rule in Fig. 6-19 with the left index (properly) equal to 1, satisfying the condition we decided on for multiplication in the discussion of the left index, and with matching scales, satisfying the condition we discussed above. Let us see whether equally spaced scales will do the job of multiplication. We might amuse ourselves by discovering what this slide rule does. By moving the hairline, we find that

$$3 \,?\, 1 = 3$$
$$3 \,?\, 2 = 4$$
$$3 \,?\, 3 = 5$$
$$\vdots$$

Whatever it does, it certainly does *not* multiply. If it did multiply, we would expect to find a 6 under the 2, a 9 under the 3, and so on, so that

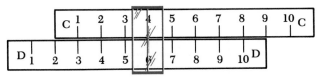

Fig. 6-19 *Here,* $3 \,?\, 4 = 6$.

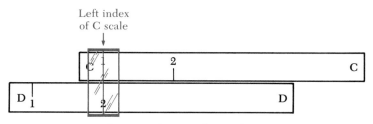

Fig. 6-20   First markings on the C and D scales.

$$3 \, ? \, 2 \, = 6$$
$$3 \, ? \, 3 = 9$$
$$\vdots$$

and the operation which we have designated as "?" would, in fact, be "$\times$".

This discussion should convince you that in a slide rule for multiplication the following conditions apply:

a. The left index is 1 for each scale.
b. The scales must match.
c. The numbers are not equally spaced on each scale.

Constructing a Scale for Multiplication

We shall start constructing a scale for multiplication by considering the problem of finding 2×2. We mark 1 and 2 anywhere on a C scale and 1 and 2 in exactly the same way (condition [*b*]) on the D scale. Then we slide the left index of the C scale to the 2 of the D scale (Fig. 6-20). What do we want under the 2 on the C scale? A 4, of course. We put it in (Fig. 6-21) and *at the same time*, because the scales must match, we mark it off on the C scale as well. Now you can see that this places the 8s in position also, because we want $2 \times 4 = 8$ (Fig. 6-22).

By starting with 1 and 2 spaced any way we please, we can, as you have seen, locate 4 and 8, also 16, 32, ... We also need 3, 5, 7, 9, . . . and the "in-between numbers." There are many methods for finding the correct spacing for a multiplication scale but they are beyond the

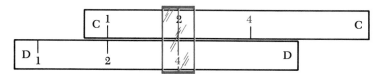

Fig. 6-21   Placing the 4s in position.

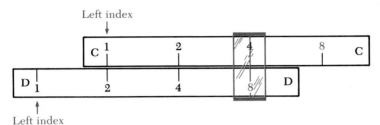

Fig. 6-22   *Now we have 1, 2, 4, and 8 in position.*

scope of this book. The result is not complicated and, in fact, you could make a simple slide rule for the integers as follows. Mark a 1 at one end and a 10 at the other. Then space the numbers as follows:

Number	Percent of Distance from Left Index
1	0.00
2	30.10
3	47.71
4	60.21
5	69.90
6	77.82
7	84.51
8	90.31
9	95.42
10	100.00

The numbers in the second column are related to *logarithms*. We shall work with them in Chap. 7.

PROBLEM SECTION 6.1

The following are for discussion.

1. What are the three important variables to control in planning a slide rule for different purposes?
2. In the figures, a slide rule is shown with matching scales, equally spaced, but with the left index at 2. Discover what this slide rule does.

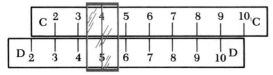

Fig. (a) for Prob. 2.

Fig. (b) for Prob. 2.

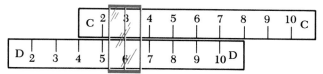

Fig. (c) for Prob. 2.

3. In the figures, a slide rule is shown with equally spaced scales, not matching, with the left index at 0. Discover what this slide rule does.

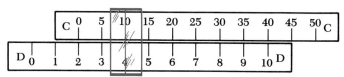

Fig. (a) for Prob. 3.

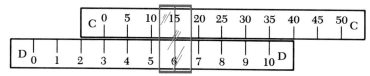

Fig. (b) for Prob. 3.

4. In the figures, a slide rule is shown with unequally spaced matched scales, with the left index equal to 1. Discover what this slide rule does.

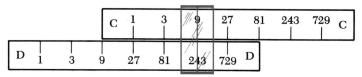

Fig. (a) for Prob. 4.

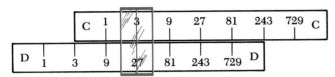

Fig. (b) for Prob. 4.

6.2   READING THE SLIDE RULE

From this point on, when we mention *slide rule* we shall be referring to the multiplication type. As indicated in the preceding section, the numbers are unequally spaced, as shown in Fig. 6-23.

Primary Graduations

The large divisions of the scale, shown in Fig. 6-23, are called the *primary* graduations. Notice that the right index is 1, not 10. On the slide rule, decimal points and zeros at *either* end are omitted, so that the numbers that appear to be 1, 2, ..., 9, 1 might just as well represent 0.001, 0.002, ..., 0.009, 0.010 or 1000, 2000, ..., 9000, 10000.

Secondary Graduations

Each primary space (between 1 and 2, or 4 and 5, or 9 and 1, for example) is divided into a second set of graduations (Fig. 6-24). The graduations between (primary) 1 and (primary) 2 are marked but the others are not. (There is no deep meaning to this. The whole thing is merely a matter of convenience. Even on a 10-inch rule, there is no room for so many markings, except between 1 and 2.)

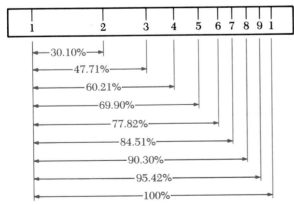

Fig. 6-23   The primary graduations.

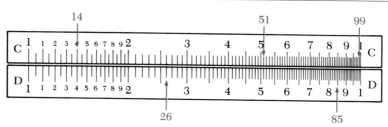

Fig. 6-24 The secondary graduations.

In Fig. 6-24, a few of the secondary graduations have been identified. Note that the marking for 14, for example, may represent 14, or 0.00014, or 14,000, or any other such number with more or fewer zeros on the right or left of the 14. Later you will see that this apparent ambiguity causes no serious problem in the use of the slide rule.

Tertiary Graduations

A complication arises in the next set of divisions. The cause of the complication is technical, not mathematical. The fact is that we should like to make one more set of graduations in order to represent numbers like 147, 362, 558, and 902 (with or without zeros and decimal points) but there is no room except between (primary) 1 and (primary) 2, even on the large-sized slide rule. Therefore, the tertiary divisions are different, depending upon the part of the slide rule with which we are working. The following divisions and markings are based upon a 10-inch inexpensive model. There are minor differences in different models and in the slide rules of different manufacturers.

Tertiary Divisions: Primary 1 to Primary 2

There are three regions on the slide rule so far as tertiary divisions are concerned.

Figure 6-25 shows the tertiary divisions for the region of the slide rule between primary 1 and primary 2. As you can see from the diagram, it is very easy to read three or even four digits in this region.

We remind you that decimal points and some zeros (at the ends) are omitted. In the diagram, if the primary graduations are considered to be 100, 200, . . . , 900, 1000, the marked points will be 105.0, 107.5, 115.0, . . . , 194.2.

If the primary graduations are considered to be 0.1, 0.2, . . . , 0.9, 1.0, then the marked points are 0.1050, 0.1075, 0.1150, . . . , 0.1831, 0.1942.

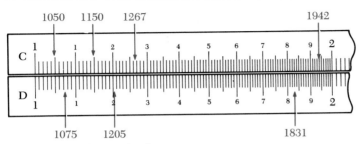

Fig. 6-25   Reading in the first region.

Tertiary Divisions: Primary 2 to Primary 4

Figure 6-26 shows the tertiary divisions for the region of the slide rule between primary 2 and primary 3. Exactly the same sort of markings are found between primary 3 and primary 4.

In this region, there is not enough room for 10 markings between secondary marks. There is room for only *five*, so that each tertiary mark counts as *two*. By estimating between the marks, you can read three or four digits, depending upon your good eye and judgment.

In the figure, if the primary graduations are considered to be 0.1, 0.2, . . . , 0.9, 1.0, the marked points are 0.2020, 0.2030, . . . , 0.2445, 0.2895. If the primary graduations are considered to be 10000, 20000, 30000, . . . , 90000, 100000, then the same markings represent 20200, 20300, . . . , 24450, 28950.

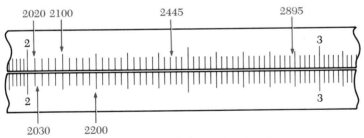

Fig. 6-26   Reading three or four digits in the second region.

Tertiary Divisions: Primary 4 to Primary 10

In this region, the space is too small to allow even five markings. Only *two* markings are found, each worth five. In Fig. 6-27, the region from primary 8 to primary 9 has been enlarged for demonstration. If the primary graduations represent 1, 2, . . . , 9, 10, the marked points are 8.05, 8.08, 8.27, 8.60, and 8.95.

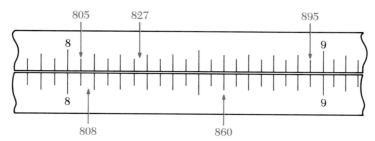

Fig. 6-27 *Reading three digits in the third region.*

PROBLEM SECTION 6.2

In each of the following diagrams, read the marked points, assuming the primary graduations as given.

1. Primary: 1, 2, . . . , 9, 10.

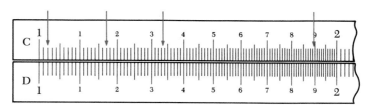

2. Primary: 10, 20, . . . , 90, 100.

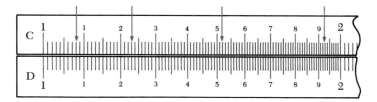

3. Primary: 10, 20, . . . , 90, 100.

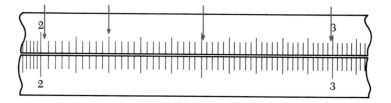

4. Primary: 0.1, 0.2, . . . , 0.9, 1.0.

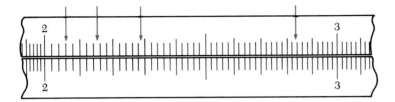

5. Primary: 100, 200, . . . , 900, 1000.

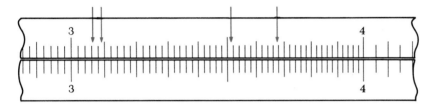

6. Primary: 1, 2, . . . , 9, 10.

7. Primary: 0.1, 0.2, . . . , 0.9, 1.0.

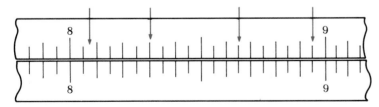

8. Primary: 10, 20, . . . , 90, 100.

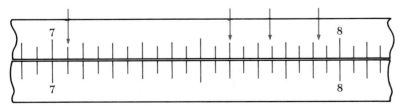

6.3   MULTIPLYING BY SLIDE RULE

You already know that the markings on a slide rule were arranged in a clever way to change a problem in *multiplication* to one in *addition*. This was accomplished by sliding a scale and moving a cursor (or your eye if you have no cursor). You also know that the slide rule does not show decimal points and certain zeros. For this reason, it is necessary to find the decimal point and the zeros by some other method in order to adjust the slide-rule reading. This method is called *estimating*. As you will see, it is fairly easy.

Estimating in Multiplication

We shall explain by doing several examples.

illustrative problem 1

Estimate 21.7×36.4.

solution

The standard procedure is to replace the actual numbers by others, usually *retaining only the first nonzero digit* and replacing the others by zeros, as necessary. We shall use the symbol $\rightarrow$ to mean *approximately equals*.

$$21.7 \rightarrow 20$$
$$36.4 \rightarrow 40 \qquad \text{(It is closer to 40 than to 30.)}$$
$$21.7 \times 36.4 \rightarrow 20 \times 40 = 800$$

This means that the answer will be somewhere around 800. The exact answer (by arithmetic) is 789.88. The answer by slide rule (we have not explained this yet) is 790. We shall not require you to calculate the slide-rule percent error, but in this case it is

$$\frac{790 - 789.88}{790} \times 100 = \frac{0.12 \times 100}{790} = 0.015 \text{ (percent)}$$

illustrative problem 2

Estimate 0.516×534.

solution

$$0.516 \rightarrow 0.5$$
$$534 \rightarrow 500$$
$$0.516 \times 534 \rightarrow 0.5 \times 500 = 250$$

The exact answer is 275.544 (by arithmetic). The answer by slide rule is 275.5. The error is 0.016 percent. We mention the error only to give you an idea of what to expect.

illustrative problem 3

Estimate 0.001024×0.873.

solution

$0.001024 \rightarrow 0.001$
$0.873 \rightarrow 0.9$ (This is closer than 0.8.)
$0.001 \times 0.9 = 0.0009$

The exact answer, by arithmetic, is 0.000893952. The answer by slide rule turns out to be 0.000895. The error of the slide-rule answer is 0.12 percent.

In all three illustrative problems, we assumed that the slide rule was used skillfully. In the exercises, a 0.3 percent error from the arithmetic correct answer is expected from a beginner. If you do better than this at the beginning, you have (1) a sharp eye and (2) very good judgment in estimating fractions of unmarked spaces. We must say that student errors are usually in placing the decimal point, not reading the scale. In other words, a typical student error is to get 0.00895 or even 895 in place of 0.000895. (A word to the wise . . . .)

Multiplication (Part I)

Multiplication, using C and D scales, leads to two slightly different situations. We shall explain one of them by two illustrative problems.

illustrative problem 4

Find 0.254×16.6.

solution

The estimate *which must be done first* is

$0.254 \times 16.6 \rightarrow 0.3 \times 20 = 6$

The slide-rule answer is found as follows:

Step 1. Set the slides at home position with both left indexes together (Fig. 6-28).

Step 2. Move the hairline to 254 on D (Fig. 6-29).

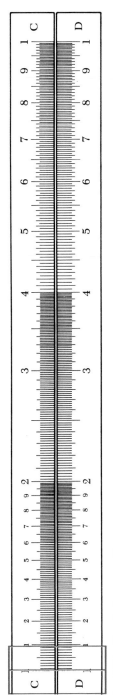

Fig. 6-28 Step 1: home position.

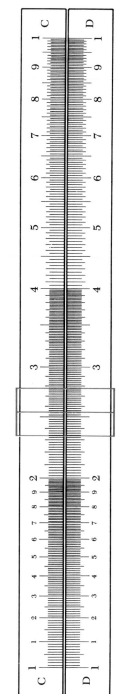

Fig. 6-29 Step 2: finding 254 on D.

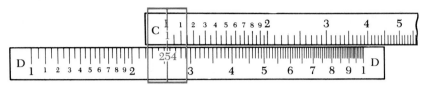

Fig. 6-30   Step 3: left index of C over 254 on D.

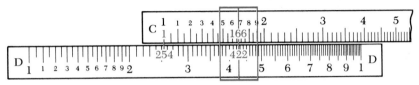

Fig. 6-31   Step 4: hairline over 166 on C; answer on D.

Step 3. Move the slide (C scale) until the left index of C is under the hairline (Fig. 6-30).

Step 4. Move the hairline to 166 on the C scale (Fig. 6-31).

Step 5. Read the number under the hairline on D (Fig. 6-31).

The slide-rule reading is 422. From the estimate, which is used to establish the position of the decimal point, the slide-rule answer is 4.22. The exact answer is 4.2164—as you see, fairly close.

illustrative problem 5

Find 0.00645 × 13,500.

solution

The estimate is 0.006 × 10,000 = 60. The final slide-rule setting is shown in Fig. 6-32. The slide-rule reading is 871. The slide-rule answer is 87.1. The exact answer, by arithmetic, is 87.075 (very close).

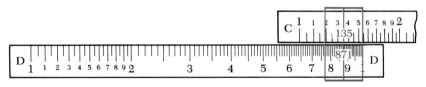

Fig. 6-32   Setting for Illustrative Problem 5.

Multiplication (Part II)

By this time, it has probably occurred to you that if we try to find 2×6 (Fig. 6-33) the method shown above will not give an answer on the slide rule because it is "off the scale." The problem is that the D scale does

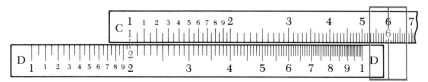

Fig. 6-33 *How do we find 2 × 6?*

not seem to be long enough. One solution would be to make a longer D scale (Fig. 6-34). This would make a very strange-looking (although possible) slide rule. Instead of doing this, we can use a trick based upon the fact that the *second* half of the D scale looks exactly like the *first* half. (We do not care about the zeros.) We shall pretend that the D scale which we have is really the second half instead of the first half. Then Fig. 6-34 becomes Fig. 6-35. Under the 6 we read 12, which is, of course, correct.

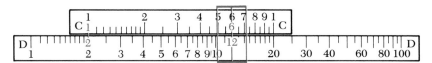

Fig. 6-34 *If the D scale were twice as long.*

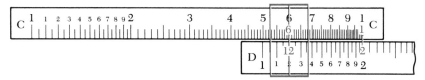

Fig. 6-35 *We pretend that the D scale is the second half of a long D scale.*

In general, if the answer is "off the scale" when the left index of C is used, we merely use the right index of C instead. This is shown in the following.

illustrative problem 6

Find 544×0.000353.

solution

The estimate is $500 \times 0.0004 = 0.2$. We set the slide rule as in Fig. 6-36. Seeing that this is unsatisfactory, we reset the slide so that the *right* index of the C scale is at 544 (Fig. 6-37). Now we move the cursor and find the slide-rule reading of 192 under the 353 on the C scale (Fig. 6-38). The decimal point, as determined by the estimate, leads to 0.192 as the answer. The exact answer, by arithmetic, is 0.192032.

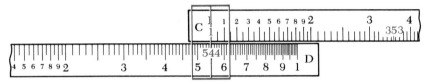

Fig. 6-36   The answer is "off the scale."

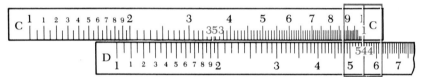

Fig. 6-37   Using the right index of the C scale.

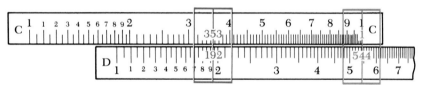

Fig. 6-38   The slide-rule reading is 192.

illustrative problem 7

Find $17{,}550 \times 0.706$.

solution

The estimate is $20{,}000 \times 0.7 = 14{,}000$. The slide-rule setting is shown in Fig. 6-39. The slide-rule reading on the D scale under 706 is 124. The slide-rule answer is 12,400. The exact answer, by arithmetic, is 12,390.300.

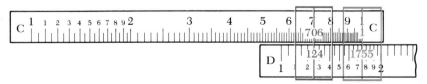

Fig. 6-39   The setting for 17,550 × 0.706.

PROBLEM SECTION 6.3

Part A. Estimate the following.

1. 0.000244×0.0838 2. 0.000198×0.629
3. $75,200 \times 31,500$ 4. $91,500 \times 4,720$

Part B. Find the slide-rule answers.

5. 13×4.2 6. 0.163×2.42
7. 0.00235×0.1945 8. $204,000 \times 42.2$

Part C. Find the slide-rule answers.

9. 0.844×35.1 10. 67.6×67.6
11. 293.5×0.457 12. 0.001762×611

6.4   CONTINUED PRODUCTS (OPTIONAL)

Another messy problem is one that involves a *continued product* such as $83.5 \times 0.276 \times 91,400$. We estimate this as

$$(80 \times 0.3) \times 90,000$$
$$24 \times 90,000 \rightarrow 20 \times 90,000 = 1,800,000$$

Remember that the purpose of the estimate is merely to place the decimal point. It does not matter if the estimate is up to five times too big or too small. For this reason, we can "shorten" the numbers at every step, as was done here.

We shall do this problem step by step to illustrate the procedure.

Step 1. Set the hairline to 835 on D (Fig. 6-40).

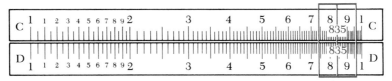

Fig. 6-40   Step 1.

Step 2a. Move the left index of C to the hairline (Fig. 6-41). A quick glance shows that 276 is off the scale.

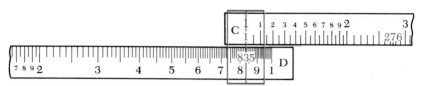

Fig. 6-41   The answer is "off the scale."

Step 2b. Change to the right index of C (Fig. 6-42).

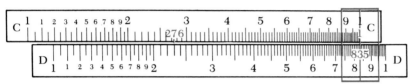

Fig. 6-42   Step 2b.

Step 3. Move the hairline to 276 on C (Fig. 6-43). The slide-rule reading for the answer is 230 on the D scale.

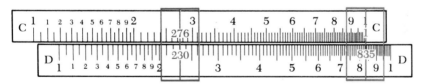

Fig. 6-43   Step 3, completing the first multiplication.

Step 4. Now we must multiply the result (230) by 914. Carefully move the slide so that the right index of C is under the hairline (Fig. 6-44). We used the right index because the left index forces the answer to be off the scale.

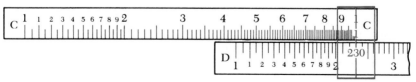

Fig. 6-44   Step 4.

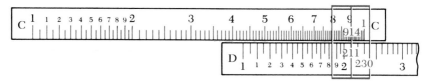

Fig. 6-45   The slide-rule reading is 211 on the D scale.

Step 5. Move the hairline to 914 (Fig. 6-45). The slide-rule reading is 211 on the D scale. Placing the decimal point in accordance with the estimate, the slide-rule answer is 2,110,000. The exact answer, by arithmetic, is 2,106,404.4000.

Notice that each multiplication involves a shift of the slide and a movement of the hairline.

There are other, more efficient ways of performing multiplications but they require better scales such as the CI and F scales. We are satisfied to give you the main idea through use of only the C and D scales.

PROBLEM SECTION 6.4

Find by slide rule. The answers given in the answer section are exact. A beginner may expect a few percent of error, but not in the position of the decimal point.

1. $38.6 \times 1.43 \times 0.887$
2. $0.441 \times 7.62 \times 0.0602$
3. $517 \times 2.92 \times 0.00943$
4. $0.00308 \times 1,635 \times 12.72$
5. $52,600 \times 20.4 \times 0.000719$
6. $0.0818 \times 37.7 \times 6,240$
7. $728 \times 934 \times 100.5$
8. $51.7 \times 105.2 \times 0.891$
9. $0.0325 \times 40.7 \times 56.9 \times 1.752$
10. $73.8 \times 25.5 \times 0.0680 \times 0.925$

6.5   DIVISION BY SLIDE RULE

Division is one of the most irritating arithmetic processes, yet it is the easiest operation on the slide rule. The theory is very simple. To explain it, let us go back to the addition slide rule (the one with equally spaced numbers on matched scales, with left indexes at 0). In Fig. 6-46, we have

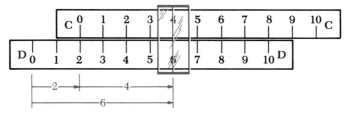

Fig. 6-46   Addition on the addition slide rule.

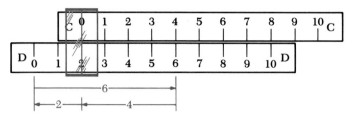

Fig. 6-47 $6 - 4 = 2$.

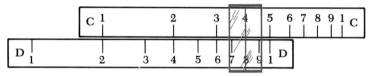

Fig. 6-48 $2 \times 4 = 8$.

shown $2 + 4 = 6$. With the very same setting, we can easily find $6 - 4$. In Fig. 6-47, we have accomplished subtraction by reading up to 6, then back 4, thus arriving at 2.

A similar principle applies to the multiplication slide rule used for division. In Fig. 6-48, we have diagramed $2 \times 4 = 8$.

If we look at this just a little differently, we see that, in this setting, $8 \div 4 = 2$ (Fig. 6-49). Reading the slide rule in this fashion, we take the length assigned to 8 and subtract the length assigned to 4. The answer is found under the index (either one) on the D scale. Students like to remember the setting by turning the fractions "upside down." In other words, the fraction ¾ appears as $\frac{4}{8}$ on the slide rule, the denominator on the C scale and the numerator on the D scale.

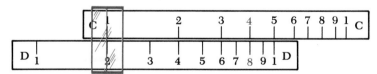

Fig. 6-49 $8 \div 4 = 2$.

illustrative problem 1

Find $75.3/2.68$.

solution

The estimate is as follows:

$75.3 \rightarrow 80$

$2.68 \rightarrow 3$

$\dfrac{75.3}{2.68} \rightarrow \dfrac{80}{3} \rightarrow 30$

Step 1. Find 753 on the D scale (Fig. 6-50).

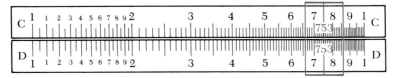

Fig. 6-50 Step 1.

Step 2. Move the C scale until 268 is under the hairline (Fig. 6-51).

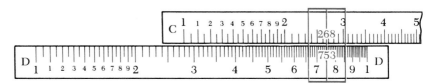

Fig. 6-51 Step 2.

Step 3. Move the hairline to the left index of C. Read the answer on D under the hairline (Fig. 6-52). The slide-rule answer is 28.1. The answer by arithmetic is 28.09701 . . . .

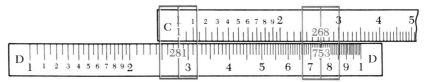

Fig. 6-52 Read 281 under the left index.

illustrative problem 2

Find 0.414/0.00760.

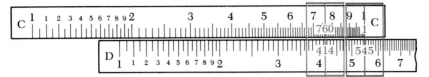

Fig. 6-53   Find 545 under the right *index.*

solution

Before estimating, we make the *denominator* a whole number:

$$\frac{0.414}{0.00760} = \frac{41,400}{760} = \frac{4,140}{76} \rightarrow \frac{4,000}{80} = 50$$

The final slide-rule setting is shown in Fig. 6-53. The answer, 54.5, is found under the *right* index. The answer by arithmetic is 54.47368 . . . .

PROBLEM SECTION 6.5

Do the following by slide rule. The answers in the answer section are correct to the number of places given. By this time, you should be able to get three figures correct most of the time, sometimes four.

1. $857 \div 24.6$
2. $438 \div 17.9$
3. $35.9 \div 56.3$
4. $60.9 \div 78.8$
5. $1.527 \div 82.6$
6. $1.814 \div 93.0$
7. $0.273 \div 625$
8. $0.391 \div 760$
9. $0.0407 \div 0.135$
10. $0.0738 \div 0.244$
11. $0.0611 \div 0.000927$
12. $0.0988 \div 0.000481$

6.6   MIXED MULTIPLICATION AND DIVISION (OPTIONAL)

In a rocket, the *burning surface area* S is given by the formula

$$S = \frac{w'}{RD} \qquad [3]$$

where w' is the weight of propellant burned per second, R is the burning rate, and D is the density of the propellant. For typical values of w', R, and D, the problem becomes

$$S = \frac{17.28}{90 \times 0.0932} \qquad [4]$$

which we shall do by slide rule.

illustrative problem 1

Find the value of S in Eq. [4].

solution

The estimate is

$$\frac{17.28}{90 \times 0.0932} \rightarrow \frac{20}{90 \times 0.09} = \frac{20}{8.10} \rightarrow \frac{20}{8} \rightarrow 2$$

There are several ways to arrive at the correct slide-rule answer. One way is shown in the following.

Step 1. Set the hairline at 1728 (Fig. 6-54).

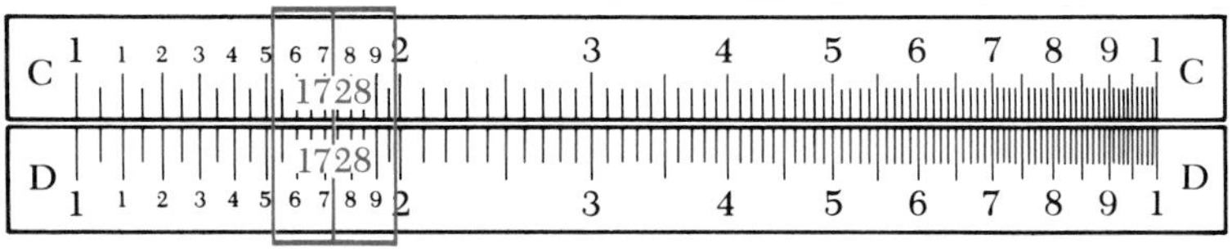

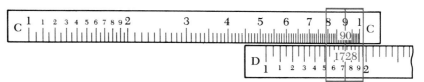

Fig. 6-54   Step 1.

Step 2. Divide by 90 (Fig. 6-55). The resulting reading, about 192, is under the hairline on the D scale (we do not need it).

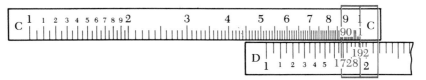

Fig. 6-55   Step 2.

Step 3. Move the hairline to the index (Fig. 6-56).

Fig. 6-56   Step 3.

Step 4. Divide by 932 (Fig. 6-57). The reading, 206, is under the index (Fig. 6-58). The slide-rule answer is 2.06. The correct answer, by arithmetic, is 2.06009 . . . .

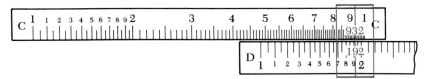

Fig. 6-57   Step 4.

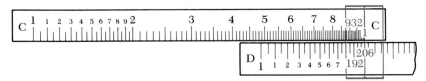

Fig. 6-58   The answer is under the index.

illustrative problem 2

The wall thickness of the combustion chamber of a rocket is found by the formula

$$t = \frac{PR}{s} \qquad [5]$$

where t is the thickness; s is the tensile strength of the wall adjusted by a safety factor, usually 4; R is the radius of the combustion chamber; and P is the combustion pressure. A typical set of values leads to

$$t = \frac{1{,}250 \times 0.812}{15{,}600} \qquad [6]$$

Find t by slide rule.

solution

The estimate is as follows:

$$\frac{1{,}250 \times 0.812}{15{,}600} \rightarrow \frac{1{,}000 \times 0.8}{20{,}000} = \frac{800}{20{,}000} = \frac{8}{200} = 0.04$$

Again, there are many ways of doing this. The most convenient method alternates division and multiplication.

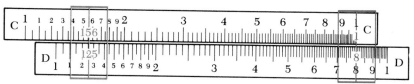

Fig. 6-59   125 ÷ 156.

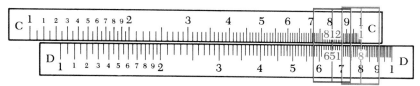

Fig. 6-60   Final setting for Illustrative Problem 2.

Step 1. Find 125 and divide by 156 (Fig. 6-59). The resulting reading, about 8, is on the D scale under the index.

Step 2. Multiply the result by 812. To do this, merely move the hairline to 812 on the C scale. It is not necessary to move the slide because it is already positioned correctly for multiplication. (In some cases, it will be necessary to interchange the right and left indexes.) This is shown in Fig. 6-60. The slide-rule reading is 651. The slide-rule answer is 0.0651 (inches). The answer, by arithmetic, is 0.06506410 . . . .

PROBLEM SECTION 6.6

Find by slide rule. The answers in the answer section are accurate to the number of figures given.

1. $\dfrac{25.6 \times 31.2}{17.6}$

2. $\dfrac{48.1 \times 52.6}{63.0}$

3. $\dfrac{75.1 \times 80.6}{96.2}$

4. $\dfrac{125 \times 20.4}{35.2}$

5. $\dfrac{40.9 \times 53.7}{62.5}$

6. $\dfrac{72.7 \times 83.4}{91.8}$

7. $\dfrac{15.6}{23.4 \times 30.7}$

8. $\dfrac{49.1}{52.6 \times 68.3}$

9. $\dfrac{77.1}{8.27 \times 0.918}$

10. $\dfrac{0.247}{0.127 \times 0.358}$

11. $\dfrac{0.0629}{0.408 \times 0.877}$

12. $\dfrac{0.529}{0.707 \times 0.0350}$

an introduction to mathematical tables

The use of mathematical tables is probably as old as or older than the use of mathematical instruments . One set of Babylonian cuneiform tablets with tables on them (Fig. 7-1) is dated as early as 2400 B.C. and another about 2100 B.C. (the time of Hammurabi).

At the present time, tables are used for astronomy, business, insurance, medicine, navigation, and, in fact, almost every field of science, industry, and commerce. We shall be concerned, in this chapter, with tables of *logarithms*.

The idea of logarithms came to John Napier in 1594, as we remarked at the beginning of Chap. 6. He was then about 44 years old. We can date the discovery this closely because of Napier's correspondence with the great astronomer Tycho Brahe. After Napier got the general idea, it took him 20 years to put it into workable form. In 1614, Napier published a book called *"Descriptio"* in which he described how logarithms could be used to make certain kinds of arithmetic calculations easier.

One of the first mathematicians to see the tremendous usefulness of logarithms was Prof. Henry Briggs, then at Gresham College in London, later at Oxford. On March 10, 1615, Briggs wrote to the Archbishop of Armagh and said that he was spending all his time "about the noble invention of logarithms." He also wrote the following[1] (his mathematics was better than his spelling):

[1] Reprinted from David Eugene Smith, "History of Mathematics," vol. 2, p. 516, Ginn, 1953.

Fig. 7-1   This is a Babylonian tablet from Nippur, from approximately 2400 B.C.

Naper, lord of Markinston, hath set my head and hands at work with his new and admirable logarithms. I hope to see him this summer, if it please God; for I never saw a book which pleased me better, and made me more wonder.

Napier and Briggs did meet at least twice, once in 1616 and once in 1617. At the first of these meetings, Briggs suggested some important improvements. The result was the so-called *Briggsian* or *common* logarithms which are actually the type we shall consider.

The table of logarithms, a shortened version of which is Table I in the Appendix, is fairly easy to make by a modern computer but, of course, there were no computers in those days. Briggs spent about 7 years calculating about one-fifth of the table. A Dutch publisher, Adriaen Vlavq (1600–1666), had the rest done, apparently for good commercial reasons.

Almost all this book is devoted to modern problems solved by modern techniques. However, in a few chapters, although the problems will still be thoroughly modern, the method will be 400 years old. For example, we shall finish Chap. 8 in a blaze of glory by calculating the *theoretical exhaust velocity* of a rocket using the formula[1]

$$V = \sqrt{\frac{2g\gamma}{\gamma - 1} RT \left[1 - \left(\frac{P_e}{P_c} \right)^{(\gamma-1)/\gamma} \right]}$$

We shall work this out by logarithms, of course. In this chapter and in Chap. 8, we shall also explain some modern applications of logarithms to problems in compound interest, amortization, annuities, and other topics in industry and commerce.

Before launching ourselves into these problems, we shall discuss logarithms slowly and carefully. You will see that working with logarithms involves mainly the ability to read a table.

7.1 A TASTE OF THEORY

In Chap. 6, we investigated a way to set up a slide rule to do multiplication and division easily and quickly (after some practice). In effect, we accomplished multiplication of numbers by *adding* their associated lengths (*logarithms*) on the slide rule. We accomplished division of numbers by *subtracting* their associated lengths (logarithms) on the slide rule. Figure 7-2 is repeated to remind you of the proper size of the associated lengths.

A natural question is: Where did these logarithms come from? In

---

[1] The symbol γ is the Greek letter *gamma*. The formula is taken from Marvin Hobbs, "Fundamentals of Rockets, Missiles and Spacecraft," p. 246, Hayden, New York, 1964.

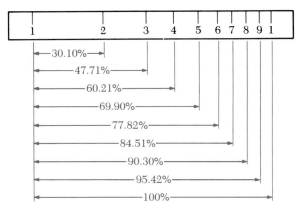

Fig. 7-2 The logarithms of certain numbers. (This is same as Fig. 6-23, page 189.)

fact, how do we know that the logarithm corresponding to 2 is 30.10 percent (or 0.3010) of the scale and that the logarithm corresponding to 3 is 47.71 percent (or 0.4771) of the scale?

Because this is a liberal arts course, we shall not even attempt a complete answer. What we shall do is identify logarithms and try to explain why it is that we can transform multiplication into addition, and division into subtraction. To do this, we shall have to go back to a topic you know something about, namely, *exponents*. Actually, logarithms came before exponents in the history of mathematical discovery but it is easier to explain the properties of logarithms in terms of exponents than the other way around.

A Review of Exponents

The symbol 2^5 is read "two to the fifth (power)" and, as you know, means $2 \times 2 \times 2 \times 2 \times 2$. By ordinary arithmetic,

$$2^5 = 2 \times 2 \times 2 \times 2 \times 2 = 32 \tag{1}$$

In Eq. [1], 2 is called a *base* and 5 is called an *exponent*. We say that in the expression 2^5 the base (2) is used as a *factor* five times. Similarly,

$$2^3 = 2 \times 2 \times 2 = 8 \tag{2}$$

Here 2 is used as a factor three times. Also,

$$3^4 = 3 \times 3 \times 3 \times 3 = 81 \tag{3}$$

Here 3 is the base and 4 is the exponent. We say that 3 is used as a factor four times.

For convenience in the illustrative problems, we furnish Table I, a partial table of numbers written as powers to bases 2 and 3:

TABLE I

Base 2 Table	Base 3 Table
$2^1\ = 2$	$3^1\ = 3$
$2^2\ = 4$	$3^2\ = 9$
$2^3\ = 8$	$3^3\ = 27$
$2^4\ = 16$	$3^4\ = 81$
$2^5\ = 32$	$3^5\ = 243$
$2^6\ = 64$	$3^6\ = 729$
$2^7\ = 128$	$3^7\ = 2,187$
$2^8\ = 256$	$3^8\ = 6,561$
$2^9\ = 512$	$3^9\ = 19,683$
$2^{10} = 1,024$	$3^{10} = 59,049$
$2^{11} = 2,048$	$3^{11} = 177,147$
$2^{12} = 4,096$	$3^{12} = 531,441$

Multiplying Numbers with Like Bases

Let us consider

$$2^5 \times 2^3 \tag{4}$$

which, we remind you, means

$$(2 \times 2 \times 2 \times 2 \times 2) \times (2 \times 2 \times 2) \tag{5}$$

This is simply the base 2 used as a factor eight times. In other words,

$$2^5 \times 2^3 = 2^{5+3} = 2^8 \tag{6}$$

Looking at the base 2 table, we see that Eq. [6] can be written

$$32 \times 8 = 256 \tag{7}$$

All we did was substitute 32 for 2^5, 8 for 2^3, and 256 for 2^8.

Do you see how important this is? Suppose you are asked to multiply 32 by 8 and you (a normal person) are too lazy to multiply but have just about enough energy to add. You look up 32 and find that it is the same as 2^5; then you look up 8 and find that it is 2^3. You *add* the exponents and decide that the answer is 2^8. You look back in the table and find that this is 256. Therefore, $32 \times 8 = 256$.

We do not really think you are too lazy to multiply 32 by 8. As you will see shortly, very complicated problems become quite simple. We just want to emphasize the main idea.

The procedure which we have illustrated will work if *both* numbers are in the same table. You undoubtedly see that there are some problems in which the numbers will not be located conveniently. Do not worry; there is a way of getting around the difficulty.

illustrative problem 1

Find 64×32 by using exponents.

solution

$$64 \times 32 = 2^6 \times 2^5 = 2^{6+5} = 2^{11} = 2,048$$

illustrative problem 2

Find $2,187 \times 81$ by using exponents.

solution

$$2,187 \times 81 = 3^7 \times 3^4 = 3^{7+4} = 3^{11} = 177,147$$

illustrative problem 3

Find 64×81 by using exponents.

Discussion: We note that 64 is 2^6, and 81 is 3^4. We do not say that a table containing both 64 and 81 does not exist. All we say is that at this point in the text we cannot complete the problem. We shall complete the general problem in Secs. 7.3 and 7.4.

Exponents and Logarithms

By this time, we hope you have noticed that, if exponents can be used in multiplication problems, the effect is to convert the problem into one in addition—the same as the effect on the slide rule. What is the difference between exponents and logarithms?

The answer is: there is no difference. *Exponents and logarithms are exactly the same things.* However, for convenience, we shall write the solutions of the problems a little bit differently when we use logarithms. For example, consider

$$3^2 = 9 \tag{8}$$

Here 3 is the base, 2 is the exponent or logarithm, and 9 is the result. Equation [8] is said to be in *exponential form.* We can express the same equation by writing

$$\log 9 = 2 \text{ (base 3)} \tag{9}$$

Equation [9] is read as follows: "Log 9, base 3, is 2." Equation [9] means that the logarithm (or exponent) corresponding to 9 is 2 when 3 is used as base. Equation [9] is said to be in *logarithmic form*.

Here are some more examples:

Exponential Form	Logarithmic Form
$2^{10} = 1{,}024$	$\log 1{,}024 \; = 10 \text{ (base 2)}$
$3^7 \; = 2{,}187$	$\log 2{,}187 \; = 7 \text{ (base 3)}$
$10^4 \; = 10{,}000$	$\log 10{,}000 = 4$

In the last line, notice that the base was not written. In computational work, when the base is omitted, it is *understood* that the base used is 10. Logarithms using base 10 are called *Briggsian* or *common logarithms*. Later in the chapter you will see why they are so convenient.

Notice that in the first column the exponents are 10, 7, and 4. In the second column, the logarithms are also 10, 7, and 4. Remember that they are always the same.

Multiplying with Logarithms

In the subsection on multiplying numbers, we found 64×32 by adding exponents, using base 2. We obtain the same result by adding the logarithms (base 2) but the solutions look a little different.

illustrative problem 4

Find 64×32.

solution 1 (exponential form)

$$64 = 2^6$$
$$32 = 2^5$$
$$64 \times 32 = 2^{11}$$
$$64 \times 32 = 2{,}048$$

solution 2 (logarithmic form)

$$\log 64 = \; 6 \text{ (base 2)}$$
$$+\log 32 = \; 5 \text{ (base 2)}$$
$$\overline{\log \text{prod} = 11 \text{ (base 2)}} \qquad (\text{``prod'' means } product)$$
$$\text{prod} = 2{,}048$$

The answer, in either case, is found by looking back to the base 2 table.

illustrative problem 5

Find $27 \times 27 \times 729$ by logarithms.

solution

$$\begin{aligned}
\log 27 &= 3 \text{ (base 3)} \\
\log 27 &= 3 \text{ (base 3)} \\
+\log 729 &= 6 \text{ (base 3)} \\
\hline
\log \text{prod} &= 12 \text{ (base 3)} \\
\text{prod} &= 531{,}441
\end{aligned}$$

At the beginning, you will find the logarithmic form to be somewhat strange. However, it turns out to be very convenient in the more complicated problems. It is important that you get used to it.

PROBLEM SECTION 7.1

Part A. Do the calculations using the logarithmic form.

1. What is meant by (a) 3^4, (b) 3^5? (c) Find 81×243.
2. What is meant by (a) 3^2, (b) 3^{10}? (c) Find $9 \times 59{,}049$.
3. Change to exponential form (a) $\log 81 = 4$ (base 3), (b) $\log 16 = 4$ (base 2).
4. Change to exponential form (a) $\log 25 = 2$ (base 5), (b) $\log 36 = 2$ (base 6).
5. Change to exponential form (a) $\log 1{,}000 = 3$, (b) $\log 10 = 1$.
6. Change to exponential form (a) $\log 100 = 2$, (b) $\log 10{,}000 = 4$.

Part B. Find by logarithms.

7. $243 \times 243 \times 3$ 8. $81 \times 27 \times 9$
9. $16 \times 8 \times 4 \times 2$ 10. $8 \times 8 \times 4 \times 8$

Part C. We did not discuss the following. See whether you can solve these by logarithms.

11. $6{,}561 \div 729$ 12. $59{,}049 \div 2{,}187$

7.2 THE LAWS OF LOGARITHMS

We have already used one law of exponents without making much fuss about it. We pause to formalize this law and mention some others we shall need. We remind you that our purpose in doing this is a practical one: to make certain calculations easier.

law of multiplication

To multiply two numbers expressed to the same base, add their exponents (or logarithms).

For example, $13^5 \times 13^2 = 13^{5+2} = 13^7$.

Division

Consider the problem $2{,}187/243$ which we wish to do by exponents or logarithms. From the table on page 213, $2{,}187 = 3^7$ and $243 = 3^5$. Then,

$$\frac{2{,}187}{243} = \frac{3^7}{3^5} = \frac{3 \times 3 \times 3 \times 3 \times 3 \times 3 \times 3}{3 \times 3 \times 3 \times 3 \times 3} = 3 \times 3 = 3^2 = 9$$

This illustrates a general rule:

law of division

To divide two numbers expressed to the same base, subtract the exponents (or logarithms) in the following order: *numerator exponent minus denominator exponent.*

illustrative problem 1

Find $x = 6{,}561 \div 81$.

solution 1 (exponential form)

$$6{,}561 = 3^8$$
$$81 = 3^4$$
$$6{,}561 \div 81 = 3^{8-4} = 3^4$$
$$6{,}561 \div 81 = 81$$

solution 2 (logarithmic form)

$$\log 6{,}561 = 8 \text{ (base 3)}$$
$$\ominus\log 81 = \ominus 4 \text{ (base 3)}$$
$$\overline{\log x = 4 \text{ (base 3)}}$$
$$x = 81$$

The encircled minus signs in color are to remind us that we are *subtracting.*

Mixed Multiplication and Division

Many problems involve both multiplication and division. When logarithms are used to solve these problems, it is convenient to treat the numerator and denominator separately, as shown in the following illustrative problems.

illustrative problem 2

Find $y = (729 \times 2{,}187)/243$.

solution 1 (exponential form)

$$y = \frac{729 \times 2{,}187}{243} = \frac{3^6 \times 3^7}{3^5} = \frac{3^{13}}{3^5} = 3^{13-5} = 3^8 = 6{,}561$$

solution 2 (logarithmic form)

We shall use "num" to mean "numerator."

$$
\begin{aligned}
\log 729 &= 6 \text{ (base 3)} \\
+\log 2{,}187 &= 7 \text{ (base 3)} \\
\hline
\log \text{num} &= 13 \text{ (base 3)} \\
\ominus\log 243 &= \ominus5 \text{ (base 3)} \\
\hline
\log y &= 8 \text{ (base 3)} \\
y &= 6{,}561
\end{aligned}
$$

illustrative problem 3

Find $z = (243 \times 81)/(9 \times 729)$.

solution 1 (exponential form)

$$\frac{243 \times 81}{9 \times 729} = \frac{3^5 \times 3^4}{3^2 \times 3^6} = \frac{3^9}{3^8} = 3^1 = 3$$

solution 2 (logarithmic form)

We shall use "den" to mean "denominator." In the following, we have omitted "(base 3)" for the logarithms to save space.

$$
\begin{array}{lll}
\log 243 = 5 & \log 9 = 2 & \log \text{num} = 9 \\
+\log 81 = 4 & +\log 729 = 6 & \ominus\log \text{den} = \ominus8 \\
\hline
\log \text{num} = 9 & \log \text{den} = 8 & \log z = 1 \\
& & z = 3
\end{array}
$$

Note: In these problems, it may appear that it is easier to work in the exponential form than in the logarithmic form. *This is quite true for simple problems.* However, as the problems become more difficult, the logarithmic form does not change much in difficulty but the exponential form becomes impractical. Please remember that the logarithmic method was not meant to be used for these easy problems. We are doing this merely for practice.

Zero Exponents or Logarithms

Consider $3^4/3^4 = 81/81 = 1$. This is a conclusion by ordinary arithmetic. Now, suppose we apply the law of division. Then we find that

$$\frac{3^4}{3^4} = 3^{4-4} = 3^0$$

Putting the two results together, we conclude that

$3^0 = 1$

and

$\log 1 = 0$ (base 3)

Now, let us try

$$\frac{2^8}{2^8} = \frac{256}{256}$$

Again, by ordinary arithmetic, the result is 1, and by the law of division it is 2^0, so that

$2^0 = 1$

and

$\log 1 = 0$ (base 2)

A complete analysis shows that it is reasonable to define a zero exponent, for any base except 0, so that the following law holds:

zero-exponent law[1]

For $b \neq 0$, $b^0 = 1$ and $\log 1 = 0$ (base b).

illustrative problem 4

Find $(243 \times 81)/(9 \times 2{,}187)$.

solution 1 (exponential form)

$$\frac{243 \times 81}{9 \times 2{,}187} = \frac{3^5 \times 3^4}{3^2 \times 3^7} = \frac{3^9}{3^9} = 3^{9-9} = 3^0 = 1$$

[1] The symbol $\neq$ is read "not equal to" or "does not equal," whichever sounds better.

solution 2 (logarithmic form)

In the following, we use "num" for "numerator," "den" for "denominator," and "res" for "result." To save space, we omit "(base 3)."

$$
\begin{aligned}
\log 243 &= 5 \\
+\log 81 &= 4 \\
\hline
\log \text{num} &= 9
\end{aligned}
\qquad
\begin{aligned}
\log 9 &= 2 \\
+\log 2{,}187 &= 7 \\
\hline
\log \text{den} &= 9
\end{aligned}
\qquad
\begin{aligned}
\log \text{num} &= 9 \\
\ominus\log \text{den} &= \ominus 9 \\
\hline
\log \text{res} &= 0 \\
\text{res} &= 1
\end{aligned}
$$

Negative Exponents or Logarithms

We turn our attention to

$$\frac{64}{512} = \frac{2^6}{2^9}$$

By ordinary arithmetic, we can rewrite and cancel as follows:

$$\frac{\cancel{2} \times \cancel{2} \times \cancel{2} \times \cancel{2} \times \cancel{2} \times \cancel{2}}{\cancel{2} \times \cancel{2} \times \cancel{2} \times \cancel{2} \times \cancel{2} \times \cancel{2} \times 2 \times 2 \times 2} = \frac{1}{2 \times 2 \times 2} = \frac{1}{2^3} = \frac{1}{8} \qquad [10]$$

However, if we apply the law of division, we find that

$$\frac{2^6}{2^9} = 2^{6-9} = 2^{-3} \qquad [11]$$

Putting Eqs. [10] and [11] together, we find that

$$2^{-3} = \frac{1}{2^3} = \frac{1}{8} \qquad [12]$$

Let us try another one.

$$\frac{9}{2{,}187} = \frac{3^2}{3^7} = \frac{\cancel{3} \times \cancel{3}}{\cancel{3} \times \cancel{3} \times 3 \times 3 \times 3 \times 3 \times 3}$$

$$= \frac{1}{3^5} = \frac{1}{243} \qquad [13]$$

By the law of division, the result should be $3^{2-7} = 3^{-5}$. To be consistent, it must be true that

$$3^{-5} = \frac{1}{3^5}$$

A full analysis shows that it is reasonable to define negative exponents and logarithms as follows:

negative-exponent law

For $b \neq 0$, $b^{-n} = 1/b^n$ and $\log(1/n) = -\log n$ (where the base is not 0).

illustrative problem 5

Find $(9 \times 729)/(243 \times 81)$.

solution

In the following, all the logarithms are to base 3.

$$
\begin{array}{lll}
\quad\log 9 = 2 & \quad\log 243 = 5 & \quad\log \text{num} = 8 \\
+\log 729 = 6 & +\log 81 = 4 & \ominus\log \text{den} = \ominus 9 \\
\hline
\quad\log \text{num} = 8 & \quad\log \text{den} = 9 & \quad\log \text{res} = -1 \\
& & \qquad\ \ \text{res} = 3^{-1} = \tfrac{1}{3}
\end{array}
$$

illustrative problem 6

Find the values of (a) 10^{-1}, (b) 10^{-2}, (c) 5^{-2}, (d) 2^{-3}.

solutions

(a) $1/10$ or 0.1, (b) $1/10^2$ or 0.01, (c) $1/5^2$ or $1/25$, (d) $1/2^3$ or $1/8$.

Fractional Exponents or Logarithms

We know, now, that $2^1 = 2$, $2^0 = 1$, and $2^{-1} = \tfrac{1}{2}$. Are there fractional exponents? What could be meant by $2^{0.5}$, for example? Let us see. If we assume that the law of multiplication holds, we know that

$$2^{0.5} \times 2^{0.5} = 2^1 \tag{14}$$

Let us give a name to $2^{0.5}$ (whatever it means). We shall call it x. Then, in Eq. [14], we have

$$x \times x = 2 \tag{15}$$
$$x^2 = 2 \tag{16}$$

This means that x is a number which, when used as a factor twice, yields the answer 2. By definition of square root, x is a square root of 2. In other words, $2^{0.5}$ is either about $1.4142 \ldots$ or $-1.4142 \ldots$ (whichever we decide). It cannot be both of them. In accordance with an international agreement among mathematicians, we shall decide that $2^{0.5}$, which can also be written as $2^{1/2}$, is the *positive* square root of 2. Similarly, $3^{0.5}$, which is about 1.7321, is the positive square root of 3.

We can write this in logarithmic form:

$$2^{0.5} = 1.4142 \ \textit{is the same as} \ \log 1.4142 = 0.5000 \ (\text{base } 2)$$

and

$$3^{0.5} = 1.7321 \ \textit{is the same as} \ \log 1.7321 = 0.5000 \ (\text{base } 3)$$

This is as far as we shall go at the moment. We merely wanted to show you, in preparation for the following sections, that exponents and logarithms may be positive, zero, or negative; also, they may be whole numbers, fractions, or decimal fractions. In Chap. 8, we shall explore fractional exponents again. Because they have to do with *roots*, they are very convenient in certain types of computations.

PROBLEM SECTION 7.2

Part A. Find (a) by exponents, (b) by logs.

1. 729×81
2. $27 \times 6{,}561$
3. $9 \times 19{,}683$
4. 243×81
5. 128×32
6. 32×32
7. 512×8
8. 64×32

Part B. Find (a) by exponents, (b) by logs.

9. $\dfrac{243 \times 27}{81}$

10. $\dfrac{729 \times 19{,}683}{243}$

11. $\dfrac{(81)^2}{729}$

12. $\dfrac{177{,}147 \times 59{,}049}{19{,}683}$

13. $\dfrac{243}{729 \times 2{,}187}$

14. $\dfrac{2{,}187}{6{,}561 \times 19{,}683}$

15. $\dfrac{243 \times 729}{2{,}187 \times 6{,}561}$

16. $\dfrac{19{,}683 \times 177{,}147}{243 \times 531{,}441}$

Part C. Find (a) by exponents, (b) by logs.

17. $\dfrac{6{,}561 \times 531{,}441 \times 19{,}683}{(177{,}147)^2 \times 2{,}187}$

18. $\dfrac{(59{,}049)^2 \times 177{,}147}{19{,}683 \times 729 \times 729}$

7.3   THE TABLE OF MANTISSAS

There is an obvious and important objection to working with logarithms using base 2 or 3. To point up the difficulty, let us look at the solution of Prob. 18 in Problem Section 7.2. In the following, all the logarithms use base 3.

$\log 59{,}049 = 10$	$\log 19{,}683 = 9$	$\log \text{num} = 31$
$\log 59{,}049 = 10$	$\log 729 = 6$	$\ominus\log \text{den} = \ominus 21$
$+\log 177{,}147 = 11$	$+\log 729 = 6$	$\overline{\log \text{res} = 10}$
$\overline{\log \text{num} = 31}$	$\overline{\log \text{den} = 21}$	$\text{res} = 59{,}049$

The obvious flaw in the method is that we can work conveniently only with certain numbers. For example, our little base 3 table would not be useful if the problem had been

$$\frac{(59,048)^2 \times 177,145}{19,680 \times 735 \times 715}$$

since none of these numbers appear in the base 3 table.

A much more convenient table for calculating is the *base 10 table* because, as you shall see, a rather short table gives us tremendous powers for calculating. Hereafter, we shall *always* use common logarithms (logarithms using base 10). In accordance with the usual practice, we shall omit mentioning the base. It will be understood to be 10.

illustrative problem 1

What does log 1,000 = 3 mean?

solution

It means that

$$\log 1,000 = 3 \text{ (base 10)} \qquad or \qquad 10^3 = 1,000$$

In this problem, 10 is the base, 3 is the logarithm (exponent), and 1,000 is called *the number*. (Of course, they are all numbers, but it has become common to speak of the result as "the number.")

illustrative problem 2

Write in logarithmic form: $10^{0.3010} = 2$.

solution

Log 2 = 0.3010. Here 2 is "the number" and 0.3010 is "the logarithm of the number." The base 10 is understood.

Mantissas and Characteristics

We have already mentioned the fact that exponents and logarithms may be positive, zero, or negative, and also whole numbers, fractions, or decimal fractions. By methods of advanced mathematics, we find, for example, that (approximately)

$10^{-0.3010} = 0.5$	or	$\log 0.5 = -0.3010$
$10^{0.6990} = 5$	or	$\log 5 = 0.6990$
$10^{1.6990} = 50$	or	$\log 50 = 1.6990$
$10^{2.6990} = 500$	or	$\log 500 = 2.6990$

We shall, for our own purposes, rewrite the logarithms as follows. Notice that the values are the same, even though they look a little different.

$$\log 0.5 = 0.6990 - 1 \qquad \text{(This is the same as } -0.3010.)$$
$$\log 5 = 0.6990$$
$$\log 50 = 0.6990 + 1 \qquad \text{(This is the same as } 1.6990.)$$
$$\log 500 = 0.6990 + 2 \qquad \text{(This is the same as } 2.6990.)$$

The *pure-decimal part* is called the *mantissa*. As you see, it turns out to be the same for 0.5, 5, 50, and 500, namely, 0.6990. (We shall explain.) The *whole-number part* is called the *characteristic* and depends upon the position of the decimal point. We shall take up an easy way to find the characteristic in Sec. 7.4.

Now we shall explain why the mantissas are the same. Consider

$$\log 5 = 0.6990 \tag{17}$$

This means that

$$10^{0.6990} = 5 \tag{18}$$

Now, multiply both members of Eq. [18] by 10^1.

$$10^{0.6990} \times 10^1 = 5 \times 10^1 \tag{19}$$

On the left side of Eq. [19], we use the law of multiplication and add the exponents. On the right side of Eq. [19], we simply multiply. The result is

$$10^{1.6990} = 50 \tag{20}$$

which is the same as

$$\log 50 = 1.6990 = 0.6990 + 1 \tag{21}$$

Now, multiply Eq. [18] by 10^2:

$$10^{0.6990} \times 10^2 = 5 \times 10^2 \tag{22}$$

Again, we add the exponents in the left member of Eq. [22]. In the right member, since 10^2 is 100, we merely multiply 5 by 100. The result is

$$10^{2.6990} = 500 \tag{23}$$

which is the same as

$$\log 500 = 2.6990 = 0.6990 + 2 \tag{24}$$

Finally, let us multiply both members of Eq. [18] by 10^{-1}, keeping in mind that $10^{-1} = \frac{1}{10} = 0.1$. Then

$$100.6990 \times 10^{-1} = 5 \times 10^{-1} \qquad\qquad\qquad [25]$$
$$10^{0.6990-1} = 0.5 \qquad\qquad\qquad\qquad [26]$$

or

$$\log 0.5 = 0.6990 - 1 \qquad\qquad\qquad [27]$$

We call your attention, once again, to the fact that the *mantissas* for the logarithms of 500, 50, 5, 0.5, 0.05, 0.005 . . . will all be the same. The characteristics will be different.

Finding the Mantissa

The following is a part of Table I of mantissas in the Appendix. Although the table is almost always called a table of logarithms, it is really a table of positive mantissas. In other words, it gives just the decimal fraction part of the logarithm.

N	0	1	2	3	4	5	6	7	8	9
55	7404	7412	7419	7427	7435	7443	7451	7459	7466	7474
56	7482	7490	7497	7505	7513	7520	7528	7536	7543	7551
57	7559	7566	7574	7582	7589	7597	7604	7612	7619	7627
58	7634	7642	7649	7657	7664	7672	7679	7686	7694	7701
59	7709	7716	7723	7731	7738	7745	7752	7760	7767	7774

This is a limited table, useful for three-digit numbers. The first two digits are given in the left-hand column, under the N, and the third digit is given in the heading. *Decimal points are omitted.* The easiest way to explain how to read the table is to illustrate.

illustrative problem 3

Find the mantissas for the logarithms of the following numbers: (*a*) 550, (*b*) 5.50, (*c*) 0.0000550, (*d*) 550,000.

solution

In all four cases, we look up 550. The mantissa is 0.7404.

illustrative problem 4

Find the mantissas for (*a*) 55.1, (*b*) 562, (*c*) 5,750, (*d*) 0.0588, (*e*) 59,900.

solution

We look up 551, 562, 575, 588, and 599. The mantissas are (*a*) 0.7412, (*b*) 0.7497, (*c*) 0.7597, (*d*) 0.7694, (*e*) 0.7774.

illustrative problem 5

Find the mantissa for 5.827.

solution

There are larger tables which take care of four-digit numbers. There are also ways of estimating the logarithm of a four-digit number even though the table was designed for three-digit numbers. However, these are details and we shall not concern ourselves with them. Instead, we shall "round off" to a three-digit number whenever the number in the problem has more than three digits. This means that the answers will not be as accurate as they should be, but that will not matter to us. In this problem, we round to 5.83, look up 583, and find that the mantissa is 0.7657.

illustrative problem 6

Find the mantissas for (a) 55.55, (b) 0.005937, (c) 592,400.

solution

We actually look for 556, 594, and 592. The mantissas are (a) 0.7451, (b) 0.7738, (c) 0.7723.

Finding "Starters" from Mantissas

After doing the calculations in a problem with logarithms, the line next to the last is usually something like

log res = 0.7536   ("res" means "result")

and we have the task of finding "the number." Thus far we have not discussed how to do this. However, we can look in the table for 0.7536 and find "the number" except for the decimal point and some zeros. In this case, when we look in the table, we find that the mantissa, 7536, corresponds to 567. So far as you know, right now, the number may be 56.7, or 0.000567, or 567,000,000. We shall call 567 the *starter*. We mean by this that after we decide that the digits are 567 we still have to place the decimal point and, possibly, some zeros.

illustrative problem 7

Find the starters for the following mantissas: (a) 0.7723 + 2, (b) 0.7413 − 1, (c) 0.7418 + 7, (d) 0.7653 − 6.

solution

(a) 592. (b) Not in the table. The closest starter is 551. We shall accept this as the correct starter. (c) Not in the table. The closest starter is 552.

(*d*) Not in the table. It is exactly between 582 and 583. We shall arbitrarily always choose the *higher* starter when the mantissa is exactly midway between two other mantissas. The answer is, therefore, 583.

PROBLEM SECTION 7.3

For the following exercises, use Table I in the Appendix.

Part A. Find mantissas for the following.

1. 10,600	2. 45,300
3. 7,310	4. 9,050
5. 439	6. 277
7. 19.9	8. 34.1
9. 5.61	10. 6.09
11. 0.837	12. 0.102
13. 0.0668	14. 0.0392
15. 0.00481	16. 0.00700

Part B. Find starters for the following mantissas.

17. $0.5587 + 1$	18. $0.8482 + 1$
19. $0.7033 + 2$	20. $0.8169 + 2$
21. $0.7340 + 3$	22. $0.8344 + 2$
23. $0.0128 + 3$	24. $0.9978 + 3$
25. $0.1970 - 1$	26. $0.9009 - 1$
27. $0.5465 - 2$	28. $0.9279 - 2$
29. $0.7067 - 3$	30. $0.9736 - 3$

Part C. Find the nearest mantissa.

31. 25.72	32. 25.75
33. 25.77	34. 4.448

Part D. Find the nearest starter.

35. $0.7017 - 3$	36. $0.5100 + 2$
37. $0.6196 + 1$	38. $0.6994 - 1$

7.4   FINDING CHARACTERISTICS

There are several methods for finding characteristics. We shall use a "trick" which will enable us to find the characteristic quickly. Before doing so, we shall define some words to help in explaining the trick.

Consider the numbers 723.45, 72.345, 7.2345, 0.72345, 0.072345, and 0.0072345. In each case the 7 is called the *first significant digit* (FSD). There may or may not be zeros left of the FSD. Between the *right* side of the FSD and the decimal point, we shall count digits. If the decimal point is to the right, we shall call them *right digits* (RD). If the decimal point is to the left, we shall call them *left digits* (LD). Remember, in both cases, we start counting from the right of the FSD. Here are some examples.

N	Comment	Characteristic	Log N
2 731.	3 RD	3	0.4362 + 3
3 85.4	2 RD	2	0.5855 + 2
4 1.48	1 RD	1	0.6201 + 1
5 .633	0 RD	0	0.7505 + 0
0.6 155	1 LD	−1	0.7896 − 1
0.07 520	2 LD	−2	0.8762 − 2
0.008 052	3 LD	−3	0.9058 − 3
0.0009 918	4 LD	−4	0.9965 − 4

As you can see, the characteristic is found by merely counting the number of right digits (RD) or left digits (LD). We are aware that this does not explain why the trick works. In general, it works because a shift in the decimal point is the same as multiplication or division by 10. For example, 23.45 becomes 234.5 by shifting the decimal point one to the right (increasing the number of RD), and 23.45 becomes 2.345 by shifting the decimal point one to the left (decreasing the number of RD). Every time the decimal point is shifted one place to the right, it is like multiplying by 10^1. By the law of multiplication, the exponent of the result is increased by 1. This means that the characteristic of the logarithm is increased by 1.

illustrative problem 1

Find (*a*) log 28.5, (*b*) log 0.0446, (*c*) log 741,236.

solution

We look up 285, 446, and 741 and get the mantissas 0.4548, 0.6493, and 0.8698. Then we do the following mentally:

2 8.5   1 RD

0.04 46   2 LD

7 41,236.   5 RD

The logarithms are (a) 0.4548 + 1, (b) 0.6493 − 2, (c) 0.8698 + 5.

illustrative problem 2

Find the numbers whose logarithms are (a) 3.5832, (b) 0.2776 − 2, (c) 0.8147.

solution

First we find the starters. They are 383, 189, and 653. We place the decimal point so that the first will have 3 RD, the second will have 2 LD, and the third will have no RD or LD. The answers are (a) 3830, (b) 0.0189, and (c) 6.53. At the beginning, this may be a little difficult. Make it a habit to check, as follows:

3 830.   3 RD

0.01 89   2 LD

6 .53   0 RD

PROBLEM SECTION 7.4

Using the problems in Problem Section 7.3, complete them by inserting characteristics in Parts A and C, and by inserting decimal points (and zeros, where necessary) in Parts B and D.

7.5 MULTIPLICATION BY LOGARITHMS

You remember that when we multiply numbers expressed to the same base we add their exponents or logarithms. We are now in a position to multiply rather easily because every (positive) number can be expressed by using the same base, namely, 10.

illustrative problem 1

Find 21.7 × 38.6 × 0.0224 × 0.00935.

solution

$$
\begin{aligned}
\log 21.7 &= 0.3365 + 1 \\
\log 38.6 &= 0.5855 + 1 \\
\log 0.0224 &= 0.3502 - 2 \\
+\log 0.00935 &= 0.9708 - 3 \\
\hline
\log \text{res} &= 2.2430 - 3 \\
&= 0.2430 + 2 - 3 \\
&= 0.2430 - 1 \\
\text{res} &= 0.175
\end{aligned}
$$

If we did this little problem by ordinary arithmetic, the answer would be 0.17543113280. The effect of our method is to give an answer accurate to three digits. It is possible to use a more detailed table, but we shall not need it. The thought is precisely the same.

illustrative problem 2

Find $0.08446 \times 1.523 \times 0.008197$.

solution

For our (limited) purposes, we shall round each number to *three* significant figures in order to make immediate use of our simplified table of mantissas.

$$
\begin{aligned}
\log 0.0845 &= 0.9269 - 2 \\
\log 1.52 &= 0.1818 \\
+\log 0.00820 &= 0.9138 - 3 \\
\hline
\log \text{answer} &= 2.0225 - 5 \\
&= 0.0225 + 2 - 5 \\
&= 0.0225 - 3 \\
\text{answer} &= 0.00105
\end{aligned}
$$

By ordinary arithmetic, the answer is 0.001,054,401,258,26. Our method is, as you see, quite painless and yields an answer which is very close to the exact one.

PROBLEM SECTION 7.5

Do by logarithms. We urge you to check by (*a*) estimate and (*b*) slide rule.

1. 384×0.0296
2. 49.1×0.583
3. $0.608 \times 735 \times 32.9$
4. $0.0891 \times 0.000914 \times 42.6$
5. $0.0000148 \times 0.00276 \times 38,400 \times 17,600$
6. $345,000 \times 72.6 \times 0.0443 \times 0.00818$

7.6   DIVISION BY LOGARITHMS

The law of division states: To divide two numbers expressed to the same base, subtract the exponents (or logarithms) in the order *numerator exponent minus denominator exponent.* Since all our numbers will be expressed in terms of logarithms to the same base (10), we can change all our division problems to problems in subtraction.

  We remind you that *subtraction,* in algebra, merely involves changing the sign of the subtrahend and then adding. Here are some examples:

1. Subtract 5 from 8

$$
\begin{array}{r}
8 \\
\ominus 5 \\
\hline
3
\end{array}
\qquad \text{(changing } +5 \text{ to } -5)
$$

2. Subtract 8 from 5

$$
\begin{array}{r}
5 \\
\ominus 8 \\
\hline
-3
\end{array}
\qquad \text{(changing } +8 \text{ to } -8)
$$

3. Subtract 5 from -8

$$
\begin{array}{r}
-8 \\
\ominus 5 \\
\hline
-13
\end{array}
\qquad \text{(changing } +5 \text{ to } -5)
$$

4. Subtract -8 from 5

$$
\begin{array}{r}
5 \\
\oplus 8 \\
\hline
13
\end{array}
\qquad \text{(changing } -8 \text{ to } +8)
$$

5. Subtract -5 from -8

$$
\begin{array}{r}
-8 \\
\oplus 5 \\
\hline
-3
\end{array}
\qquad \text{(changing } -5 \text{ to } +5)
$$

6. Subtract -8 from -5

$$
\begin{array}{r}
-5 \\
\oplus 8 \\
\hline
3
\end{array}
\qquad \text{(changing } -8 \text{ to } +8)
$$

The Simplest Case

illustrative problem 1

Find $38.6/21.7$.

solution

$$\log 38.6 = 0.5855 + 1$$
$$\ominus \log 21.7 \overset{\ominus}{=} 0.3365 \overset{\ominus}{+} 1 \qquad \text{(Note } \textit{three} \text{ changes of sign.)}$$
$$\overline{\log \text{res} = 0.2490 + 0}$$
$$= 0.2490$$
$$\text{res} = 1.77$$

If we wanted to write this in exponential form (we are doing it just for explanatory purposes), the solution would look like this:

$$\frac{38.6}{21.7} = \frac{10^{1.5855}}{10^{1.3365}} = 10^{1.5855-1.3365} = 10^{0.2490} = 1.77$$

illustrative problem 2

Find $84.6/0.00229$.

solution

$$\log 84.6 = 0.9274 + 1$$
$$\ominus \log 0.00229 \overset{\ominus}{=} 0.3598 \overset{\oplus}{-} 3 \qquad (\textit{Three} \text{ changes})$$
$$\overline{\log \text{answer} = 0.5676 + 4}$$
$$\text{answer} = 37,000$$

In this problem, as in the others, the table gives us only three significant figures. By arithmetic, the answer is $36,943.231\ldots$. You may notice that the first *two* of the significant figures are correct and the *third* is off by 1. This is a common situation in working with approximations. The last significant figure may be off by 1, sometimes more if it is a long calculation.[1]

Avoiding Negative Mantissas

In many division problems, the subtraction step looks something like this:

$$0.3365$$
$$\ominus 0.5855$$
$$\overline{-0.2490}$$

---

[1] A more careful discussion of significance and approximations can be found in Dodes and Greitzer, "Numerical Analysis," chap. 1, Hayden, 1964.

so that the mantissa of the result is *negative*. This is not incorrect, but it is very inconvenient because the table of mantissas supplied in mathematical handbooks (and in the Appendix of this book) is a set of *positive* mantissas. Furthermore, our trick for finding and using characteristics is based upon the use of positive mantissas.

To avoid this problem, we may rewrite the negative mantissa as a positive mantissa with a negative characteristic. In this specific case, we may add and subtract 1. (This does not change the value of the number.)

$$
\begin{aligned}
-0.2490 &= 1 - 0.2490 - 1 \\
&= (1 - 0.2490) - 1 \\
&= 0.7510 - 1
\end{aligned}
$$

To get the answer in the table of mantissas, in this little example, we would look up 7510.

This method is satisfactory, and you are welcome to use it if you prefer. However, a little planning will avoid the necessity of doing this. We remind you that the following logarithms are all the same:

0.3365
1.3365 − 1   (The characteristic is still 0.)
2.3365 − 2

and so on. If we notice that the subtrahend, 0.5855, is large enough to cause a negative mantissa for the result, we may adjust the *minuend* (the upper number) instead. The following shows the two ways of doing the subtraction. You may make your own choice.

Method 1:
$$
\begin{array}{r}
0.3365 \\
\ominus\,0.5855 \\
\hline
-0.2490 \\
+1.0000 - 1 \\
\hline
0.7510 - 1
\end{array}
$$

Method 2:
$$
\begin{array}{r}
1.3365 - 1 \\
\ominus\,0.5855 \\
\hline
0.7510 - 1
\end{array}
$$

We shall always use method 2 in the illustrative problems.

illustrative problem 3

Find 21.7/38.6.

solution

When we first set this up, it looks like this:

$$\log 21.7 = 0.3365 + 1$$
$$\underline{^\ominus\log 38.6 = {}^\ominus 0.5855 \overset{\ominus}{+} 1}$$

We note that this will give us a negative mantissa. We therefore change the minuend so that the problem looks like the following:

$$\log 21.7 = 1.3365$$
$$\underline{^\ominus\log 38.6 = {}^\ominus 0.5855 \overset{\ominus}{+} 1}$$
$$\log \text{res} = 0.7510 - 1$$
$$\text{res} = 0.564$$

illustrative problem 4

Find 0.0224/38.6.

solution

When we first set this problem up, it looks like this:

$$\log 0.0224 = 0.3502 - 2$$
$$\underline{^\ominus \log 38.6 = {}^\ominus 0.5855 \overset{\ominus}{+} 1}$$

and we note that the logarithm of the result will have a negative mantissa. We change $0.3502 - 2$ to $1.3502 - 3$ and obtain

$$\log 0.0224 = 1.3502 - 3$$
$$\underline{^\ominus\log 38.6 = {}^\ominus 0.5855 \overset{\ominus}{+} 1}$$
$$\log \text{res} = 0.7647 - 4$$
$$\text{res} = 0.000582$$

illustrative problem 5

Find 0.0000371/0.00908.

solution

$$\log 0.0000371 = 0.5694 \ -5$$
$$\underline{^\ominus\log 0.00908 = {}^\ominus 0.9581 \ \overset{\oplus}{-}3}$$

We change the minuend to $1.5694 - 6$, which is the same as $0.5694 - 5$, and obtain

$\log 0.0000371 = 1.5694 - 6$

$\ominus \log 0.00908 = \overset{\ominus}{}0.9581 \overset{\oplus}{=} 3$

$\overline{\quad \log \text{answer} = 0.6113 - 3 \quad}$

$\quad\quad\quad \text{answer} = 0.00409$

PROBLEM SECTION 7.6

Do by logarithms. We urge you to check by (a) estimate and (b) slide rule.

Part A

1. $423 \div 175$ 2. $897 \div 158$
3. $75.4 \div 2.63$ 4. $81.9 \div 9.22$
5. $1.35 \div 0.447$ 6. $5.07 \div 0.384$
7. $0.229 \div 0.159$ 8. $0.957 \div 0.463$
9. $0.339 \div 0.0244$ 10. $0.917 \div 0.00817$

Part B

11. $58.6 \div 351$ 12. $63.7 \div 492$
13. $712 \div 250$ 14. $892 \div 3,110$
15. $0.277 \div 8.35$ 16. $0.419 \div 12.6$
17. $0.0538 \div 0.714$ 18. $0.0829 \div 0.173$
19. $0.0000885 \div 0.0161$ 20. $0.0000727 \div 0.0917$

7.7 GROWTH AND DECAY PROBLEMS

Review of Linear Graphs

Before getting into our main topic, we remind you that formulas like

$$y = 3x \quad\quad\quad\quad\quad\quad\quad [28]$$
$$y = 2x + 1 \quad\quad\quad\quad\quad [29]$$
$$2y = 3x - 6 \quad\quad\quad\quad\quad [30]$$

lead to straight-line (*linear*) graphs (Fig. 7-3) when plotted in the usual fashion. The key fact is that in formulas [28] to [30] the exponents of x and y are both 1. A useful form of the linear formula is

Linear formula: $y = ax + b$ [31]

We are interested in the fact that any formula which cannot be put into form [31] is not linear. In other words, the graph will not be a straight line.

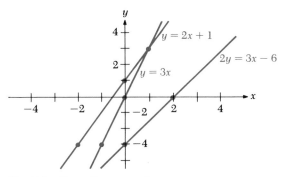

Fig. 7-3   Some linear graphs.

Growth Formulas

We shall investigate certain formulas which look like the following. Notice that we are using t and y instead of x and y.

$y = 10^t$	[32]
$y = 0.5 \times 10^t$	[33]
$y = 0.785 \times 10^{0.24t}$	[34]

where t and y are *variables*. In general, t may stand for a number representing something like a time interval, i.e., 0.38 second, and then y is calculated by logarithms. We are especially interested in this type of formula because it occurs in *growth* problems: the growth of living things, the growth of a crystal, some problems in business, and so on.

The general form of the growth formula is

Growth formula: $y = Ab^{kt}$ [35]

where A, b, and k are positive constants. There are some growth curves with variable A and k, but we shall not consider them.

If we plot formulas [32] and [33] in the usual fashion, Fig. 7-4 results. On the whole, curves like those in Fig. 7-4 are difficult to draw with precision even though there are certain commercial devices (Figs. 7-5 and 7-6) which are helpful.

As usual, brains are more powerful than computers or instruments. We note that

$y = 10^t$ [36]

is an exponential equation exactly equivalent to

$\log y = t$ [37]

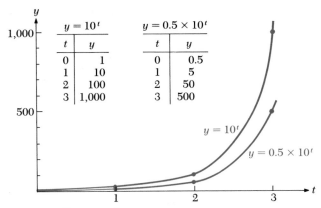

Fig. 7-4   *Two growth curves.*

Now, imagine that the vertical axis in Fig. 7-4 is replaced by a new one divided logarithmically, and let log y be replaced by z. Then, formula [37] becomes

$$z = t \qquad\qquad\qquad\qquad [38]$$

which is linear.

To restate this, it appears that if the y-axis is replaced by a logarithmic scale (so that it is really log y instead of y) formula [36] should give us a straight line. This is so important that a special kind of graph paper called *semilogarithmic graph paper* is manufactured to process growth-type formulas. This paper has one axis divided logarithmically. It looks like a long C or D scale of a slide rule, as a matter of fact.

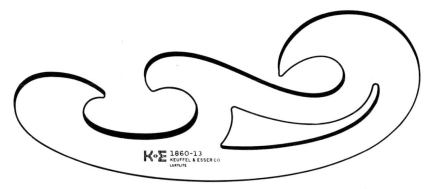

Fig. 7-5   *A French curve. By careful choice of a part of this instrument, a smooth curve can be drawn. (Keuffel & Esser Company.)*

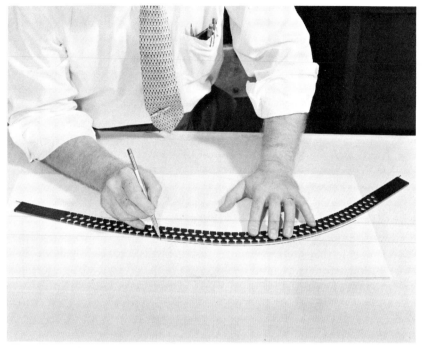

Fig. 7-6   A flexible ruler. This can be bent into a variety of shapes. (Keuffel & Esser Company.)

In Fig. 7-7, we have plotted formulas [32] and [33] on this special kind of paper. You see that they are really straight lines, as promised. In fact, any simple growth formula of the form

$$y = Ab^{kt}$$

is easily plotted on semilogarithmic paper. It always turns out to be a straight line if A and k are constants. (Of course, b is a constant because it is the *base*.)

illustrative problem 1

Plot the semilogarithmic curve

$$y = 0.785 \times 10^{0.24t}$$

From this, read values and draw a growth curve.

solution

For the line, we *need* only two values. Ordinarily, we calculate *three* values, the third one being used as a check point.

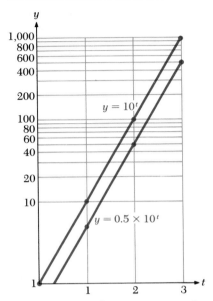

t	y
0	0.785
5	12.4
7	37.6

Fig. 7-7   Growth curves on semilog paper.

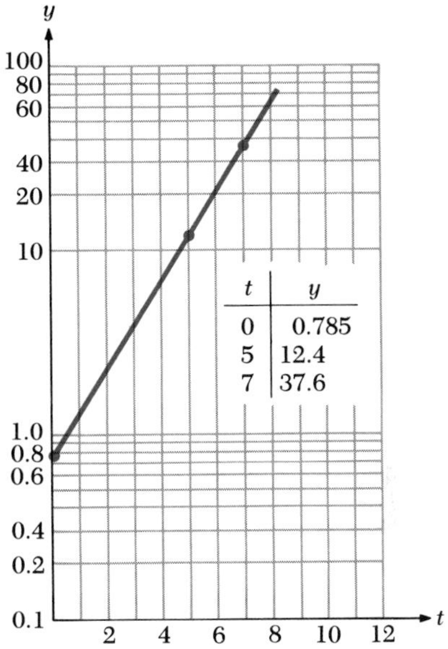

Fig. 7-8   Semilogarithmic graph for $y = 0.785 \times 10^{0.24t}$.

When $t = 0$, $y = 0.785 \times 10^0 = 0.785 \times 1 = 0.785$.

When $t = 5$, $y = 0.785 \times 10^{1.2000}$. We find $10^{1.2000}$ by looking in the table of mantissas for 2000. The starter is 158. The value of $10^{1.2000}$ is, therefore, 15.8 because the characteristic, in 1.2000, is 1. Then $y = 0.785 \times 15.8$, which equals 12.4 (easy by logarithms).

When $t = 7$, $y = 0.785 \times 10^{1.6800} = 0.785 \times 47.9 = 37.6$. Using these three values, we plot the line shown in Fig. 7-8.

A "standard" growth curve can be drawn by reading values from Fig. 7-8. Some possible values are

$t =$	0	1	2	3	4	5	6	7	8
$y =$	0.785	1.33	2.3	4.0	7.1	12.4	21.5	37.6	65

We omit the curve. It looks like all growth curves.

Decay Curves

We shall discuss, very briefly, a change in the exponents of formulas [32] and [33]. Consider

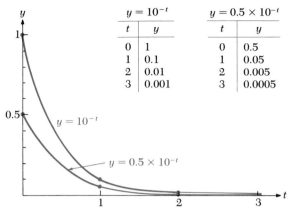

Fig. 7-9   *Two decay curves.*

$$y = 10^{-t} \tag{39}$$

and

$$y = 0.5 \times 10^{-t} \tag{40}$$

where *t* is positive. The curves are shown in Fig. 7-9.

The general form of a simple decay formula is

Simple decay formula: $y = Ab^{-kt}$ [41]

where *A*, *b*, and *k* are positive constants. As in the case of the simple growth curve, if the *t*-axis is equally divided and the *y*-axis is divided logarithmically, straight lines result. This is shown in Fig. 7-10.

Radioactive Half-life

Radioactive elements decay in accordance with formulas like [41]. For example, the formula for the decay of radium is

$$P = 10^{-0.000182t} \tag{42}$$

where *P* is the percent of the original that remains active after *t* years. (The rest disintegrates into nonradioactive elements.) For example, after 1,000 years (when $t = 1,000$), about 66 percent remains ($P = 0.658$) so that about 34 percent of the radium has changed into other elements.

illustrative problem 2

Using the formula for radium, (*a*) make a semilogarithmic decay curve using units of hundreds of years for *t*. (*b*) From this, read values and

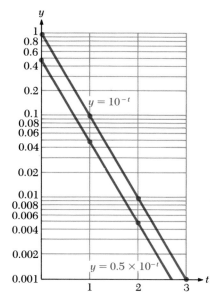

Fig. 7-10   *Decay curves plotted semi-logarithmically.*

draw a standard decay curve. (c) From the semilogarithmic decay curve (actually, a line) find the *half-life* of radium; that is, find out how long it will take for a quantity of radium to lose half its radioactivity (find t with $P = 50$ percent).

solution

(a) To make the semilogarithmic curve, we calculate three points (one for check). We convert Eq. [42] into logarithmic form for convenience:

$$\log P = -0.000182t \qquad [43]$$

We arbitrarily choose $t = 0$, $t = 1,000$, and $t = 3,000$. (Some trial and error preceded this. We wanted to be sure the result would fit on the paper. It does not matter what you choose.)

For $t = 0$: $\log P = 0$, so that $P = 1$.

For $t = 1,000$: $\log P = -0.182$. This is a negative mantissa, and so we add and subtract 1. Then $\log P = 0.8180 - 1$. From the table, the closest number is $P = 0.658$.

For $t = 3,000$: $\log P = -0.546$. Adding and subtracting 1, we get $\log P = 0.4540 - 1$. Then $P = 0.284$.

The graph is shown in Fig. 7-11.

(b) To draw the standard decay curve, it is convenient to read values from Fig. 7-11. For example, when $t = 2,500$, $P = 0.35$, as shown by

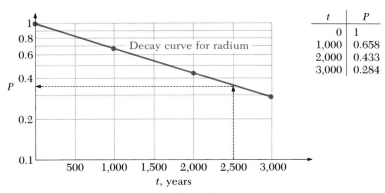

t	P
0	1
1,000	0.658
2,000	0.433
3,000	0.284

Fig. 7-11 Semilogarithmic curve for radium decay.

the dotted lines in Fig. 7-11. Reading values this way, we can easily plot the standard decay curve shown in Fig. 7-12.

(c) To find the half-life of radium, we go back to Fig. 7-11 and find $P = 0.50$ on the vertical axis. We read across (to the right) until we touch the line and then drop down to the t-axis. The value is about 1,660 (years). This means that half the radium will have decayed in about 1,660 years.

This does not mean that all the radium will be gone in twice 1,660 years. As a matter of fact, the half-life of the remainder, after the first 1,660 years, is still 1,660 years so that, in 3,320 years one-quarter of the original radium is still unchanged.

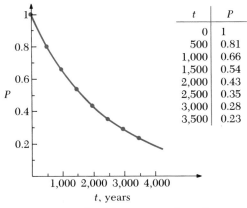

t	P
0	1
500	0.81
1,000	0.66
1,500	0.54
2,000	0.43
2,500	0.35
3,000	0.28
3,500	0.23

Fig. 7-12 Standard decay curve for radium.

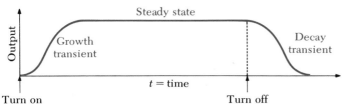

Fig. 7-13   *Growth and decay transients.*

Transients

When you turn on an electric light, it takes a little time for the filament to warm up and give out light, even though you may not notice it. (This effect is more noticeable if you have an old-time radio set or a TV set with vacuum tubes. It takes time for the tubes to warm up enough to provide the proper conditions for generating the sounds.) After this short time, the bulb emits a fairly steady light. (Actually there is a pulsation because of the alternating current but we cannot go into that.) When you turn the light off, it takes a little time for the filament to cool down. (In the old-time radio or TV, it takes a little time for the sound to go off.)

A simplified diagram of the situation we are trying to describe is shown in Fig. 7-13. The growth and decay parts of the curve are called *transients*. They are very important in engineering work. We cannot go into a discussion because problems in transients involve much more advanced mathematics, but we wanted you to know that growth and decay curves are important.

PROBLEM SECTION 7.7

Part A. For these problems, use Fig. 7-11 or a copy on your own paper.

1. After 750 years, what percent of the radium is unchanged?
2. After 1,250 years, what percent of the radium is unchanged?
3. After 1,750 years, what percent of the radium is unchanged?
4. After 2,250 years, what percent of the radium is unchanged?
5. After how many years will 90 percent of the radium be unchanged?
6. After how many years will 70 percent of the radium be unchanged?
7. After how many years will 40 percent of the radium be unchanged?
8. After how many years will 30 percent of the radium be unchanged?

Part B

9. A generator having an electromotive force (emf) of 100 volts is connected in series with a 10-ohm resistor and an inductor of 2 henrys.

A decay transient associated with the resulting current is

$$I = 10 \times 10^{-2.17t}$$

where I = number of amperes (current), and t = number of seconds after the switch is turned off. (a) Make a semilogarithmic decay graph using intervals of 0.1 second. (b) Make a standard decay graph. (c) After how many seconds is the current down to 5 amperes?

10. In a certain chemical reaction, one substance is being transformed into another at a rate proportional to the amount of the original substance left. The formula for the percent of original substance left is

$$P = 10^{-0.25t}$$

where t = time in hours. (a) Make a semilogarithmic graph of decay, using intervals of 1 hour. (b) Make a standard decay graph. (c) After how many hours is 25 percent of the original chemical left?

11. A thousand bacteria are multiplying continuously at the rate of 4 percent per hour. The growth formula is

$$B = 1,000 \times 10^{0.01736t}$$

where B = number of bacteria and t = number of hours. (a) Make a semilogarithmic graph, using intervals of 10 hours. (b) Make a standard growth curve. (c) After how many hours will the number of bacteria be doubled (i.e., what is the value of t when $B = 2,000$)? (d) After how many hours will there be 1 million bacteria?

12. The figures for the population of the United States from 1790 to 1950 are as follows:

Year	Population (millions)
1790	3.9
1800	5.3
1810	7.2
1820	9.6
1830	12.9
1840	17
1850	23
1860	31
1870	39
1880	50
1890	63
1900	76
1910	92
1920	108
1930	122
1940	135
1950	150

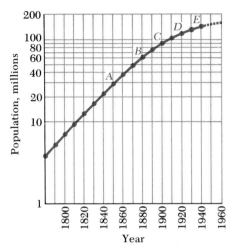

Fig. 7-14   *Population of the United States.*

These are plotted semilogarithmically in Fig. 7-14. The result is not a single straight line, as it would be if this were a single growth curve. Instead, it appears to be a series of straight lines ending at A, B, C, D, and E. As a rough approximation, we shall assume that the formula for the dotted portion of the curve is

$$P = 0.0343 \times 10^{0.0187t}$$

where P is the population (in millions) and t is the year. (*a*) Make a semilogarithmic graph of this formula from 1950 to 2000 in 10-year intervals. (*b*) From this, draw a standard growth curve. (*c*) From the semilogarithmic line, make a prediction for the population in 1960, 1970, 1980, 1990, 2000. (These will not check with actual figures. There was a sudden spurt in population due to a variety of causes. Mathematics cannot take account of unexpected variables.)

applications
of
logarithms

Innocent Byer was rather enthusiastic about the house, especially since the price tag was a mere $30,000. He asked the real estate agent whether it was possible to pay for the house in 30 yearly payments. "Certainly," said the agent, "we'll help you arrange the whole thing with the bank." Mr Byer beamed. "That's just fine," he said, "now . . . let me see. Thirty thousand dollars in 30 annual payments means, uh, it will cost me $1,000 a year. That's easy."

After Mr. Byer picked himself off the ground outside the real estate office, he said to himself, "I *really* should have learned about amortization, but I didn't know enough about logarithms to understand the explanation."

In the previous chapter, we discussed some of the theory of logarithms and then showed you how to calculate things like

$$27.8 \times 0.0432 \times 73,990$$

and

$$0.00563 \div 91.8$$

easily, just by referring to tables of mantissas. Unfortunately, most practical problems are not this short. In addition to the problem of amortization with which Mr. Byer had his difficulties, here are some other real problems which can be done by logarithms:

1. When a force is applied to a steel bar, it stretches. The elongation of the bar, in inches, is given by the formula

$$e = \frac{Pl}{AE} \qquad\qquad [1]$$

where e is the number of inches of elongation, P is the number of pounds of force applied, l is the length of the bar in inches, A is the cross-section area in square inches, and E is a constant depending upon the material. For steel, E is about 29 million. This formula would be useful, for example, if a very heavy object (like a train) were resting on pieces of steel (like rails). It is also useful for a rocket on its guide bars.

2. Ten years ago you deposited $50 at 4½ percent compounded semi-annually. How much is in the account now, provided you have made no withdrawals or deposits?

3. You deposit $25 a month for 10 years in a generous bank which offers interest at 6 percent compounded quarterly. How much is in the account at the end of the 10 years?

4. When you are 65, you wish to retire on an income of $500 a month guaranteed for 20 years. How much will this *annuity* cost?
5. The designer of your little transistor radio had to calculate the *resonance frequency f,* for which the formula is

$$f = \frac{1,000,000}{2\pi \sqrt{LC}} \qquad [2]$$

where π is a constant (about 3.14159), L is the inductance of the coil (in microhenrys), and C is the capacitance of a capacitor (in microfarads).

Involved in these and many, many other calculations is a knowledge of how to do problems which have mixed multiplication, division, powers, and roots. This is the subject of this chapter. You will see that it takes very little more than the ability to read a table to be able to do these calculations. (Of course, you must learn which table to use.)

8.1 MIXED MULTIPLICATION AND DIVISION

You already know how to do multiplication and division. Instead of going into a long explanation, we shall merely illustrate the procedure with five examples.

illustrative problem 1

Find $A = (32.3 \times 1.741)/2.819$.

solution

It is always wise to *set up* the problem first, as follows, before looking up any mantissas.

$$
\begin{array}{r}
\log 32.3 = \\
+\log 1.74 = \\
\hline
\log \text{num} = \\
\ominus\log 2.82 = \\
\hline
\log A = \\
A =
\end{array}
$$

Note that we rounded 1.741 to 1.74, and we rounded 2.819 to 2.82. We remind you that this is not a limitation on the method of logarithms but, instead, a result of the limited table in this book.

When you look up the mantissas, the problem looks like this:

$$\begin{array}{rl}
\log 32.3 = & 0.5092 + 1 \\
+\log 1.74 = & 0.2405 \\
\hline
\log \text{num} = & 0.7497 + 1 \\
\ominus\log 2.82 = & \ominus 0.4502 \\
\hline
\log A = & 0.2995 + 1 \\
A = & 19.9
\end{array}$$

To make sure there are no tremendous errors, we *estimate* the answer. The original problem is approximately

$$\frac{30 \times 2}{3}$$

which is about 20. This is close enough. (Up to *five* times too large or too small is close enough. This merely checks the decimal point.) To check the actual digits, use your slide rule.

illustrative problem 2

Find $A = (165 \times 0.00814)/35.7$.

solution

$$\begin{array}{rl}
\log 165 = & 0.2175 + 2 \\
+\log 0.00814 = & 0.9106 - 3 \\
\hline
\log \text{num} = & 1.1281 - 1 \\
\ominus\log 35.7 = & \ominus 0.5527 \overset{\ominus}{+} 1 \\
\hline
\log A = & 0.5754 - 2 \\
A = & 0.0376
\end{array}$$

Estimate: $\dfrac{200 \times 0.008}{40} = 5 \times 0.008 = 0.04$ (very close)

illustrative problem 3

Find $A = (165 \times 0.00814)/35{,}700$.

solution

$$\begin{array}{rl}
\log 165 = & 0.2175 + 2 \\
+\log 0.00814 = & 0.9106 - 3 \\
\hline
\log \text{num} = & 1.1281 - 1 \\
\ominus\log 35{,}700 = & \ominus 0.5527 \overset{\ominus}{+} 4 \\
\hline
\log A = & 0.5754 - 5 \\
A = & 0.0000376
\end{array}$$

illustrative problem 4

Find $A = 49.2/(16.8 \times 0.0727)$.

solution

First, we calculate the logarithm of the *denominator*. Then we subtract that from the logarithm of the numerator.

$$\begin{array}{ll}
\log 16.8 = 0.2253 + 1 \\
\underline{+\log 0.0727 = 0.8615 - 2} \\
\quad \log \text{den} = 1.0868 - 1 \\
\qquad\qquad\; = 0.0868
\end{array}
\qquad
\begin{array}{ll}
\log 49.2 = \quad 1.6920 \\
\ominus \log \text{den} = \ominus 0.0868 \\
\quad \log A = \quad 1.6052 \\
\qquad A = \quad 40.3
\end{array}$$

illustrative problem 5

Find $(93.6 \times 0.4127)/(0.826 \times 0.00612)$.

solution

We calculate the logarithms of the numerator and denominator separately and then subtract the logarithm of the denominator from that of the numerator.

$$\begin{array}{l}
\log 93.6 = 0.9713 + 1 \\
\underline{+\log 0.413 = 0.6160 - 1} \\
\quad \log \text{num} = 1.5873 \\
\qquad\qquad\; = 0.5873 + 1
\end{array}$$

$$\begin{array}{l}
\log 0.826 = 0.9170 - 1 \\
\underline{+\log 0.00612 = 0.7868 - 3} \\
\quad \log \text{den} = 1.7038 - 4 \\
\qquad\qquad\; = 0.7038 - 3
\end{array}$$

$$\begin{array}{l}
\quad \log \text{num} = \quad 1.5873 \\
\ominus \log \text{den} = \ominus 0.7038 \overset{\oplus}{=} 3 \\
\quad \log \text{ans} = \quad 0.8835 + 3 \\
\qquad\quad \text{ans} = 7650
\end{array}$$

Estimate: $\dfrac{90 \times 0.4}{0.8 \times 0.006} \to \dfrac{36}{0.0048} \to \dfrac{40}{0.005} \to 8{,}000 \qquad$ (close)

PROBLEM SECTION 8.1

Do by logarithms. We encourage you to check by slide rule and estimate.

Part A

1. $\dfrac{175 \times 245}{926}$

2. $\dfrac{358 \times 412}{837}$

3. $\dfrac{52.6 \times 613}{7.81}$

4. $\dfrac{71.8 \times 822}{6.19}$

5. $\dfrac{9.26 \times 0.114}{75.3}$

6. $\dfrac{1.81 \times 0.249}{86.5}$

Part B

7. $\dfrac{150}{964 \times 8.51}$

8. $\dfrac{372}{727 \times 6.41}$

9. $\dfrac{54.7}{58.9 \times 0.418}$

10. $\dfrac{72.8}{39.1 \times 0.218}$

11. $\dfrac{9.62}{1.84 \times 0.00912}$

12. $\dfrac{4.17}{8.31 \times 0.00727}$

Part C

13. $\dfrac{123 \times 234}{345 \times 456}$

14. $\dfrac{567 \times 678}{789 \times 901}$

15. $\dfrac{17.8 \times 3.51}{5.69 \times 0.728}$

16. $\dfrac{24.6 \times 4.18}{6.35 \times 0.819}$

17. $\dfrac{0.353 \times 0.00462}{5.18 \times 63.2}$

18. $\dfrac{0.528 \times 0.00773}{9.35 \times 31.4}$

8.2 POWERS

The Compound-interest Formula

The interest rate for money deposited in a savings bank varies. Typical rates are somewhere between 4 and 6 percent compounded quarterly. This means that if, for example, the rate is 4 percent the bank adds 1 percent ($= \frac{1}{4} \times 4\%$) of your account to your account every 3 months. If you start with $100, then at the end of 3 months your account is altered to $101, the extra dollar being the interest.

Suppose you deposit $500 on January 1. (We know the banks are closed on that day but we want to make the explanation easy.) Then on April 1 (3 months later), your interest is $1\% \times \$500 = 0.01 \times \$500 = \$5.00$, and your new *balance* is $\$500 + \$5.00 = \$505.00$. You can save a step by multiplying $500 by 1.01:

$$
\begin{array}{r}
\$5\,00 \\
\times 1.01 \\
\hline
5\,00 \\
500\,0 \\
\hline
\$505.00
\end{array}
$$

After another 3 months, on July 1 (because we are assuming that interest is *compounded* every 3 months), your interest is 1% × $505 = 0.01 × $505 = $5.05, and your new balance is $505.00 + $5.05 = $510.05. Again, you can save a step by multiplying $505 by 1.01. We remind you that we are using 1 percent because the given interest rate is 4 percent, but this is a yearly rate and we are calculating the interest four times a year, so that each time, the interest rate is one-quarter of 4 percent.

$$
\begin{array}{r}
\$5\ 05 \\
\times 1.01 \\
\hline
5\ 05 \\
505\ 0 \\
\hline
\$510.05
\end{array}
$$

Now, let us go back and see what we have done. First, we calculated $500 × 1.01, and then we multiplied the result of this calculation by 1.01, again. In other words, the last result we got was really

($500 × 1.01) × 1.01 = $500 × (1.01 × 1.01) = $500 × (1.01)^2

To check, let us find out how much $(1.01)^2$ is; then multiply $500 by this. It is not easier but (as you have probably guessed) we are leading up to an easy method.

$$
\begin{array}{r}
1.01 \\
\times 1.01 \\
\hline
1\ 01 \\
1\ 01\ 0 \\
\hline
1.02\ 01
\end{array}
\qquad
\begin{array}{r}
\$500 \\
1.0201 \\
\hline
500 \\
10\ 000 \\
500\ 0 \\
\hline
\$510.0500
\end{array}
$$

If you have followed this argument successfully, you see that on October 1, after three *interest periods*, each interest period being 3 months long, the new balance would be

$500 × (1.01)^3

We shall, hereafter, omit the symbol ×. The balance after three interest periods is, then,

$500(1.01)^3

and on January 1 of the next year, after *four* interest periods, the new balance is

$500(1.01)^4

A generalization of this is given in the following formula.

Compound-interest Formula: The amount A of the balance after n interest periods is equal to the original principal P multiplied by $(1 + r)^n$, where r is the rate of interest for each interest period:

$$A = P(1 + r)^n \hspace{4cm} [3]$$

illustrative problem 1

A man deposits \$625 at 6 percent compounded semiannually. (*a*) What is the interest rate per interest period? (*b*) How many interest periods are there in 12 years? (*c*) Write the formula to find the balance after 12 years, but do not calculate.

solution

(*a*) There are *two* interest periods each year. The interest rate per year is 6 percent, and so the interest rate per interest period is $6\%/2 = 3\% = 0.03$. (*b*) In 12 years, there will be 24 interest periods. (*c*) $A = \$625(1.03)^{24}$.

illustrative problem 2

A man deposits \$575 at 5 percent compounded quarterly. (*a*) What is the interest rate per interest period? (*b*) How many interest periods are there in 10 years? (*c*) Write the formula to find the balance after 10 years, but do not calculate.

solution

(*a*) There are four interest periods each year. The interest rate per year is 5 percent, and so the interest rate per interest period is $5\%/4 = 0.05/4 = 0.0125$. (*b*) In 10 years, there will be 40 interest periods. (*c*) $A = \$575(1.0125)^{40}$.

The Power Law

There are few calculations more irritating than trying to find $(1.03)^{24}$ or $(1.0125)^{40}$ by direct multiplication. We are going to show you how to get an approximate answer easily by logarithms but we hasten to say that our tables are not precise enough to do a very good job. In our own defense, let us say that the *method* is exactly the same. If you really need the correct answer, just consult a handbook with more complete tables.

We introduce the method by investigating a very simple exercise. Consider

$$Q = (35)^3$$

As you know, this is the same as

$$Q = 35 \times 35 \times 35$$

To solve by logarithms, we proceed in the usual way:

$$\log 35 = 0.5441 + 1$$
$$\log 35 = 0.5441 + 1$$
$$+\log 35 = 0.5441 + 1$$
$$\overline{\log Q = 1.6323 + 3}$$
$$= 0.6323 + 4$$
$$Q = 42{,}900$$

This is satisfactory, but we can speed up the calculations by doing the following:

$$\log 35 = 0.5441 + 1$$
$$\times 3$$
$$\overline{\log Q = 1.6323 + 3}$$
$$= 0.6323 + 4$$
$$Q = 42{,}900$$

Now, let us tackle $Q = (1.03)^4$ in the same way:

$$\log 1.03 = 0.0128$$
$$\times 4$$
$$\overline{\log Q = 0.0512}$$
$$Q = 1.13$$

This illustrates the power law:

power law

To raise a number to a power, multiply the logarithm of the number by the power; then find the result by using a table of mantissas.

Computing Balances

We are now almost ready to complete the problems with which we started. In Illustrative Problem 1, we have to evaluate

$$A = \$625(1.03)^{24}$$

and in Illustrative Problem 2, we have to evaluate

$$A = \$575(1.0125)^{40}$$

We could use our present table to do these, but the answers would be off by quite a bit. We shall not attempt to eliminate the error completely (we leave that to the banks). However, in the interest of getting somewhat more sensible answers, we include Table I, a small piece of a more accurate table.

TABLE I.   PORTION OF A
FIVE-PLACE TABLE

N	Log N
1.0075	0.00325
1.0100	0.00432
1.0125	0.00539
1.0150	0.00647
1.0175	0.00753
1.0200	0.00860
1.0250	0.01072
1.0300	0.01284
1.0350	0.01494
1.0400	0.01703

illustrative problem 3

Complete Illustrative Problem 1 by calculating $A = \$625(1.03)^{24}$.

solution

We shall do this in two parts. First, we take care of the power, using the five-place table. Let

$$Q = (1.03)^{24}$$

Then

$$\begin{array}{r} \log 1.03 = 0.01284 \\ \times 24 \\ \hline \log Q = 0.30816 \end{array}$$

We do not need the value of Q. We round the value of $\log Q$ to four places and continue as follows:

$$\begin{array}{r} \log 625 = 0.7959 + 2 \\ + \log Q = 0.3082 \\ \hline \log A = 1.1041 + 2 \\ = 0.1041 + 3 \\ A = \$1,270 \qquad \text{(approximately)} \end{array}$$

The correct answer is about half a dollar more than this.

illustrative problem 4

Complete Illustrative Problem 2 by calculating $A = \$575(1.0125)^{40}$.

solution

Let $Q = (1.0125)^{40}$.

$$\begin{aligned} \log 1.0125 &= 0.00539 \\ &\underline{\times 40} \\ \log Q &= 0.21560 \end{aligned}$$

$$\begin{aligned} \log 575 &= 0.7597 + 2 \\ +\log Q &= 0.2156 \\ \hline \log A &= 0.9753 + 2 \\ A &= \$945 \end{aligned}$$

The correct answer is about 77¢ more.

illustrative problem 5

A certain property accrues in value at the rate of 7 percent compounded semiannually. If its original value is $5,000, what will its value be in 10 years?

solution

$A = \$5,000(1.035)^{20}$

Let $Q = (1.035)^{20}$.

$$\begin{aligned} \log 1.035 &= 0.01494 \\ &\underline{\times 20} \\ \log Q &= 0.29880 \end{aligned}$$

$$\begin{aligned} \log 5,000 &= 0.6990 + 3 \\ +\log Q &= 0.2988 \\ \hline \log A &= 0.9978 + 3 \\ A &= \$9,950 \end{aligned}$$

Answer: The value of the property will be about $9,950.

The Compound-interest Table

We are reading your mind; we see in it the question whether bankers actually do these multiplications, and whether they actually look in these tables of mantissas. We must admit that we have been guilty of a slight fib. What happens is that what we have been calling Q exists in tables all by itself. A short version is given as Table II in the Appendix.

We shall do Illustrative Problem 3 by using this table. In that problem, $r = 3\%$ and $n = 24$. Looking in the table, we find 2.0328, which is the *compound amount factor per dollar.* (That is what we have been calling Q.) Our principal is, however, $625. We now multiply,

$\$625 \times 2.0328 = \$1,270.5000$

which we round to $1,270.50.

All the problems up to 50 interest periods for certain interest rates can be done easily by Table II.

Extending the Compound-interest Table (Optional)

Although the table goes up to only 50 interest periods, it is not difficult to extend it to larger numbers of interest periods. To find the factor for, say, 70 years, we choose any two convenient years that *add* up to 70, then *multiply* the factors. [We are actually using the fact that, for example, $(1.03)^{70} = (1.03)^{40} \times (1.03)^{30}$.] We could, for example, multiply the factors for 42 and 28, or 50 and 20.

illustrative problem 6

If \$25 is deposited for 35 years at 6 percent compounded quarterly, how much is it worth at the end of the 35 years?

solution

We shall need a value for $4 \times 35 = 140$ interest periods. We shall use $50 + 50 + 40 = 140$. To find the factor for 140 interest periods, we multiply

$$2.1052 \times 2.1052 \times 1.8140 = 8.0394$$

Then

$$A = \$25 \times 8.0394$$
$$= \$200.99$$

Obviously, if much of this kind of thing has to be done, it is better to purchase a better set of tables—or a computer, which will do it by logarithms.

PROBLEM SECTION 8.2

Part A. Using the four-place table, find each of the following.

1. $(35.4)^2$ 　　　2. $(48.7)^2$
3. $(0.0129)^3$ 　　4. $(0.0257)^3$
5. $(1.83)^{10}$ 　　6. $(8.76)^{10}$

Part B. In each of the following, find the amount for the principal deposited, after the time given, at the interest stated. Use either logarithms or Table II of the Appendix (where convenient).

7. \$25, 4 percent quarterly, 10 years
8. \$35, 6 percent quarterly, 20 years
9. \$1, 5 percent quarterly, 100 years
10. \$300, 7 percent quarterly, 15 years

Part C

11. A man sets aside a trust fund of \$5,000 at the birth of his son, the amount to become available when the son is 21 years old. The bank

offers 6 percent compounded quarterly for long-term deposits. How much will the trust fund be worth at maturity?

12. A man borrows $1,500 for a 10-year business-expansion loan, interest to accrue at 8 percent compounded semiannually. How much is owed at the end of 10 years? (In this problem, we are making the unrealistic assumption that the interest is allowed to grow for 10 years.)

8.3   SAVINGS PLANS

In 1854, a British geologist found two mathematical tablets at Senkereh, the site of an ancient Babylonian city on the Euphrates. Since that time, about 50,000 tablets have been found at Nuffar (ancient Nippur), a town south of the site of Babylon. These appear to be from a large library destroyed about 2150 B.C. or even earlier. An examination of the tables seems to show that the Babylonians, more than 4,000 years ago, might have been able to solve some of the modern problems which we are about to investigate.

Some Theory

Let us form the *geometric sequence*

$$1, 3, 9, 27, 81, 243 \qquad [4]$$

How were the numbers chosen? Obviously, each number (except the first one) is three times the one before it. We shall say that the *first term, a*, is equal to 1 and that the *multiplying factor, m*, is equal to 3. We could have written [4] as follows:

$$1, 1 \times 3, 1 \times 3^2, 1 \times 3^3, 1 \times 3^4, 1 \times 3^5 \qquad [5]$$

This sequence has *six* terms. We say that $n = 6$.

Here is another geometric sequence:

$$2, 10, 50, 250 \qquad [6]$$

Can you find a, m, and n? The first term is 2, and so $a = 2$. Each term (except the first one) is found by multiplying by 5, so that $m = 5$. Also, there are four terms, and so $n = 4$. We could have written [6] as

$$2, 2 \times 5^1, 2 \times 5^2, 2 \times 5^3 \qquad [7]$$

Notice that in [5], where $n = 6$, the last exponent is 5. In [7], where $n = 4$, the last exponent is 3.

In general, a geometric sequence is defined as a sequence in which the terms look like this:

$$a, a(m^1), a(m^2), a(m^3), \ldots, a(m^{n-1}) \tag{8}$$

where the last exponent, as usual, is 1 less than n.

Our problem is to find the *sum* of a *geometric series*. A geometric series is one in which the terms are in geometric sequence, like [4] or [6]. Of course, in these easy cases, the wisest thing to do is just add:

$$S_6 = 1 + 3 + 9 + 27 + 81 + 243 = 364 \tag{9}$$
$$S_4 = 2 + 10 + 50 + 250 = 312 \tag{10}$$

where S_6 (*S sub* 6) means "the sum of six terms" and S_4 (*S sub* 4) means "the sum of four terms." However, we are interested (just as the Babylonians were, 4,000 years ago) in a lazy way to do this kind of problem when there are a great many terms.

We shall illustrate with Eq. [9] and use a little trickery which we shall explain promptly. If

$$S_6 = 1 + 3 + 9 + 27 + 81 + 243 \tag{9}$$

then

$$3S_6 = 3 + 9 + 27 + 81 + 243 + 729 \tag{11}$$

We obtained Eq. [11] from [9] by multiplying each term by m which, in this case, is 3. Now we shall "line up" Eqs. [9] and [11] as shown below and subtract, term by term:

$$3S_6 = \qquad\;\; 3 + 9 + 27 + 81 + 243 + 729 \tag{11}$$
$$\ominus S_6 = \;\; \ominus 1 \;\overset{\ominus}{+}\; 3 \;\overset{\ominus}{+}\; 9 \;\overset{\ominus}{+}\; 27 \;\overset{\ominus}{+}\; 81 \;\overset{\ominus}{+}\; 243$$

$$\overline{2S_6 = -1 \qquad\qquad\qquad\qquad\qquad\quad\; + 729} \tag{12}$$
$$2S_6 = 728$$
$$S_6 = 364$$

To emphasize our general plan of operations, we repeat the trick with Eq. [10], where $m = 5$.

$$5S_4 = \qquad\;\; 10 + 50 + 250 + 1{,}250 \tag{13}$$
$$\ominus S_4 = \;\; \ominus 2 \;\overset{\ominus}{+}\; 10 \;\overset{\ominus}{+}\; 50 \;\overset{\ominus}{+}\; 250$$

$$\overline{4S_4 = -2 \qquad\qquad\qquad\qquad + 1{,}250}$$
$$4S_4 = 1{,}248$$
$$S_4 = 312$$

Now we are ready to obtain the general rule. The following proof is *optional*. It leads to formula [16].

Proof (Optional): Let

$$S_n = a + am^1 + am^2 + am^3 + \cdots + am^{n-1} \tag{14}$$

We multiply by m and "line up" the results as follows. Notice that $am^{n-1} \times m^1 = am^{n-1+1} = am^n$.

$$mS_n = \quad\quad am^1 + am^2 + \cdots + am^{n-1} + am^n \quad\quad\quad [15]$$

$$\ominus S_n = \ominus a \ominus{+} am^1 \ominus{+} am^2 \ominus{+} \cdots \ominus{+} am^{n-1} \quad\quad\quad\quad [14]$$

$$\overline{\begin{array}{l} mS_n - S_n = -a \quad\quad\quad\quad\quad\quad\quad\quad\quad + am^n \\ (m-1)S_n = am^n - a = a(m^n - 1) \end{array}}$$

$$S_n = \frac{a(m^n - 1)}{m - 1} \quad\quad\quad\quad [16]$$

Formula [16] tells us how to find the sum of the terms of a geometric series when we know a, m, and n.

theorem for a geometric series

The sum S_n of the terms of a geometric series is given by

$$S_n = \frac{a(m^n - 1)}{m - 1} \quad\quad\quad\quad [16]$$

where a is the first term, m is the multiplying factor, and n is the number of terms.

The Problem (Method 1)

John Thrifty deposits $300 every 3 months in a savings bank which offers 6 percent compounded quarterly. (This means that the interest rate is 1½ percent, or 0.015, each quarter year.) How much will be in his account at the end of exactly 2 years? We assume that a deposit is made on the first and the last day of the two years.

By this time, you know that there are nine deposits of $300 but you are too wise to believe that the account has only $9 \times \$300 = \$2,700$ in it. Let us investigate the situation carefully.

1. The first deposit. This is $300 compounded at 1½ percent *eight* times. Therefore,

$$\begin{aligned} A_1 &= P(1 + r)^n \\ &= \$300(1.015)^8 \\ &= \$300(1.1265) \quad\quad \text{using Table II of Appendix} \\ &= \$337.95 \end{aligned}$$

2. The second deposit. This is $300 compounded at 1½ percent *seven* times. Therefore,

TABLE II

Deposit Number	Interest Periods	Table II (App.) Factor	Amount
1	8	1.1265	$337.95
2	7	1.1098	332.94
3	6	1.0934	328.02
4	5	1.0773	323.19
5	4	1.0614	318.42
6	3	1.0457	313.71
7	2	1.0302	309.06
8	1	1.0150	304.50
9	0	1.0000	300.00
Total			$2,867.79

$$
\begin{aligned}
A_2 &= P(1 + r)^n \\
&= \$300(1.015)^7 \\
&= \$300(1.1098) \qquad \text{from Table II of Appendix} \\
&= \$332.94
\end{aligned}
$$

3. The last deposit. This is $300. Because it is made on the last day, it does not have time to earn any interest.

   Table II above summarizes all the calculations.

The Problem (Method 2)

For only a few interest periods, method 1 is not too bad, but it might become rather painful for a more normal 20- or 30-year savings plan. We shall try another method. (You will not use either of these methods in doing the problems on savings plans, but we are going through them to remove the mystery from the method we shall actually use.)

In the problem we posed above, the amounts are

$$300 + 300(1.015)^1 + 300(1.015)^2 + 300(1.015)^3 + \cdots + 300(1.015)^8$$

Notice that each amount (except the first one) can be obtained by multiplying the previous one by 1.015. Then this is the sum of the terms of a geometric sequence. Here, $a = 300$, $m = 1.015$, and $n = 9$. Using formula [16],

$$S_9 = \frac{300(1.015^9 - 1)}{1.015 - 1} \tag{17}$$

The denominator is simply 0.015. By logs, we find that $(1.015)^9 = 1.1435$ so that Eq. [17] becomes

$$S_9 = \frac{(300)(1.1435 - 1)}{0.015}$$

$$S_9 = \frac{(300)(0.1435)}{0.015} \qquad \text{[18]}$$

We can set this up as a problem, using logarithms in the usual way:

$$\begin{array}{rl}
\log 300 = & 0.4771 + 2 \\
+\log 0.1435 = & 0.1569 - 1 \\
\hline
\log \text{num} = & 0.6340 + 1 \\
\ominus\log 0.015 = & \ominus 0.1761 \; \oplus 2 \\
\hline
\log S_9 = & 0.4579 + 3 \\
S_9 = & \$2,870
\end{array}$$

The difference in answers between method 1 and method 2 is caused by the fact that in method 1 we used a four-place table of logarithms. (We used a better table for 1.015^9.)

At this moment, method 1 may seem easier, but if there were a great many deposits, method 2 would be much easier.

The Problem (Solution by Table)

As we have mentioned, these important calculations are done by an easy method based upon method 2. All the usual problems have been done, and the results are tabulated in Table III in the Appendix.

We shall restate the problem, just in case you have forgotten it.

illustrative problem 1

John Thrifty deposits $300 every 3 months in a savings bank which offers 6 percent compounded quarterly. How much is in his account at the end of exactly 2 years (a) if the ninth deposit is made on the last day and (b) if no deposit is made at that time?

solution

(a) We look at Table III of the Appendix under $1\frac{1}{2}$ percent with $n = 9$. The factor is 9.5593. The account then has

$$\begin{aligned}
S &= \$300(9.5593) \\
&= \$2,867.79
\end{aligned}$$

(b) If no deposit was made on the last day, we subtract $300. Then $S = \$2,567.79$.

illustrative problem 2

Suppose the deposits continue for 10 years. How much will be in the account?

solution

Here $n = 41$, provided a deposit is made on the last day of the 10 years. The factor, from Table III, is 56.0819. Then

$$S = \$300(56.0819)$$
$$= \$16,824.57$$

illustrative problem 3

In a payroll savings plan, $260 is deposited every 6 months at a bank which offers 5 percent compounded semiannually. How much is in the plan at the end of 20 years?

solution

We shall assume that the first deposit is made at the end of the first 6 months of employment. Then there are only 40 deposits. (In the other problems, we started with a deposit at the beginning.) The interest rate is 2½ percent per interest period. Looking in Table III, we find that the factor is 67.4026. Then

$$S = \$260(67.4026)$$
$$= \$17,524.6760$$
$$= \$17,524.68 \qquad \text{(assuming normal roundoff)}$$

In this problem, if the money had been kept in a shoe box under the bed, it would have amounted to only $40 \times \$260 = \$10,400$.

illustrative problem 4

An employee on a payroll savings plan deposits at the rate of $15 a week, the money being placed in the bank every 13 weeks ($13 \times \$15 = \$195$). The deposits are compounded quarterly at 6 percent. He does this regularly for 10 years except that the sixteenth deposit is skipped because of illness. How much is there in his account at the end of 10 years?

solution

We are including this problem to show the use of Appendix Tables II and III together. First, we shall forget about the skipped payment and calculate what the account would have been worth if no payments had been skipped. For 40 payments at 1½ percent, we find a factor of 54.2679 in Table III. Then

$$S_{40} = \$195(54.2679)$$
$$= \$10,582.2405$$

However, the sixteenth deposit was skipped. The *first* deposit was compounded 39 times. The *second* deposit was compounded 38 times. The *sixteenth* deposit would have been compounded 24 times. (The easiest way to remember this is to note that the numbers add to 40. For example, $1 + 39 = 40$, $2 + 38 = 40$, $16 + 24 = 40$.) Now how much would the skipped \$260 have contributed to the total amount after being compounded 24 times? We look in Appendix Table II for this kind of information (single deposit) and find a compound factor of 1.4295. Then

$$A = \$260(1.4295) = \$371.6700 = \$371.67$$

Subtracting, we find

$$\$10,582.24 - \$371.67 = \$10,210.57$$

This is the amount in the account.

Extending the Table

If you need a longer table than Table III, you can find it in books on *annuities*. We mention, without proof, that the table can be extended by the formula

$$S_{x+y} = S_x + S_y + rS_xS_y \tag{19}$$

where S_x is the factor for x interest periods, S_y is the factor for y interest periods, and r is the interest rate per period. For example, from Table III with $r = 2\%$,

$$S_{20} = 24.2974$$
$$S_{30} = 40.5681$$

Then

$$S_{50} = 24.2974 + 40.5681 + 0.02(24.2974)(40.5681)$$
$$= 64.8655 + 19.7140$$
$$= 84.5795$$

which checks with the value for S_{50} in Table III.

PROBLEM SECTION 8.3

Part A (Optional). Use the theorem for a geometric series and logarithms.

1. Find the sum of 20 terms of the series $2 + 6 + 18 + \cdots$.
2. Find the sum of 10 terms of the series $5 + 10 + 20 + \cdots$.
3. Find the sum of 10 terms of the series $8 + 4 + 2 + \cdots$.
4. Find the sum of 15 terms of the series $25 + 5 + 1 + \cdots$.

Part B. Use Appendix Table III.

5. You deposit $150 in a bank at 5 percent compounded semiannually, and another $150 every 6 months. (*a*) How many deposits are there at the end of 23 years? (*b*) How much is in the account?
6. Pete deposits $200 every 3 months in a bank account paying 6 percent per year compounded quarterly. (*a*) How many deposits are there at the end of 12 years? (*b*) How much is in the account?
7. If an employee contributes $1,000 every 6 months in a pension plan paying 4 percent semiannually, (*a*) how many contributions are there at the end of 25 years, if the first contribution is made at the end of the first 6 months? (*b*) How much is in the plan at the end of 25 years?
8. An employee contributes $1,250 every 6 months in a pension plan paying 6 percent semiannually. (*a*) How many contributions are there at the end of 15 years, if the first contribution is made after the first 6 months? (*b*) How much is in the plan at the end of 15 years?

Part C

9. In Prob. 5, what would be in the account if the tenth deposit had been skipped?
10. In Prob. 6, what would be in the account if the tenth and twentieth deposits were both skipped?

8.4 ANNUITIES

The Problem

A certain insurance policy has the provision that, at the age of 65, the beneficiary will receive $600 semiannually for 5 years. (This is a simplified situation. We just want to illustrate the general idea.) The payment of $1,200 per annum (each year) is called the *annual rent*. The entire set of payments is called an *annuity*.

The problem is: How much money must be in the beneficiary's

account to guarantee these payments? At first thought, you might guess that $6,000 would be the answer. However, this is not so. Actually, if $6,000 were in the account, the insurance company would make a lot of extra money at the beneficiary's expense. Let us show you why this is so by considering just the first few payments.

To be specific, suppose the $6,000 is deposited on January 1 and the first payment of $600 is made on July 1, 6 months later. By the time the first payment is made, the insurance company has had $6,000 for 6 months. For illustrative purposes, suppose the company is investing its money at 6 percent annually, compounded semiannually. Then, by July 1, the company is entitled to 3 percent interest. In other words, the original $6,000 has become $6,000(1.03) = $6,180. The company now pays out $600, leaving $5,580 in the account. To summarize, here is the situation after 6 months:

1. One payment has been made ($600).
2. The amount left in the account is $5,580.
3. Only $5,400 is needed to make the other nine payments.
4. On the face of it, the company is ahead by $5,580 − $5,400 = $180, plus some interest to be earned.

Now, let us get to the second payment. This takes place on January 1 of the next year. However, $5,580 has been at interest for 6 months, so that it has become $5,580(1.03) = $5,747.40. After paying $600, the account has $5,147.40. Then:

1. Two payments have been made ($1,200).
2. The account now has $5,147.40.
3. Only $4,800 is needed for the other eight payments.
4. The company is ahead by $5,147.40 − $4,800 = $347.40 plus some interest to be earned.

Just one more. On July 1, the account of $5,147.40 has grown to $5,147.40(1.03) = $5,301.82, and another payment of $600 is made. Then:

1. Three payments have been made ($1,800).
2. The account now has $4,701.82.
3. Only $4,200 is needed for the other seven payments.
4. The company is ahead by $501.82, plus interest to be earned.

A company could get fairly rich if anyone were foolish enough to invest in an annuity under these conditions.

It should be very clear that *less* than $6,000 should be deposited to guarantee the annuity as described.

Present Value

The fact is that "future" money is worth more than "present" money. For example, if the prevailing interest rate is 6 percent per annum compounded quarterly, the value of (present) $1 a year from now is

$$A = \$1(1.015)^4 \tag{20}$$

because $\frac{1}{4} \times 6\% = 1\frac{1}{2}\% = 0.015$, and there are *four* interest periods per year. We could calculate this by logarithms, but we shall just look in Table II of the Appendix instead and find, for $r = 1\frac{1}{2}\%$ and $n = 4$, that $1 now is the same as $1.0614 a year from now. We say that the *present value* of (next year's) $1.0614 is $1, under the conditions of interest noted.

Suppose that we wish to find the present value of (future) $1 at 6 percent interest compounded quarterly for 1 year. Then

$$\$1 = P(1.015)^4 \tag{21}$$

and

$$P = \frac{\$1}{(1.015)^4} = (1.015)^{-4} \tag{22}$$

Using logarithms, we have

$$P = (1.015)^{-4}$$

$$\log 1.015 = \quad 0.00647$$
$$\underline{\qquad\qquad \times\ -4}$$
$$\log P = -0.02588$$
$$= 0.9741 - 1$$
$$P = 0.942$$

Fortunately, these calculations have been collected into tables. Table IV in the Appendix is a short version of such a table. Looking under $1\frac{1}{2}$ percent with $n = 4$, we find

$$P = \$0.94218 \tag{23}$$

or about 94¢, the same answer as that by logarithms. In other words, for the interest situation described (6 percent interest compounded quarterly), a deposit of 94¢ now will be worth $1 in a year (approximately).

illustrative problem 1

What is the present value of (future) $120 deposited for 5 years at 4 percent compounded semiannually? This means the account *will be* worth $120 after 5 years.

solution

First, find the present value for (future) $1 in Table IV. We use $r = \frac{1}{2} \times 4\%$, and $n = 5 \times 2 = 10$. The factor is 0.82035. Then we multiply by $120. The result is $98.44200 which we round to $98.44. In other words, a present value of $98.44 is the same as a future value of $120 (in 5 years), under the interest conditions specified.

The Present Value of an Annuity

No one expects a company to work for nothing, and so the actual cost of an annuity includes (1) a profit which the company earns by taking care of the annuity and (2) the actual present value required to grow into the amounts needed for the payments. The actual amount is called the *present value of the annuity*. In all our explanations, we shall assume that the interest rate stated takes care of all costs so that we shall not have to separate the two parts.

We shall do a calculation in two ways, once to explain the thought behind it and once to show the use of another table like the one used by banks and insurance companies. Let us return to the problem with which we started this section. At the time of the first payment (after 6 months), the present value of the (future) $600 payment is $600(1.03)^{-1}$ and can be found in Table IV as $600(0.97087) = $582.52200. This means that $582.522 now will be worth $600 by the time of the first payment. At the time of the second payment, the present value of the (future) $600 payment is $600(1.03)^{-2} = $600(0.94260) = $565.56000.

A complete list for the 10 payments is as follows:

Payment	Factor (Table IV)	Present Value
1	0.97087	$582.52200
2	0.94260	565.56000
3	0.91514	549.08400
4	0.88849	533.09400
5	0.86261	517.56600
6	0.83748	502.48800
7	0.81309	487.85400
8	0.78941	473.64600
9	0.76642	459.85200
10	0.74409	446.45400
Total		$5,118.12000

According to this, $5,118.12 is the present value of an annuity that will pay $600 each 6 months 10 different times in the future.

The Annuity Table

The calculation illustrated above is not very difficult but it involves a certain amount of annoying arithmetic. Table V in the Appendix gives the same result per dollar of payment. In the problem given, $r = \frac{1}{2} \times 6\% = 3\%$, and $n = 5 \times 2 = 10$. Looking in Table V, we find a factor of 8.5302. Multiplying by $600, we quickly obtain $5,118.12, the same answer, much more easily.

illustrative problem 2

What is the present value of an annuity to consist of a payment of $500 every 3 months for 10 years if the prevailing rate of interest is 6 percent compounded quarterly? What is the annual rent?

solution

$r = \frac{1}{4} \times 6\% = 1\frac{1}{2}\%$, $n = 10 \times 4 = 40$. From Table V, the factor is 29.9158. Multiplying by $500, the present value of the annuity is $14,957.90. The annual rent is $500 \times 4 = $2,000.

PROBLEM SECTION 8.4

Part A. In each of the following, find (a) the annual rent and (b) the present value of the annuity for the payments required under the interest conditions specified.

1. $250 every 6 months for 25 years, 5 percent semiannually.
2. $1,000 every 3 months for 10 years, 6 percent quarterly.
3. $500 every 4 months for 12 years, 6 percent compounded three times a year.
4. $5,000 a year for 30 years, 5 percent annually.

Part B. In the following, Table V cannot be used. Using Table IV or logarithms, as you please, find (a) the annual rent; (b) the present value of the annuity.

5. $200 every 3 months for 5 years, 5 percent compounded quarterly.
6. $500 every 6 months for 5 years, 5½ percent compounded semiannually.
7. $1,500 annually for 5 years, 7½ percent compounded annually.
8. $1,000 quarterly for 3 years, 5½ percent compounded quarterly.

8.5   AMORTIZATION

The Problem

We left Mr. Byer somewhat unhappy at the beginning of the chapter. Let us see why his offer (paying $1,000 a year for 30 years) was rejected so indignantly.

If the agent receives $30,000 all at once then, at the end of 30 years, it will be worth

$30,000(1.06)^{30}$

at an interest rate of 6 percent compounded annually (to make things easy). By using logs or from Table II in the Appendix, this will be equal to about $172,305 at the end of the 30 years.

Now suppose Mr. Byer pays $1,000 at the end of the first year and $1,000 for 29 more years, and suppose the agent deposits each payment promptly. As you see, this is like a savings-plan problem. Looking in Table III under 6 percent and $n = 30$, we find a factor of 79.0582. Then,

$$S_{30} = \$1,000(79.0582)$$
$$= \$79,058.20 \qquad\qquad [24]$$

Mr. Byer's scheme costs the agent the difference between $172,305 and $79,058, or about $93,247.

It should be clear that if Mr. Byer chooses to pay the money in equal installments (the set of payments is called an *amortization*), he must pay much more than $1,000 a year.

The Solution

The key to this problem is the recognition that the amortization problem is similar to the annuity problem. As a matter of fact, if Mr. Byer pays $2,179.47 a year (instead of $1,000 a year), then, instead of Eq. [24], we would have

$$S_{30} = \$2,179.47(79.0582)$$
$$= \$172,304.98 \qquad\qquad [25]$$

which is approximately the correct total for the agent.

Now, where did we get the strange amount $2,179.47? We merely took $172,305, which we know was the correct *future* value of the $30,000, and divided by the factor 79.0582.

This is a very hard way to do the problem. Let us see. We already know that, for an annuity,

$$PV = \text{annual payment} \times \text{Table V factor} \qquad\qquad [26]$$

where PV is the present value of the annuity. We can avoid all the intermediate calculations by using this formula. We look up the factor for 30 years at 6 percent in Table V. It is 13.7648. Then

$$\$30,000 = P(13.7648) \tag{27}$$

$$P = \frac{\$30,000}{13.7648} = \$2,179.47 \tag{28}$$

What we are saying, in effect, is that a payment of $30,000 *now* is equivalent to an annuity of $2,179.47 a year for 30 years which is, in turn, equivalent to a future value of $172,305 at the end of the 30 years.

illustrative problem 1

A student buys two Marcos automobiles (one for weekends). After the down payment, he wishes to pay the $15,000 balance in equal installments for 5 years. The interest rate is 5 percent per annum, compounded annually. How much will he pay each year?

solution

The factor for 5 years at 5 percent, in Table V, is 4.3295. Then

$$\$15,000 = P(4.3295)$$

$$P = \frac{\$15,000}{4.3295}$$

$$P = \$3,464.60 \text{ to be paid each year}$$

The *total* amortization is $5 \times \$3,464.60 = \$17,323$.

illustrative problem 2

A man buys a TV set listed at $600. He makes a down payment of $150 and arranges to pay off the balance of $450 in 12 equal monthly installments. The interest rate is 1½ percent per month, including all supplementary charges and insurance. What are his payments, and how much is the total amortization? What did the set cost?

solution

The factor for 12 months at 1½ percent (Table V) is 10.9075.

$$\$450 = P(10.9075)$$

$$P = \frac{\$450}{10.9075}$$

$$P = \$41.26 \text{ to be paid each month}$$

The total amortization is $12 \times \$41.26 = \$495.12$. The cost of the set was \$150 (down payment) $+ \$495.12 = \$645.12$.

PROBLEM SECTION 8.5

In each of the following, find the payment and calculate the total cost of the article. Assume all payments are amortized. *Note:* If divisions are done by logarithms or by slide rule, your answers will probably agree to three significant figures, after rounding.

1. You borrow \$1,000 to be repaid in six installments, 3 months apart. The rate of interest is 6 percent compounded quarterly.
2. You buy a badly used Rolls Royce which, after some haggling, comes to \$4,537. Your trade-in counts for \$1,200. The remainder is to be paid in 12 installments every 3 months. The rate of interest is 2 percent for each 3-month period (including charges and insurance).
3. A certain house has a list price of \$25,000, of which \$5,000 must be paid down. The rest is paid in a 20-year mortgage at 5 percent.
4. In Prob. 3, calculate the results if the mortgage had been a 30-year mortgage.
5. A man wants to sell his store for \$50,000, including fixtures, stock, and goodwill. The buyer offers to pay 10 percent down and the rest in a 10-year mortgage at 6 percent compounded annually.
6. A corporation borrows \$100,000 for expansion. The payments are amortized over 15 years at 5 percent compounded annually.

8.6   ROOTS

Many problems in science, industry, and commerce require finding roots such as $\sqrt{85.2}$ (the *square* root of 85.2), $\sqrt[3]{0.172}$ (the *cube* root of 0.172), $\sqrt[5]{0.00239}$ (the *fifth* root of 0.00239). We cannot cite any very complicated problems in this book because they involve ideas beyond the scope of the subjects we have discussed, but here are some examples which may give you the basic idea.

1. According to Einstein's theory of relativity, if a body has a mass of m_0 when at rest, then its mass (m) in motion is given by

$$m = \frac{m_0}{\sqrt{1 - v^2/c^2}} \qquad [29]$$

where v is the speed of its motion and c is the speed of light (about 186,000 miles per second). Formula [29] says that the faster a body moves, the more massive it becomes. If a body could actually move at the speed of light, then v and c would be equal and m would become infinite, an impossibility.

2. The period (T) of a pendulum (the time needed for the pendulum bob to complete one swing) is given by

$$T = 2\pi \sqrt{\frac{L}{g}} \qquad [30]$$

where T is in seconds, L is the length in feet, and g is the acceleration of gravity, about 32.2 feet per second per second.

3. A company wishes to design a soup can with volume V and height h. The diameter of the cylinder is given by

$$d = \sqrt{\frac{4V}{\pi h}} \qquad [31]$$

where π is about 3.14159.

4. The radius of a golf ball of volume V is given by

$$r = \sqrt[3]{\frac{3V}{4\pi}} \qquad [32]$$

Exponents and Square Roots (Review)

You remember that

$$x^2 \cdot x^3 = x^{2+3} = x^5 \qquad [33a]$$

and

$$y^{72} \cdot y^{12} \cdot y^{15} = y^{72+12+15} = y^{99} \qquad [33b]$$

We remind you that, if two numbers are expressed in exponential form with the same base, their product is found by retaining the base and adding the exponents.

Now, suppose that we wish to find two equal positive numbers whose product is 64. (We know that each of the two numbers is 8, but let us pretend we do not know.) We shall say that there is a number r such that

$$r^2 = 64 \qquad [34]$$

or

$$r \cdot r = 64 \qquad [35]$$

Now, for explanatory purposes, let us write 64 in exponential form with 2 as base:

$$r \cdot r = 2^6 \qquad [36]$$

We would like to write r in exponential form also. Let us suppose that there is an exponent, x, such that r and 2^x represent the same number.

$$r = 2^x \qquad\qquad [37]$$

Substituting Eq. [37] into [36], we have

$$2^x \cdot 2^x = 2^6 \qquad\qquad [38]$$
$$2^{x+x} = 2^6 \qquad\qquad [39]$$
$$2^{2x} = 2^6 \qquad\qquad [40]$$

Comparing the two members of Eq. [40], we see that it must be true that

$$2x = 6$$
$$x = 3 \qquad\qquad [41]$$

Backtracking to Eq. [37], we have

$$r = 2^3 = 8 \qquad\qquad [42]$$

checking our observation that, if $r^2 = 64$, then $r = 8$. (We are limiting ourselves to *principal* roots. For positive numbers, the principal roots are *positive*. It would also be true that $-8 \cdot -8 = 64$, so that -8 is a square root of 64, but it is not the principal square root, as we have defined it.)

This seems to be a hard way to do an easy problem. However, let us find $\sqrt{65}$ in a similar fashion and you will see that there is some sense in what we are doing.

$$x = \sqrt{65} \qquad\qquad [43]$$
$$x^2 = 65 \qquad\qquad [44]$$

Looking in the table of mantissas, and supplying the characteristic of 1, we have

$$x^2 = 10^{0.8129+1} \qquad\qquad [45]$$

Then,

$$x \cdot x = 10^{0.8129+1} \qquad\qquad [46]$$

Each of the x's can be expressed as a number in exponential form with base 10 and an exponent equal to one-half of the exponent $(0.8129 + 1)$ or, more simply in this case, 1.8129.

$$2)\overline{1.8129}$$
$$0.90645$$

In other words, $x = 10^{0.90645}$. Looking in the table again, we find that the closest starter is 806. The characteristic is 0, and so

$$\sqrt{65} = 8.06 \qquad \text{(approximately)}$$

By arithmetic, the answer is about 8.062257 . . . (very good agreement within the limitations of our log table).

We pause to summarize what we have done to find a (positive) square root:

Step 1. Express the number in exponential form with base 10. (The exponent is the logarithm to base 10.)

Step 2. For square root, divide the logarithm by 2.

Step 3. Find the answer by referring, once again, to the table of logarithms.

We shall summarize by a few illustrative problems without going through all the intermediate steps.

illustrative problem 1

Find $\sqrt{275}$.

solution 1

$275 = 10^{2.4393}$
$2\overline{)2.4393}$ (Step 2 of the rule)
1.21965
$10^{1.21965} =$ approximately 16.6
$\phantom{10^{1}}\sqrt{275} =$ approximately 16.6

solution 2

Let $x = \sqrt{275}$. Then

$\log x = \tfrac{1}{2} \log 275$ (Step 2 of the rule)
$ = \tfrac{1}{2}(2.4393)$
$ = 1.21965$
$ x =$ approximately 16.6

illustrative problem 2

Find $\sqrt{186,215}$.

solution

We round the number to 186,000 because our log table will not serve for so many significant figures. Let $x = \sqrt{186,000}$.

$\log x = \tfrac{1}{2}(5.2695)$
$ = 2.63475$
$ x =$ approximately 431

You may wonder how much we lost by rounding. The square root of 186,215, by arithmetic, is 431.5264. Our error is only 0.5264, and our *percent error* is $(0.5264 \times 100)/431.5264$ which means that the error is about 0.12 percent. Not too bad!

In the next problem, we have a difficulty which is, however, not hard to take care of. Before doing the problem, we remind you that

$$0.9063 - 7$$

is the same as

$$1.9063 - 8$$

and as

$$2.9063 - 9$$

This is because $0 - 7$, $1 - 8$, and $2 - 9$ are the same.

illustrative problem 3

Find $\sqrt{0.000,000,806}$.

solution

Let $x = \sqrt{0.000,000,806}$.

$$\log x = \tfrac{1}{2} \log 0.000,000,806$$
$$= \tfrac{1}{2}(0.9063 - 7)$$

Now, if we continue as we did in the previous problems, we get

$$2)\overline{0.9063 \quad - 7}$$
$$0.45315 - 3.5000$$

which is correct but inconvenient because the result does not have a "separate" mantissa and characteristic. We could do the addition, get -3.04685, then add and subtract 4 to get $0.95315 - 4$. However, there is an easier way: We rewrite the logarithm as $(1.9063 - 8)$:

$$\log x = \tfrac{1}{2}(1.9063 - 8)$$
$$= 0.95315 - 4$$
$$x = 0.000898 \qquad \text{approximately}$$

The "trick" is to adjust the *form* of the logarithm any way you like, while looking ahead to see that the result will be a separate mantissa and characteristic. Notice that if we adjusted the form of the logarithm to $3.9063 - 10$ we would have

$$\log x = \tfrac{1}{2}(3.9063 - 10)$$
$$= 1.98315 - 5$$
$$= 0.95315 - 4$$

which is almost as convenient, but if we adjusted the form of the logarithm to $2.9063 - 9$, we would have

$$\log x = \tfrac{1}{2}(2.9063 - 9)$$
$$= 1.45315 - 4.50000$$
$$= -3.04685$$
$$= (4 - 3.04685) - 4$$
$$= 0.93515 - 4$$

which is not nearly as convenient.

illustrative problem 4

Find $\sqrt{0.0581}$.

solution

Let $x = \sqrt{0.0581}$.

$$\log x = \tfrac{1}{2} \log 0.0581$$
$$= \tfrac{1}{2}(0.7642 - 2)$$
$$= 0.3821 - 1$$
$$x = 0.241 \qquad \text{approximately}$$

Cube Roots

The work for cube roots is very similar. Suppose we wish to find $\sqrt[3]{125}$. (We know the principal cube root is 5, because $5 \times 5 \times 5 = 125$.) We can, for explanatory purposes, arrange the work as follows:

$$r \cdot r \cdot r = 125$$
$$\text{Let } r = 10^x$$
$$10^x \cdot 10^x \cdot 10^x = 10^{2.0969}$$
$$10^{x+x+x} = 10^{2.0969}$$
$$10^{3x} = 10^{2.0969}$$
$$3x = 2.0969$$
$$x = \tfrac{1}{3}(2.0969)$$
$$x = 0.69897$$
$$r = 10^x = 10^{0.69897} = 5$$

The steps in finding cube root are:

Step 1. Express the numbers in exponential form with base 10, or use logarithms with base 10.

Step 2. For cube root, divide the logarithm by 3.

Step 3. Find the answer by using the table of logarithms.

illustrative problem 5

Find $\sqrt[3]{275}$.

solution

Let $x = \sqrt[3]{275}$.

$\log x = \frac{1}{3} \log 275$
$ = \frac{1}{3}(2.4393)$
$ = 0.8131$
$ x = 6.50 \qquad$ approximately

illustrative problem 6

Find $\sqrt[3]{186,215}$.

solution

Let $x = \sqrt[3]{186,000}$.

$\log x = \frac{1}{3} \log 186,000$
$ = \frac{1}{3}(5.2695)$
$ = 57.1 \qquad$ approximately

illustrative problem 7

Find $\sqrt[3]{0.0581}$.

solution

Let $x = \sqrt[3]{0.0581}$.

$\log x = \frac{1}{3}(0.7642 - 2)$

We shall change $0 - 2$ to $1 - 3$ in order to get a separate characteristic. We could, just as well, use $4 - 6$, or $28 - 30$. The main thing is that the divisor must go evenly into the right-hand part of the characteristic.

$\log x = \frac{1}{3}(1.7642 - 3)$
$ = 0.58807 - 1$
$ x = 0.387 \qquad$ approximately

Other Roots

By this time, we hope you have grasped the main thought behind finding roots with the help of logarithms. We shall illustrate to make sure.

illustrative problem 8

Find the fifth root of 33.5.

solution

Let $x = \sqrt[5]{33.5}$.

$$\log x = \tfrac{1}{5} \log 33.5$$
$$= \tfrac{1}{5}(1.5250)$$
$$= 0.3050$$
$$x = 2.02 \qquad \text{approximately}$$

illustrative problem 9

Find $\sqrt[10]{0.0581}$.

solution

Let $x = \sqrt[10]{0.0581}$.

$$\log x = \tfrac{1}{10} \log 0.0581$$
$$= \tfrac{1}{10}(0.7642 - 2)$$
$$= \tfrac{1}{10}(8.7642 - 10)$$
$$= 0.87642 - 1$$
$$x = 0.752$$

PROBLEM SECTION 8.6

Find, by logarithms, the principal roots indicated below.

1. $\sqrt{83.1}$, $\sqrt[3]{83.1}$
2. $\sqrt{607}$, $\sqrt[3]{607}$
3. $\sqrt{0.418}$, $\sqrt[3]{0.418}$
4. $\sqrt{0.0738}$, $\sqrt[3]{0.0738}$
5. $\sqrt{0.00926}$, $\sqrt[5]{0.00926}$
6. $\sqrt{0.000158}$, $\sqrt[4]{0.000158}$
7. $\sqrt{0.0000663}$, $\sqrt[6]{0.0000663}$
8. $\sqrt{0.0000834}$, $\sqrt[7]{0.0000834}$

8.7   FRACTIONAL EXPONENTS

As this book is being written, the United States of America and other countries are busy experimenting with satellites. As you probably know, satellites usually travel in ellipses (Fig. 8-1). The point of greatest distance from the Earth is called the *apogee* and the nearest point is called the *perigee*. If we let d be the distance in miles from the center of the earth to the apogee, it can be proved that the period T (the number of minutes to go around the Earth once) is given by the formula

$$T = \left(\frac{d}{205.82}\right)^{3/2} \tag{47}$$

We call your attention to the strange exponent $\tfrac{3}{2}$. It turns out, from this formula, that if the apogee is 100 miles above the surface of the earth and

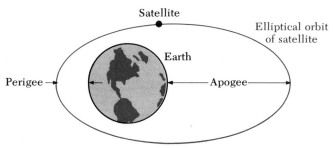

Fig. 8-1 Satellite orbit.

d is equal to 4,063 miles (we added 100 to the radius of the earth, which is 3,963 miles), then the satellite will take 87.7 minutes to make one complete orbit.

In this section, we shall merely investigate the handling of simple expressions with fractional exponents.

The Meaning of Fractional Exponents

At the very beginning, an expression like b^3 merely meant $b \times b \times b$. It was a kind of shorthand notation. As we described in Chap. 7, it became *convenient* to define a *zero* exponent so that

$$b^0 = 1 \qquad\qquad [48]$$

provided $b \neq 0$. (If b is zero, the symbol b^0 is without meaning.) Furthermore, it became *convenient* to define a *negative* exponent so that, for example,

$$b^{-2} = \frac{1}{b^2} \qquad\qquad [49]$$

provided $b \neq 0$. (If b were 0, the right member would involve division by zero, which is not permissible.) We are stressing *convenience* because we wish to decide how to interpret symbols like

$$b^{2/3}, \; b^{3/2}, \; b^{-1/2}$$

and so on. We are going to restrict ourselves to *positive* numbers for b. It happens to be all right if b is negative but we shall not need to consider the meaning of these symbols under those conditions.

We have already explained that it is convenient and proper to define $b^{1/2}$ as the positive square root of b, and $b^{1/3}$ as the positive cube root of b. Without further explanation, we see that $b^{1/4}$ is the positive *fourth* root of b and, in general,

definition: positive nth root

$b^{1/n}$ = positive nth root of b = $\sqrt[n]{b}$ where b is positive   [50]

illustrative problem 1

Find (a) $27^{1/3}$; (b) $25^{1/2}$; (c) $32^{1/5}$.

solution

(a) 3, (b) 5, (c) 2.

     The problem of $b^{2/3}$ is simplified by noticing that

$$b^{2/3} = b^{1/3} \cdot b^{1/3} = \sqrt[3]{b} \cdot \sqrt[3]{b} = (\sqrt[3]{b})^2 \tag{51}$$

Similarly,

$$b^{3/2} = b^{1/2} \cdot b^{1/2} \cdot b^{1/2} = \sqrt{b} \cdot \sqrt{b} \cdot \sqrt{b} = (\sqrt{b})^3 \tag{52}$$

In accordance with these observations, we shall define fractional exponents so that:

definition: fractional exponents

$b^{m/n} = (\sqrt[n]{b})^m$ or $\sqrt[n]{b^m}$ where b is positive

In other words, the *numerator* of the fractional exponent tells to what power the number is raised, and the *denominator* tells which (principal) root is to be used. It can be shown that it does not matter whether the power or the root is calculated first.

illustrative problem 2

Find (a) $27^{2/3}$, (b) $25^{3/2}$, (c) $32^{4/5}$.

solution

(a) $27^{2/3} = (\sqrt[3]{27})^2 = 3^2 = 9$
(b) $25^{3/2} = (\sqrt{25})^3 = 5^3 = 125$
(c) $32^{4/5} = (\sqrt[5]{32})^4 = 2^4 = 16$

     To complete this set of decisions about the meanings of fractional exponents, let us decide that the negative fractional exponent merely forms the reciprocal, as usual, as shown in the following.

illustrative problem 3

Find (a) $27^{-2/3}$, (b) $25^{-3/2}$, (c) $32^{-4/5}$.

solution

(a) $27^{-2/3} = \dfrac{1}{(\sqrt[3]{27})^2} = \dfrac{1}{3^2} = \dfrac{1}{9}$ (b) $25^{-3/2} = \dfrac{1}{(\sqrt{25})^3} = \dfrac{1}{5^3} = \dfrac{1}{125}$

(c) $32^{-4/5} = \dfrac{1}{(\sqrt[5]{32})^4} = \dfrac{1}{2^4} = \dfrac{1}{16}$

Fractional Exponents and Logs

To find a root, you *divide* the logarithm. To find a power, you *multiply* the logarithm. To solve a problem where the exponent is a fraction, you multiply *and* divide in either order. We shall multiply first, in the following problems, because it is a little easier.

illustrative problem 4

Find $65^{3/2}$.

solution

Let $x = 65^{3/2}$. Then

$\log x = \frac{3}{2}(\log 65)$
$\quad = \frac{3}{2}(1.8129)$
$\quad = \frac{1}{2}(5.4387)$
$\quad = 2.71935$
$\quad x = 524 \qquad$ approximately

illustrative problem 5

Find $65^{-3/2}$.

solution

Let $x = 65^{-3/2}$. Then

$\log x = -\frac{3}{2} \log 65$

$\quad = -\frac{3}{2}(1.8129)$
$\quad = -\frac{1}{2}(5.4387)$
$\quad = -2.71935$

To convert this to a logarithm with a positive mantissa, we add and subtract 3. Unfortunately, there is no easy way to avoid this without a lot of careful planning. In this case, it turns out to be easier to add and subtract, and this is what we recommend.

$\log x = (3 - 2.71935) - 3$
$\log x = 0.28065 - 3$
$\quad x = 0.00191 \qquad$ approximately

PROBLEM SECTION 8.7

Part A. Simplify the following.

1. $32^{1/5}$
2. $81^{1/4}$
3. $16^{3/4}$
4. $16^{3/2}$
5. $36^{3/2}$
6. $64^{2/3}$
7. $32^{-3/5}$
8. $81^{-1/4}$
9. $16^{-1/4}$
10. $16^{-5/2}$

Part B. Find by logarithms.

11. $33.5^{1/2}$
12. $28.9^{1/3}$
13. $7.56^{1/5}$
14. $9.19^{1/4}$
15. $0.263^{1/2}$
16. $0.826^{1/3}$
17. $7.58^{2/3}$
18. $1.59^{3/4}$
19. $45.6^{3/2}$
20. $61.5^{4/3}$

Part C. Find by logarithms.

21. $33.5^{-1/2}$
22. $28.9^{-1/3}$
23. $7.58^{-2/3}$
24. $45.6^{-3/2}$

8.8 COMBINED OPERATIONS (OPTIONAL)

In the previous sections, we practiced some rules for finding roots and powers. This is not quite enough. Let us reintroduce the examples from the beginning of Sec. 8.6:

Period of a pendulum: $\quad T = 2\pi \sqrt{\dfrac{L}{g}}$ [53]

Soup-can diameter: $\quad d = \sqrt{\dfrac{4V}{\pi h}}$ [54]

Golf-ball radius: $\quad r = \sqrt[3]{\dfrac{3V}{4\pi}}$ [55]

Relativistic mass: $\quad m = \dfrac{m_0}{\sqrt{1 - v^2/c^2}}$ [56]

To these, we add (from Sec. 8.7)

Period of a satellite: $\quad T = \left(\dfrac{d}{205.82}\right)^{3/2}$ [57]

and, from the introduction to Chap. 7,

Theoretical exhaust velocity of a rocket:

$$V = \sqrt{\frac{2g\gamma}{\gamma - 1} RT \left(1 - \frac{P_e}{P_c}\right)^{(\gamma-1)/\gamma}} \qquad [58]$$

We shall consider these problems in this section.

Problems Not Involving Addition and / or Subtraction

Formulas [53] to [55] and [57] involve no additions or subtractions. They require some planning but are not difficult to do.

illustrative problem 1

Find the period T of a pendulum with a string of length 5.18 inches. In formula [53], π is about 3.14, L is the length in feet, and g is approximately 32.2 feet per second per second on the Earth. The answer comes out in seconds.

solution

First we must convert 5.18 inches to feet. We divide by 12 to accomplish this, because there are 12 inches in a foot. The formula becomes

$$T = 2(3.14) \sqrt{\frac{5.18}{12(32.2)}} \qquad [59]$$

Before doing anything else, we plan the order of operations. As a rule of thumb, we shall work from inside out, as follows:

Step 1. Investigate $5.18/12(32.2)$. We do not actually need the value of this fraction, which we shall call Q, but we shall need log Q. You will see why in a moment.

Step 2. Investigate $\sqrt{Q}$. This just means taking log Q and dividing by 2. The result of $\sqrt{Q}$ is a number which we shall call S. We shall not actually need S, as a matter of fact; we shall be satisfied with log S. This is explained in step 3.

Step 3. Now $T = 2(3.14)S$. This is straightforward multiplication. As you see, we do not need S because the next step will be to find log 2, log 3.14, and log S. There is no harm in finding Q and S, but it is a waste of valuable time.

The problem is set up as follows before looking up any logarithms.

Step 1. log Q

$$\begin{array}{ll} \log 12 = & \log 5.18 = \\ +\log 32.2 = & \ominus\log \text{den} = \\ \hline \log \text{den} = & \log Q = \end{array}$$

Step 2. log S

$\log S = \tfrac{1}{2} \log Q = \tfrac{1}{2}(\qquad) =$

Step 3. *T*

$$\begin{array}{l} \log 2 = \\ \log 3.14 = \\ +\log S = \\ \hline \log T = \\ \quad T = \end{array}$$

It is *strongly* urged that every complicated problem be set up, as above, before looking up a single logarithm. All the logarithms can be looked up together. This saves a *lot* of time.

When we look up the logarithms, the solution looks like this:

Step 1. log Q

$$\begin{array}{ll} \log 12 = 0.0792 + 1 & \log 5.18 = \quad 0.7143 \\ +\log 32.2 = 0.5079 + 1 & \ominus\log \text{den} = \ominus 0.5871 \overset{\ominus}{+} 2 \\ \hline \log \text{den} = 0.5871 + 2 & \log Q = \quad 0.1272 - 2 \end{array}$$

We remind you, now, that it is easy enough to find Q (it is about 0.0134) but we do not need it.

Step 2. log S

$\log S = \tfrac{1}{2} \log Q = \tfrac{1}{2}(0.1272 - 2) = 0.0636 - 1$

From this, we could find $S =$ about 0.116, but we do not need it.

Step 3. *T*

$$\begin{array}{l} \log 2 = 0.3010 \\ \log 3.14 = 0.4969 \\ +\log S = 0.0636 - 1 \\ \hline \log T = 0.8615 - 1 \\ \quad T = 0.727 \qquad \text{approximately} \end{array}$$

Answer: The pendulum will make one (complete) swing in about 0.727 second.

illustrative problem 2

Using formula [57], find the period of a satellite orbiting at an apogee of 50 miles from Earth. (Remember that 3,963 miles has to be added to the 50 miles to obtain the distance from the center of the Earth.) The answer will come out in minutes.

solution

We set up the problem as follows

$$
\begin{array}{l}
\log 4{,}010 = \\
\ominus\log 206 = \\
\hline
\quad \log Q = \\
\qquad\qquad \times 3 \\
\hline
2) \\
\hline
\quad \log T = \\
\qquad T =
\end{array}
$$

With the logarithms filled in, we have

$$
\begin{array}{lll}
\log 4{,}010 = & 0.6031 & + 3 \\
\ominus\log 206 = & \ominus 0.3139 & \overset{\ominus}{+} 2 \\
\hline
\log Q = & 0.2892 & + 1 \\
\log Q = & 1.2892 & \\
& \times 3 & \\
\hline
2) & 3.8676 & \\
\hline
\log T = & 1.9338 & \\
T = & 85.9 \text{ minutes} &
\end{array}
$$

Answer: The satellite will circle the Earth in 85.9 minutes if its apogee is 50 miles above the surface.

Complicated Problems

Formulas [56] and [58] illustrate situations that involve addition and subtraction. These are a great deal more difficult because they must be done in segments. Logarithms are not well suited to problems which have addition and subtraction. This is most unfortunate, but the only other practical alternative is the use of a computer. (We shall discuss computing in the last chapter of the book.)

We illustrate with formula [58] which is rather complicated. The values of the variables are taken from Hobbs' book[1] as follows:

g = gravitational acceleration = 32.2 feet per second per second
γ = specific heat ratio = 1.25 for a propellant with 2.04 parts of zinc to 1 part of sulfur
R = gas constant = 15.8 feet per degree
T = combustion-chamber temperature = 3060°
P_c = combustion-chamber pressure = 1,000 pounds per square inch
P_e = exhaust pressure = 14.7 pounds per square inch

We wish to find V, the theoretical exhaust velocity of the rocket, in feet per second. The *actual velocity* is about 50 percent of the theoretical velocity.

Substituting, we have the following. We have used $\gamma - 1 = 0.25$ and $(\gamma - 1)/\gamma = 0.25/1.25 = 1/5$.

$$V = \sqrt{\frac{2(32.2)(1.25)(15.8)(3,060)}{0.25}\left[1 - \left(\frac{14.7}{1,000}\right)^{1/5}\right]}$$

solution

We rewrite the problem as

$$V = \sqrt{A(1 - B)}$$

where

$$A = \frac{2(32.2)(1.25)(15.8)(3,060)}{0.25}$$

and

$$B = \left(\frac{14.7}{1,000}\right)^{1/5}$$

Step 1. Find log A (we do not need A).

$$
\begin{array}{rl}
\log 2 = & 0.3010 \\
\log 32.2 = & 0.5079 + 1 \\
\log 1.25 = & 0.0969 \\
\log 15.8 = & 0.1987 + 1 \\
+\log 3,060 = & 0.4857 + 3 \\
\hline
\log \text{num} = & 1.5902 + 5 \\
\ominus \log 0.25 = & \ominus 0.3979 \oplus 1 \\
\hline
\log A = & 1.1923 + 6 \\
\log A = & 0.1923 + 7
\end{array}
$$

[1] Marvin Hobbs, "Fundamentals of Rockets, Missiles and Spacecraft," p. 246, Hayden, New York, 1964.

Step 2. Find *B*.

$$\begin{aligned}
\log 14.7 &= 1.1673 = 3.1673 - 2 \\
\ominus\log 1{,}000 &= \ominus 3.0000 = \ominus 3.0000
\end{aligned}$$

$$\begin{aligned}
\log \text{frac} &= 0.1673 - 2 \\
5)\quad &= 3.1673 - 5 \\
\log B &= 0.6335 - 1 \\
B &= 0.430 \qquad \text{(We need it because the problem} \\
& \text{involves } 1 - B.)
\end{aligned}$$

Step 3. Find $1 - B$.

$$1 - B = 1 - 0.430 = 0.570$$

Step 4. Find *V*.

$$\begin{aligned}
\log A &= 0.1923 + 7 \\
+\log (1 - B) &= 0.7559 - 1 \\
2)\quad \log \text{prod} &= 0.9482 + 6 \\
\log V &= 0.4741 + 3 \\
V &= 2{,}980 \text{ feet per second}
\end{aligned}$$

PROBLEM SECTION 8.8

Part A

1. Using formula [53], find the period of a pendulum, with a string of length 2.15 feet.
2. Using formula [54], find the diameter (in inches) of a soup can with a volume of 32.6 cubic inches and a height of 4.38 inches.
3. Using formula [55], find the radius (in inches) of a ball with a volume of 4.09 cubic inches.
4. Using formula [57], find the period of a satellite whose apogee is 100 miles from the surface of the Earth.

Part B. These are *much* more difficult.

5. Use formula [56] to find out how much mass (m) in tons a rocket traveling 150,000 miles per second (v) would have if the speed of light (c) is 186,000 miles per second and the mass of the rocket at rest (m_0) is 120 tons.
6. According to Kepler's third law, the period P of a planet (the time in earth days required for a planet to go around the Sun) is given by

$$P = 365 \left(\frac{A}{93{,}000{,}000} \right)^{3/2} \qquad\qquad [60]$$

where A is the average distance of the planet from the Sun. If Mars is 142 million miles from the Sun, find the number of earth days in a Mars year. (*Note:* Your answer will be about 2 days too large because of roundoff errors.)

the
mathematics
of
management

9999999999

In this century, an awakened knowledge of the power of mathematics to solve "ordinary" problems has led to new, rather pretty techniques. Executives study the problems and their solutions in a series of courses usually called *management science*. Included in this new branch of mathematics are such topics as *linear programming*, the *theory of games, simulation, PERT*, and *forecasting*. We have already discussed the first two topics at some length (although there is much more that could be said about each of them). In this chapter, we shall introduce the other topics for the purpose of letting you know that they exist and to give you an idea of what mathematicians are contributing to management.

We shall start, in the first section, with a topic having nothing to do with management (we hope). We need this topic in order to give you some practice with *random numbers*. One problem we shall attack is:

A drunkard can stagger north and south or east and west. Describe a "typical" random path from the street corner where he is leaning on a lamppost to his home in the southwest portion of the town.

9.1   THE DRUNKARD'S WALK

The Problem

We shall assume that the drunkard starts at the *origin* (point *A*) in Fig. 9-1. He lives in the southwest part of town at the place marked *B*.

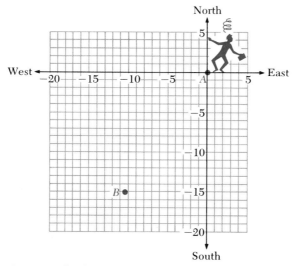

Fig. 9-1   *The drunkard is at A. His home is at B.*

We shall assume that if he gets within a block and a half of point B his butler will come out and get him.

In order to plot a "random walk," we shall need to invent a way to decide *at random* how many blocks in any direction the drunkard will stagger before changing his direction.

The Table of Random Numbers

There are many ways of deciding upon numbers "at random." We could use the watch second-hand method described on page 138 and illustrated in Figs. 5-4 and 5-5. For example, we could decide that 0 to 14 represents staggering east, 15 to 29 represents staggering north, 30 to 44 represents staggering west, and 45 to 59 represents staggering south. This would be a rough way of making the decisions on the random sequence of staggers for the drunkard.

However, we shall be interested in using a table, an excerpt of which is shown in Fig. 9-2. In this version, the numbers (produced by a computer) are supplied in pairs and may be read in any order and any direction.

To solve our problem, we decided, *before looking at the numbers in the table,* to start with row 10, left to right, and (if that was not enough) to continue with row 3, right to left. In each case, the left number of the pair might represent "number of blocks east" and the right number of the pair might represent "number of blocks north." We could have chosen any other rows and directions.

Because all the numbers in the table are positive, we must think of a device to change some of the entries to negative ones in order to allow the drunkard to stagger in any of the four directions. For exam-

	1	2	3	4	5	6	7	8	9	10	11	12	13	14	15	16	17	18
1	03	47	43	73	86	36	26	62	38	97	75	84	27	42	37	86	53	48
2	97	74	24	67	62	42	23	42	40	64	74	82	00	39	68	29	61	66
3	16	76	62	27	66	56	52	36	28	19	95	50	29	94	98	94	24	68
4	12	56	85	99	26	96	37	85	94	35	12	83	16	90	82	66	59	83
5	55	59	56	35	64	38	70	29	17	12	13	40	11	27	94	75	06	06
6	16	22	77	94	39	49	56	62	18	37	35	96	35	24	10	16	20	33
7	84	42	17	53	31	57	99	49	57	22	77	88	38	23	16	86	38	42
8	63	01	63	78	59	16	16	08	15	04	72	33	31	96	25	91	47	96
9	33	21	12	34	29	78	31	16	93	32	43	50	60	67	40	67	14	64
10	57	60	86	32	44	09	68	34	30	13	70	55	14	90	84	45	11	75
11	18	18	07	92	46	44	74	57	25	65	76	59	68	05	51	18	00	33

Fig. 9-2   Excerpt from a table of random numbers.

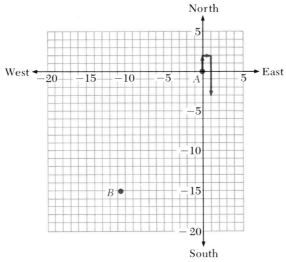

Fig. 9-3   *The first few stumbles: zero blocks east, then two blocks north, then one block east, then five blocks south. This corresponds to the random sequence 0, 2, 1, −5.*

ple, we can subtract 5 from each individual number. Then 5, 7 becomes 0, 2, meaning "no blocks east, two blocks north," and 6, 0 becomes 1, −5, meaning "one block east, five blocks *south.*" We shall discuss this further in the subsection on bias. The first few stumbles are shown in Fig. 9–3.

The Solution

In Fig. 9–4, the entire set of stumbles and staggers has been plotted. The distance from A to B is actually $10\frac{1}{2}$ blocks west and 15 blocks south, for a total of $25\frac{1}{2}$ blocks. In the random walk shown in the figure, the drunkard has actually traveled about 66 blocks.

A Problem with Bias

We assumed that the drunkard would stagger in each of four directions with almost equal probability. For that reason, we changed

$$0, \quad 1, \quad 2, \quad 3, \quad 4, \quad 5, \quad 6, \quad 7, \quad 8, \quad 9 \qquad [1]$$

to

$$-5, \quad -4, \quad -3, \quad -2, \quad -1, \quad 0, \quad 1, \quad 2, \quad 3, \quad 4 \qquad [2]$$

Actually there are many assumptions here. For example, the drunkard would not stagger in any direction for 10 percent of the time (at 0), would

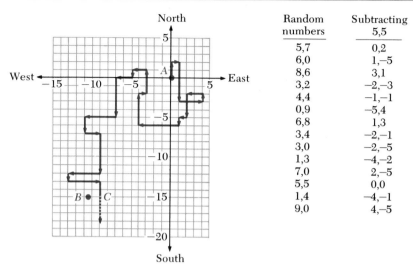

Random numbers	Subtracting 5,5
5,7	0,2
6,0	1,−5
8,6	3,1
3,2	−2,−3
4,4	−1,−1
0,9	−5,4
6,8	1,3
3,4	−2,−1
3,0	−2,−5
1,3	−4,−2
7,0	2,−5
5,5	0,0
1,4	−4,−1
9,0	4,−5

Fig. 9-4   *When the drunkard reaches point C, the butler comes out and gets him.*

stagger in a *positive* direction (north or east) 40 percent of the time (at 1, 2, 3, 4), and would stagger in a *negative* direction (south or west) 50 percent of the time (at −5, −4, −3, −2, −1). Furthermore, we limited staggers in a positive direction to a maximum of four blocks, and in a negative direction to a maximum of five blocks. We do not apologize for this because the purpose of the example was to teach the use of the table but we want you to know that the assumptions were what a mathematician would call "heavy."

Now, suppose that the drunkard realizes that his home is south and west and suppose he can control his staggers to some extent. Then most of the staggers should be south and west. We should have more negative random numbers than positive ones. If we subtract 7 from each entry in line [1], we increase the *bias* in the direction we want. Then line [1] changes to line [3] as shown below:

$$0, \quad 1, \quad 2, \quad 3, \quad 4, \quad 5, \quad 6, \quad 7, \quad 8, \quad 9 \qquad\qquad [1]$$
$$-7, \quad -6, \quad -5, \quad -4, \quad -3, \quad -2, \quad -1, \quad 0, \quad 1, \quad 2 \qquad\qquad [3]$$

Under these conditions, the drunkard staggers north or east in only 20 percent of the staggers, and south or west in 70 percent of them. The result is shown in Fig. 9-5.

Brownian Motion

In 1827, the English botanist Robert Brown (1773–1858) discovered that tiny grains of pollen suspended in water move about apparently at

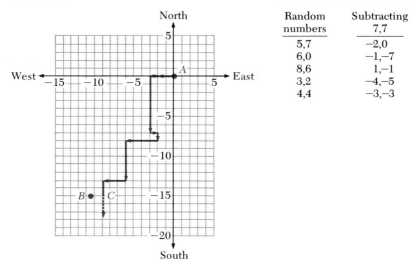

Random numbers	Subtracting 7,7
5,7	−2,0
6,0	−1,−7
8,6	1,−1
3,2	−4,−5
4,4	−3,−3

Fig. 9-5 *If the drunkard staggers south and west more often, his path is shorter. The butler picks him up at point C. If the drunkard misses by chance, he may never get home.*

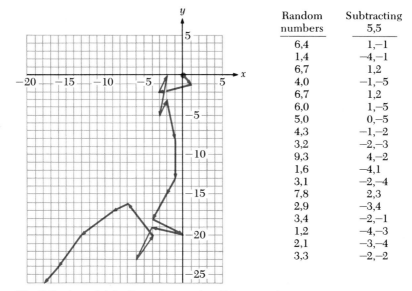

Random numbers	Subtracting 5,5
6,4	1,−1
1,4	−4,−1
6,7	1,2
4,0	−1,−5
6,7	1,2
6,0	1,−5
5,0	0,−5
4,3	−1,−2
3,2	−2,−3
9,3	4,−2
1,6	−4,1
3,1	−2,−4
7,8	2,3
2,9	−3,4
3,4	−2,−1
1,2	−4,−3
2,1	−3,−4
3,3	−2,−2

Fig. 9-6 *A model for Brownian motion (18 impacts).*

random. At first, Brown thought this was because pollen is alive. Later observations led him to conclude that any finely divided materials in a suspension will show the same erratic motion. This phenomenon is called *Brownian motion*. The explanation is that different numbers of molecules in the liquid or gas hit the small body from different sides and cause it to bounce away.

We are going to make a model of Brownian motion with our table of random numbers. To do this, we choose row 9 right to left. We shall pick up the numbers in pairs. In order to have both positive and negative directions, we shall subtract 5, 5 from each pair, exactly as we did before. Then 6, 4 becomes 1, -1 and 1, 4 becomes -4, -1. The first move is from the origin $(0,0)$ to $(1, -1)$. The second move is 4 to the *left* and 1 *down*, landing at $(-3, -2)$.

The graph is shown in Fig. 9-6. It is not true to life because of the heavy assumptions already mentioned, but it will serve our present purpose, to show how the table of random numbers is used.

PROBLEM SECTION 9.1

We cannot provide answers for this Problem Section. We suggest that different members of the class choose different rows or columns of the table of random numbers, and then compare results.

1. For the drunkard's walk, choose a row or column, or a combination, and plot the result, assuming 6, 6 is subtracted from the number pairs in the table. (He may miss!)
2. For Brownian motion, choose two rows and plot the result, assuming 5, 5 is subtracted from each entry in the table.

9.2 SIMULATION

The Problem

You are considering opening a very small market. After some research (watching other markets in this and similar areas), you discover that there is a probability of 10 percent that customers will arrive in 3-minute intervals, 30 percent that they will arrive in 2-minute intervals, and 60 percent that they will arrive in 1-minute intervals. After arriving, there is a probability of 80 percent that they will shop for 5 minutes before going to a check-out counter and 20 percent that they will shop for 10 minutes. A 5-minute shopper needs 2 minutes to check out, and a 10-minute shopper needs 4 minutes. (A) Assuming there is *one* check-out counter, find out what happens for the first 12 customers in the morning. (B) Assuming there are *two* check-out counters, find out what happens for the first 20 customers in the morning.

What are we looking for? We are interested in the time wasted in line (the *average queuing time*), the total *idle* time for the check-out clerk(s), and the *percent busy time* for the check-out clerk(s). This is a simplified version of a very real problem that is usually done on a computer.

Using the Table

We shall use row 10 in the table of random numbers, reading from left to right. The first number in each pair will indicate whether the arrival interval is 1, 2, or 3 minutes, as follows:

Random Number	Arrival Interval	
0	3 minutes	
1, 2, 3	2 minutes	[4]
4, 5, 6, 7, 8, 9	1 minute	

This means that the customers will arrive *at random* at 3-minute intervals 10 percent of the time, at 2-minute intervals 30 percent of the time, and at 1-minute intervals 60 percent of the time. This is so because in a random sample of numbers from 0 through 9 each of these numbers appears 10 percent of the time. Obviously, we could have chosen any combinations that would give us *one* number for the 3-minute interval, *three* for the 2-minute interval, and *six* for the 1-minute interval.

For shopping intervals, we use the second number of the pair. We assign values as follows:

Random Number	Shopping Interval	
0, 1, 2, 3, 4, 5, 6, 7	5 minutes	
8, 9	10 minutes	[5]

Do you see why this meets the conditions?

Solution A

In Fig. 9-7, you see an outline of the work for the first 12 customers. We have filled in the random numbers 57, 60, 86, . . . , from top to bottom, using row 10.

RANDOM PROBLEM: SUPERMARKET, ONE CHECK-OUT COUNTER

Customer No.	Random No. 1	Arrival Interval	Start Shopping	Random No. 2	Shopping Interval	End Shopping	Start Check-out	Check-out Interval	End Check-out	Wait
1	5			7						
2	6			0						
3	8			6						
4	3			2						
5	4			4						
6	0			9						
7	6			8						
8	3			4						
9	3			0						
10	1			3						
11	7			0						
12	5			5						
						Totals				

Fig. 9-7   The chart for solution A (one check-out counter) with random numbers entered.

The purpose of the random numbers is merely to get a random sequence of intervals. We now fill in the intervals using the information in [4] and [5]. The result is shown in Fig. 9-8. We have also filled in the check-out times (2 or 4 minutes, depending upon how much shopping was done).

RANDOM PROBLEM: SUPERMARKET, ONE CHECK-OUT COUNTER

Customer No.	Random No. 1	Arrival Interval	Start Shopping	Random No. 2	Shopping Interval	End Shopping	Start Check-out	Check-out Interval	End Check-out	Wait
1	5	1		7	5			2		
2	6	1		0	5			2		
3	8	1		6	5			2		
4	3	2		2	5			2		
5	4	1		4	5			2		
6	0	3		9	10			4		
7	6	1		8	10			4		
8	3	2		4	5			2		
9	3	2		0	5			2		
10	1	2		3	5			2		
11	7	1		0	5			2		
12	5	1		5	5			2		
							Totals			

Fig. 9-8   *The intervals filled in.*

Now we consider the first customer. She arrives after 1 minute. We fill in 9:01. She shops for 5 minutes, ending at 9:06. The check-out counter is empty, and so she starts checking out immediately, with no wait, at 9:06. She finishes at 9:08 (see Fig. 9-9). The second customer comes a minute after the first one, at 9:02. She finishes shopping at 9:07. The counter is busy. She queues (lines up) for 1 minute. She finishes at 9:10. Figure 9-9 shows the situation for the first five customers.

RANDOM PROBLEM: SUPERMARKET, ONE CHECK-OUT COUNTER

Customer No.	Random No. 1	Arrival Interval	Start Shopping	Random No. 2	Shopping Interval	End Shopping	Start Check-out	Check-out Interval	End Check-out	Wait
1	5	1	9:01	7	5	9:06	9:06	2	9:08	0
2	6	1	9:02	0	5	9:07	9:08	2	9:10	1
3	8	1	9:03	6	5	9:08	9:10	2	9:12	2
4	3	2	9:05	2	5	9:10	9:12	2	9:14	2
5	4	1	9:06	4	5	9:11	9:14	2	9:16	3
6	0	3		9	10			4		
7	6	1		8	10			4		
8	3	2		4	5			2		
9	3	2		0	5			2		
10	1	2		3	5			2		
11	7	1		0	5			2		
12	5	1		5	5			2		
						Totals				

Fig. 9-9   The first five customers.

In Fig. 9-10, we have filled in the start- and end-shopping times for all 12 customers. Notice that customer 6 is ready to get in line at 9:19, but customer 8 is already on line. (She finished shopping at 9:17.) We have indicated, by small numbers, the order in which the customers get on line. (Customers 6 and 9 are ready at the same time. We tossed a coin to decide which one was to be first.)

Note that the order of queuing is *not* the same as the order of arrival.

RANDOM PROBLEM: SUPERMARKET, ONE CHECK-OUT COUNTER

Customer No.	Random No. 1	Arrival Interval	Start Shopping	Random No. 2	Shopping Interval	End Shopping	Start Check-out	Check-out Interval	End Check-out	Wait
1	5	1	9:01	7	5	9:06 ①	9:06	2	9:08	0
2	6	1	9:02	0	5	9:07 ②	9:08	2	9:10	1
3	8	1	9:03	6	5	9:08 ③	9:10	2	9:12	2
4	3	2	9:05	2	5	9:10 ④	9:12	2	9:14	2
5	4	1	9:06	4	5	9:11 ⑤	9:14	2	9:16	3
6	0	3	9:09	9	10	9:19 ⑦		4		
7	6	1	9:10	8	10	9:20 ⑨		4		
8	3	2	9:12	4	5	9:17 ⑥		2		
9	3	2	9:14	0	5	9:19 ⑧		2		
10	1	2	9:16	3	5	9:21 ⑩		2		
11	7	1	9:17	0	5	9:22 ⑪		2		
12	5	1	9:18	5	5	9:23 ⑫		2		
							Totals			

Fig. 9-10   The queuing times of the customers.

In Fig. 9-11, we have filled in the data for customers 8, 6, and 9 *in that order.* The next one in line is customer 7 who finished shopping at 9:20. That is when she gets on line. She has to wait until 9:25 (when customer 9 has finished).

RANDOM PROBLEM: SUPERMARKET, ONE CHECK-OUT COUNTER

Customer No.	Random No. 1	Arrival Interval	Start Shopping	Random No. 2	Shopping Interval	End Shopping	Start Check-out	Check-out Interval	End Check-out	Wait
1	5	1	9:01	7	5	9:06 ①	9:06	2	9:08	0
2	6	1	9:02	0	5	9:07 ②	9:08	2	9:10	1
3	8	1	9:03	6	5	9:08 ③	9:10	2	9:12	2
4	3	2	9:05	2	5	9:10 ④	9:12	2	9:14	2
5	4	1	9:06	4	5	9:11 ⑤	9:14	2	9:16	3
6	0	3	9:09	9	10	9:19 ⑦	9:19	4	9:23	0
7	6	1	9:10	8	10	9:20 ⑨		4		
8	3	2	9:12	4	5	9:17 ⑥	9:17	2	9:19	0
9	3	2	9:14	0	5	9:19 ⑧	9:23	2	9:25	4
10	1	2	9:16	3	5	9:21 ⑩		2		
11	7	1	9:17	0	5	9:22 ⑪		2		
12	5	1	9:18	5	5	9:23 ⑫		2		
							Totals			

Fig. 9-11 By 9:19, a customer has to wait 4 minutes to start checking out.

In Fig. 9-12, we display the complete table. You can see that the check-out clerk worked for 28 minutes out of 35, and the 12 customers waited a total of 44 minutes. This represents 80 percent busy time and an average of 3.7 minutes queuing time.

From a management viewpoint, the busy time is fine, but the queuing time is definitely very bad, especially since the store has just opened. There will be a real pileup later in the day, as you can see by continuing the table. Under these conditions, the customers would soon learn to trade elsewhere. We shall now test the situation with two check-out counters.

RANDOM PROBLEM: SUPERMARKET, ONE CHECK-OUT COUNTER

Customer No.	Random No. 1	Arrival Interval	Start Shopping	Random No. 2	Shopping Interval	End Shopping	Start Check-out	Check-out Interval	End Check-out	Wait
1	5	1	9:01	7	5	9:06 [1]	9:06	2	9:08	0
2	6	1	9:02	0	5	9:07 [2]	9:08	2	9:10	1
3	8	1	9:03	6	5	9:08 [3]	9:10	2	9:12	2
4	3	2	9:05	2	5	9:10 [4]	9:12	2	9:14	2
5	4	1	9:06	4	5	9:11 [5]	9:14	2	9:16	3
6	0	3	9:09	9	10	9:19 [7]	9:19	4	9:23	0
7	6	1	9:10	8	10	9:20 [9]	9:25	4	9:29	5
8	3	2	9:12	4	5	9:17 [6]	9:17	2	9:19	0
9	3	2	9:14	0	5	9:19 [8]	9:23	2	9:25	4
10	1	2	9:16	3	5	9:21 [10]	9:29	2	9:31	8
11	7	1	9:17	0	5	9:22 [11]	9:31	2	9:33	9
12	5	1	9:18	5	5	9:23 [12]	9:33	2	9:35	10
							Totals	28		44

Fig. 9-12   The complete table for the first 12 customers (one check-out counter).

Solution B

For the problem with two check-out counters, we shall use row 10 left to right and row 11 right to left. Figure 9-13 shows the random numbers and intervals, and the times for starting and ending shopping.

RANDOM PROBLEM: SUPERMARKET, TWO CHECK-OUT COUNTERS

Customer No.	Rand. No. 1	Arrival Interval	Start Shopping	Rand. No. 2	Shopping Interval	End Shopping	Start Check-out 1	2	Check-out Interval 1	2	End Check-out 1	2	Wait
1	5	1	9:01	7	5	9:06 ①							
2	6	1	9:02	0	5	9:07 ②							
3	8	1	9:03	6	5	9:08 ③							
4	3	2	9:05	2	5	9:10 ④							
5	4	1	9:06	4	5	9:11 ⑤							
6	0	3	9:09	9	10	9:19 ⑦							
7	6	1	9:10	8	10	9:20 ⑨							
8	3	2	9:12	4	5	9:17 ⑥							
9	3	2	9:14	0	5	9:19 ⑧							
10	1	2	9:16	3	5	9:21 ⑩							
11	7	1	9:17	0	5	9:22 ⑪							
12	5	1	9:18	5	5	9:23 ⑫							
13	1	2	9:20	4	5	9:25 ⑬							
14	9	1	9:21	0	5	9:26 ⑭							
15	8	1	9:22	4	5	9:27 ⑮							
16	4	1	9:23	5	5	9:28 ⑯							
17	1	2	9:25	1	5	9:30 ⑰							
18	7	1	9:26	5	5	9:31 ⑱							
19	3	2	9:28	3	5	9:33 ⑲							
20	0	3	9:31	0	5	9:36 ⑳							
						Totals							

Fig. 9-13 The situation for two check-out counters.

We shall assume that customers prefer check-out counter 1 to check-out counter 2. In other words, if both counters are available, they go to counter 1. Of course, if only one is available, they go to that one. This assumption does not change the problem at all, and so we need not worry about it. Filling in the table as before, we obtain Fig. 9-14.

As you can see, the situation is much better from the viewpoint of the customers, and it is not too bad from the viewpoint of the check-out clerks, either. In solution A (Fig. 9-12) we found that the one clerk was busy for 80 percent of the time and idle for 20 percent of the time. The

RANDOM PROBLEM: SUPERMARKET, TWO CHECK-OUT COUNTERS

Customer No.	Rand. No. 1	Arrival Interval	Start Shopping	Rand. No. 2	Shopping Interval	End Shopping	Start Check-out 1	Start Check-out 2	Check-out Interval 1	Check-out Interval 2	End Check-out 1	End Check-out 2	Wait
1	5	1	9:01	7	5	9:06 ①	9:06		2		9:08		0
2	6	1	9:02	0	5	9:07 ②		9:07		2		9:09	0
3	8	1	9:03	6	5	9:08 ③	9:08		2		9:10		0
4	3	2	9:05	2	5	9:10 ④	9:10		2		9:12		0
5	4	1	9:06	4	5	9:11 ⑤		9:11		2		9:13	0
6	0	3	9:09	9	10	9:19 ⑦	9:19		4		9:23		0
7	6	1	9:10	8	10	9:20 ⑨		9:21		4		9:25	1
8	3	2	9:12	4	5	9:17 ⑥	9:17		2		9:19		0
9	3	2	9:14	0	5	9:19 ⑧		9:19		2		9:21	0
10	1	2	9:16	3	5	9:21 ⑩	9:23		2		9:25		2
11	7	1	9:17	0	5	9:22 ⑪	9:25		2		9:27		3
12	5	1	9:18	5	5	9:23 ⑫		9:25		2		9:27	2
13	1	2	9:20	4	5	9:25 ⑬	9:27		2		9:29		2
14	9	1	9:21	0	5	9:26 ⑭		9:27		2		9:29	1
15	8	1	9:22	4	5	9:27 ⑮	9:29		2		9:31		2
16	4	1	9:23	5	5	9:28 ⑯		9:29		2		9:31	1
17	1	2	9:25	1	5	9:30 ⑰	9:31		2		9:33		1
18	7	1	9:26	5	5	9:31 ⑱		9:31		2		9:33	0
19	3	2	9:28	3	5	9:33 ⑲	9:33		2		9:35		0
20	0	3	9:31	0	5	9:36 ⑳		9:36		2		9:38	0
						Totals	24	20					15

Fig. 9-14   The complete table for the first 20 customers (two check-out counters).

idle time is also called *slack time*. (This was only at the beginning of the day. Under normal conditions, there would be no more slack time for the rest of the day.)

In solution B, the slack time was 14 minutes out of 38 for clerk 1 and 18 minutes out of 38 for clerk 2. This would undoubtedly be evened out in practice, so that we can consider total slack time as 32 minutes out of 76, or 42.1 percent. The 20 customers waited a total of 15 minutes, or an average queuing time of 0.75 minute. At first glance, it seems that the management would get more for its salary dollar in solution A, but this is an illusion. Actually, he would go out of business.

We must remind you that this is just the start of the simulation. With a computer, we could make a model of the entire day in a few thousandths of a second. This would provide ammunition for timing coffee breaks, reliefs, lunch hours, extra packers, etc.

PROBLEM SECTION 9.2

We cannot offer solutions for these problems. We suggest that different members of the class choose different rows and columns of the table of random numbers and compare results.

Part A

1. Choose other rows of the table of random numbers and extend Fig. 9-12 to 30 customers.
2. Choose other rows of the table of random numbers and extend Fig. 9-14 to 40 customers.

Part B

3. A barber is considering opening a barbershop with two or three chairs. After a survey, it is found that the probabilities of arrival are 40 percent for 5-minute intervals between customers, 30 percent for 10-minute intervals between customers, and 30 percent for 20-minute intervals between customers. The probabilities for various customer-service requirements are 10 percent for 40 minutes of barbering work, 30 percent for 30 minutes of barbering work, and 60 percent for 20 minutes of barbering work. For (*a*) two chairs and (*b*) three chairs, simulate the arrival and servicing of 20 customers and find (i) the average queuing time, (ii) slack time for each barber (one to a chair), (iii) percent of time each barber is busy. It is all right to assume that customers prefer chair 1 to chair 2, and chair 2 to chair 3. The shop opens at 8:30 A.M.
4. In a very small telephone-answering service, it is found that the probabilities of telephone-call intervals are 50 percent for a 1-minute interval between calls, 30 percent for a 2-minute interval between

calls, and 20 percent for a 3-minute interval between calls. The durations of the calls are divided as follows: 60 percent for 2 minutes, 30 percent for 4 minutes, and 10 percent for 6 minutes. After a 2-minute call, the telephone clerk needs 2 minutes to write the order; after a 4-minute call, she needs 3 minutes; after a 6-minute call, she needs 4 minutes. While she is writing the order, she does not answer her phone.

For (a) three telephones and (b) four telephones, simulate the calls and the servicing of the first 40 customers. Find (i) the average time a customer has to wait until the telephone is answered, (ii) slack time for each clerk, (iii) percent of busy time for the clerks. The service opens at 10 A.M.

9.3 PERT

The term *PERT* stands for *Program Evaluation and Review Technique.* This is a method of planning a program of operations. It was developed by the United States Navy in 1958 and used to plan the Polaris submarine project. It deals with the time, resources, and technical performance, and the relationships between them in a project.

PERT has become very important in the planning of complex operations by our government and by large corporations. As a matter of fact, major projects for the government must be accompanied by a PERT analysis. We shall merely illustrate with simple examples in order that you, as a liberal arts student, can learn how these plans are made.

A Simple Schedule

For the purpose of explaining some language, consider the following simple situation. You wish to get to the theater on a school night by 7:20 P.M. when the first complete evening show starts. The final time is called the *target*. Here are the *activities* which must take place, but not necessarily in the order shown. (The following schedule is for males. Females have their own methods.)

List of Activities

1. Talk roommate into lending (a) money and (b) car.
2. Call girl friend and persuade her to go.
3. Get washed and dressed.
4. Drive to girl friend's house.
5. Wait for her.

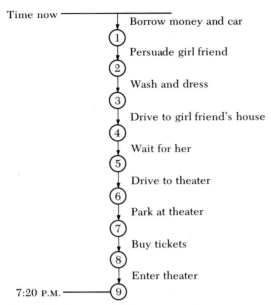

Time now

Borrow money and car
Persuade girl friend
Wash and dress
Drive to girl friend's house
Wait for her
Drive to theater
Park at theater
Buy tickets
Enter theater

7:20 P.M.

Fig. 9-15 *A network of activities and events.*

6. Drive to theater.
7. Park at theater.
8. Buy tickets.
9. Enter theater, buy candy, find seats.

The successful conclusion of each activity or set of activities is called an *event*. Figure 9-15 is a graph of the *network* of activities and events. The arrows represent the activities, and the circles represent the events ending the activities.

Each of the activities in Fig. 9-15 takes time. In Fig. 9-16, we have put our estimate for the *most likely time* (m) needed for each activity. According to this, the most likely estimate of *total elapsed time* is 130 minutes, i.e., 2 hours and 10 minutes. Then, to satisfy our target time, you must start on activity 1 that much before 7:20 P.M. The PERT schedule shows that you must start persuading at 5:10 P.M. (If you wish to eat a meal, this must be included as an activity.)

If the estimates are correct, this schedule will work about 98 percent of the time. For the other 2 percent of the time, you will be too early or too late. In the next subsection, we discuss how professionals revise the estimate.

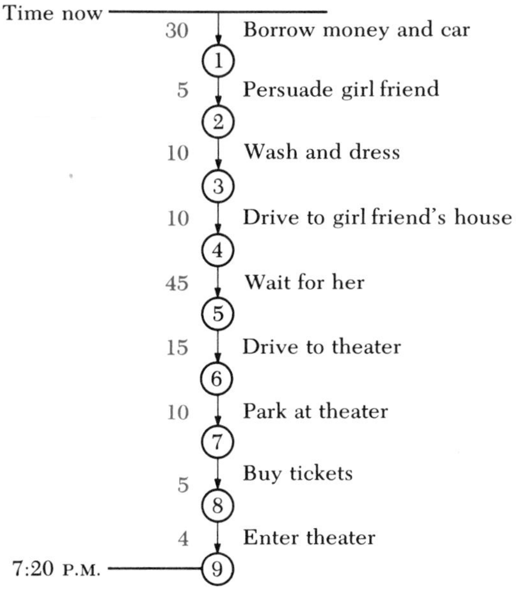

Time now ───────────────

30 ↓ Borrow money and car

①

5 ↓ Persuade girl friend

②

10 ↓ Wash and dress

③

10 ↓ Drive to girl friend's house

④

45 ↓ Wait for her

⑤

15 ↓ Drive to theater

⑥

10 ↓ Park at theater

⑦

5 ↓ Buy tickets

⑧

4 ↓ Enter theater

7:20 P.M. ────── ⑨

Fig. 9-16 The "most likely times," in minutes.

Time Estimates

In professional work, *three* time estimates are made for each activity:

1. *Optimistic time* (*a*): the shortest possible time in which the activity can be accomplished. This is the 1 percent of the trials when everything breaks just right.
2. *Most likely time* (*m*).
3. *Pessimistic time* (*b*): the longest time that the activity would take, once in a hundred times. This is the 1 percent when all the breaks are against you.

For example, in Fig. 9-16, we used 30 minutes as the most likely time for activity 1 (persuading roommate). Once in a hundred times, it might take only 5 minutes and once in a hundred times it might take an hour. In industry, the *elapsed time* (*t*) for the activity would be calculated by the formula

$$t = \frac{a + 4m + b}{6} \qquad [6]$$

which is, for activity 1,

$$t = \frac{5 + 120 + 60}{6}$$

$$t = \frac{185}{6}$$

$$t = 30\frac{5}{6} \text{ minutes}$$

In the table which follows, we have made some estimates as to a, m, and b, and then we have calculated t, using formula [6]. These are entered in Fig. 9-17 with a, m, and b in parentheses and t below. Ac-

Activity	a	m	b	t
1. Persuading roommate	5	30	60	30.8
2. Girl friend	1	5	30	8.5
3. Wash and dress	8	10	20	11.3
4. Drive to house	5	10	20	10.8
5. Wait	25	45	60	44.2
6. Drive to theater	10	15	30	16.7
7. Park at theater	1	10	20	10.2
8. Buy ticket	1	5	30	8.5
9. Enter, buy candy, sit	2	4	10	4.7
Elapsed time				145.7

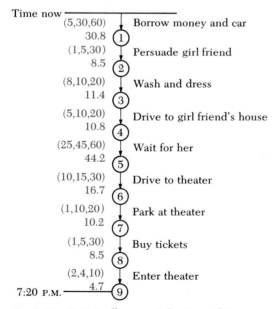

Time now

(5,30,60) 30.8 ① Borrow money and car
(1,5,30) 8.5 ② Persuade girl friend
(8,10,20) 11.4 ③ Wash and dress
(5,10,20) 10.8 ④ Drive to girl friend's house
(25,45,60) 44.2 ⑤ Wait for her
(10,15,30) 16.7 ⑥ Drive to theater
(1,10,20) 10.2 ⑦ Park at theater
(1,5,30) 8.5 ⑧ Buy tickets
(2,4,10) 4.7 ⑨ Enter theater

7:20 P.M.

Fig. 9-17 *Statistically corrected estimated times.*

cording to this improved method, the estimated elapsed time is 2 hours and 26 minutes. Therefore, you must start the first activity at 4:59 P.M. (We still did not allow for a meal.)

Critical Path

The preceding problem was both straight and straightforward. There was a single *path* from beginning to end. Sometimes there are several activities leading into a single event, and the times for the various activities leading into a single event, and the times for the various activities are different. For example, in Fig. 9-18, after event 1 occurs, the activities for events 2 and the 3-4 combination take place beginning at the same time. The numbers in color under the activities represent the calculated values of *t*.

When event 2 and events 3-4 have *both* occurred, then event 5 can occur. The upper path is the longer one, in this case, for a total of $5 + 6 + 8 = 19$ days, so that it will take 19 days to complete the project. The other path uses $5 + 2 + 3 + 5 = 15$ days, so that there are 4 days of *slack time*. If this represents an industrial project, the men and machinery needed for activities 3 and 4 may be used in other projects for 4 days in order to lower the overall cost of the project. In Fig. 9-18, the heavy lines represent the *critical path*. It is called the critical path because any delay in the activities along that path will delay the entire project. (A delay of less than 4 days in the other path will not delay the completion time of this project; that is why the other path is not "critical.")

illustrative problem 1

In the PERT network shown in Fig. 9-19, find the critical path and the slack times. The times given are in days. How long will the entire job take?

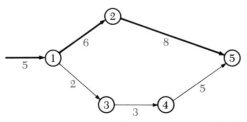

Fig. 9-18   Event 2 and events 3-4 must both take place before event 5 can occur.

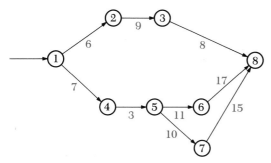

Fig. 9-19 PERT network for Illustrative Problem 1.

solution

Path 1-2-3-8 requires 23 days. Path 1-4-5-6-8 requires 38 days. Path 1-4-5-7-8 requires 35 days. The critical path is 1-4-5-6-8. The slack in path 1-2-3-8 is $38 - 23 = 15$ days. The slack in path 1-4-5-7-8 is $38 - 35 = 3$ days. The job will probably take 38 days. Notice that each day of delay *along the critical path* will delay completion. That path must be watched most carefully. Delay along the other paths will not delay completion until the slack is used up.

A Critical-path Problem

Critical-path problems occur in all branches of industry. They are easiest to illustrate when something is to be built.

illustrative problem 2

We wish to build a birdhouse mounted on a pole which is set in concrete. Make a PERT network of activities and events. Find the critical path. How long will the job take?

solution

We begin by listing all the activities we can think of (as shown in the accompanying table). We estimate the times (in days).

At this point, we are ready to draw the network (Fig. 9-20). The critical path is shown by heavy lines. The project will take 11.5 days (the length of the critical path). The upper path requires 8.0 days (with 3.5 days of slack), and the middle path requires 8.2 days (with 3.3 days of slack). Because the ordering of the post is on the critical path, each day's delay in receiving the order will delay the job. On the other hand, even if the concrete arrives 3 days late, the completion date will not be affected.

Activities	Pessimistic	Most Likely	Optimistic	t
1. Make design	3	2	1	2.0
2. Order post	10	5	3	5.5
3. Get lumber and paint	1	1	1	1.0
4. Get concrete for footing	1	1	1	1.0
5. Put house together	3	2	1	2.0
6. Pour concrete, make footing	2	1	1	1.2
7. Mount post in concrete	1	1	1	1.0
8. Place house on post	1	1	1	1.0
9. Paint house and post	1	1	1	1.0
10. Clean up	1	1	1	1.0

You can see that this kind of analysis may point up the weak link in a chain of activities. In this case, if there is some way of speeding up the purchase of the post, the length of the task will be reduced until the slack is taken up. If this is done, the critical path may, of course, shift to another sequence.

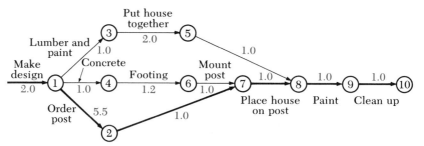

Fig. 9-20   Illustrative Problem 2.

illustrative problem 3

A PERT analysis shows that a critical path involves $126\frac{5}{6}$ hours. If the target is Thursday, 2:13 P.M., what is the starting date?

solution

First, $126\frac{5}{6}$ hours = 126 hours 50 minutes = 5 days, 6 hours, 50 minutes. Now we choose a (previous) day as day 0. We shall arbitrarily take the Thursday a week previous as day 0. Then the target is 7 days, 14 hours, 13 minutes (2 P.M. = 12 + 2 = 14 hours). The length of the critical path must be subtracted from the target:

7 days, 14 hours, 13 minutes
5 days, 6 hours, 50 minutes

We cannot subtract 50 minutes from 13 minutes. Therefore, we borrow 1 hour from the 14 hours and add 60 minutes to the 13 minutes:

  7 days, 13 hours, 73 minutes
− 5 days, 6 hours, 50 minutes
——————————————————————————
  2 days, 7 hours, 23 minutes

The starting date is day 2. The previous Thursday was day 0, and so the previous Friday is day 1 and the previous Saturday is day 2. The starting date is Saturday, 7:23 A.M. (If it had turned out 2 days, 19 hours, 23 minutes, the starting date would have been Saturday, 7:23 P.M.)

illustrative problem 4

Suppose the critical path had had a length of 5 days, 16 hours, 50 minutes in the previous problem. What would the starting date have been?

solution

We write

  7 days, 14 hours, 13 minutes
− 5 days, 16 hours, 50 minutes
——————————————————————————

First we borrow to adjust the minutes, and get

  7 days, 13 hours, 73 minutes
− 5 days, 16 hours, 50 minutes
——————————————————————————

Then we must borrow a day (24 hours) to adjust the hours:

  6 days, 37 hours, 73 minutes
− 5 days, 16 hours, 50 minutes
——————————————————————————
  1 day, 21 hours, 23 minutes

which corresponds to the previous Friday at 9:23 P.M.

In both illustrative problems, if there is no work on Saturday and Sunday, the starting date must be pushed back 2 days. In the problems which follow, we shall disregard this possibility in the answer section. In actual practice, it must be taken into account, of course.

PROBLEM SECTION 9.3

In Probs. 1 to 10, calculate the lengths of the various paths, find the critical path, and give a starting date or time. Where a single figure is given, assume it is t. If three figures are given, assume they are a, m, and b in that order and calculate t from these. Problems 11 and 12 are class projects and no answers for them are given in the answer section.

Part A

1.

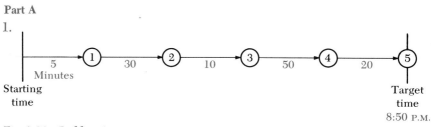

Fig. 9-21   *Problem 1.*

2.

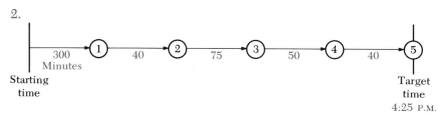

Fig. 9-22   *Problem 2.*

3.

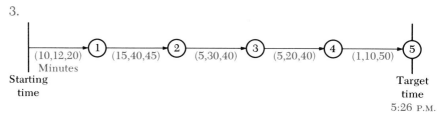

Fig. 9-23   *Problem 3.*

4.

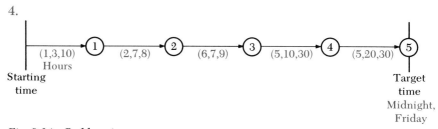

Fig. 9-24   *Problem 4.*

5.

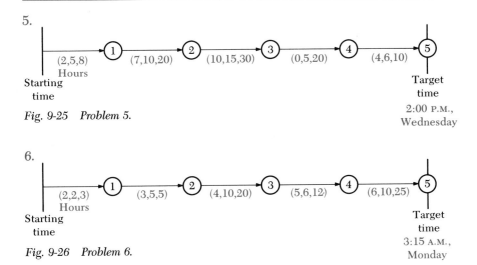

Fig. 9-25   *Problem 5.*

6.

Fig. 9-26   *Problem 6.*

7.

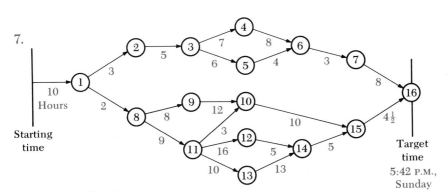

Fig. 9-27   *Problem 7.*

8.

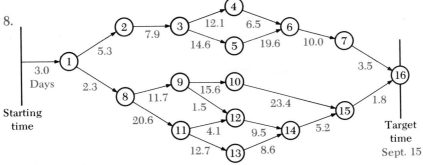

Fig. 9-28   *Problem 8.*

9.

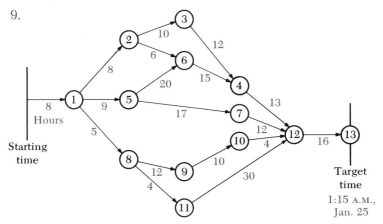

Fig. 9-29   Problem 9.

10.

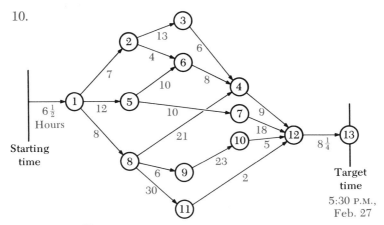

Fig. 9-30   Problem 10.

Part B. These are class projects.

11. You are going to build a barbecue in your backyard. Among the activities are designing the barbecue, getting bricks, digging the footing, getting materials for concrete, getting the grating, mixing the concrete, pouring the footing, building the brickwork, fitting the grating, and cleaning up. You may think of other activities for your own situation, such as preparing the space. Make a PERT network and determine the critical path. Assuming a certain target date in June, find the starting date. Disregard fractions of a day.

12. (Difficult). In order to allow students to graduate on June 15, it is

necessary that Student Services (or the Guidance Department) have all the grades by June 10. For the grades to be in, all examinations must be in by June 8. Following that, final grades are computed and entered into students' permanent records. The project starts with the assignment of teacher committees to submit questions for the final examinations. These must be assembled, checked for validity, length, and correctness; typed; collected; run off; collated; and stuffed into envelopes along with answer booklets and other materials. Among other things to be done are the printing of the graduation announcement and pamphlet, practicing for graduation, preparation of diplomas, getting signatures, etc. Make a PERT network to determine when the project must begin and when examinations should be given. Get estimates of a, m, and b to calculate t.

9.4 FORECASTING (PART I)

Mr. Nasty, President and owner of the Nasty Manufacturing Company, called in his new Vice President in charge of Everything. He said, "Well, what about it? Have you forecast the sales for the next three months yet? We have to know how much raw material to order, how much overtime to allow, how many temporary employees to hire, how much warehouse space to reserve, and so on. I should tell you that I had to fire your predecessor because he didn't guess right!"

The new Vice President said, "I'm sorry, sir, but this has nothing to do with guessing, and I've only been on the job for 13 minutes and 47 seconds. I don't even know whether your key items are *horizontal, trend,* or *seasonal.*"

"What does that mean?" said the President.

Categories of Items

We shall explain some of the commoner categories of items. In most corporations, there is more than one item, and a separate analysis must be made for key items and for groups of similar items.

We should say that there are two large classes of factors that influence consumer demand. In the first class, there are *extrinsic* factors such as the nature of the economy, the gross national product (GNP), the industrial index, and various other long-range considerations. This class of forecasting is usually done by *regression analysis,*[1] a topic too

[1] For an elementary discussion, see Dodes and Greitzer, "Numerical Analysis," chap. 6, Hayden, New York, 1964.

specialized for this book. It is studied in a subject called *econometrics* and in *advanced statistical analysis*. Large corporations almost always employ an economist who knows advanced statistics.

A second class of forecasting deals with *intrinsic* factors, often unknown, which cause demand to fluctuate. These are usually, but not always, short-range factors. At any rate, if you have a weekly or monthly record of demand for at least 5 years, it is possible to forecast with satisfactory accuracy.

We shall deal with industrial rule-of-thumb methods for doing the *second* kind of forecasting. There are four main types of variation in this second class: *horizontal, trend, seasonal,* and *mixed*.

Horizontal Variation

Some items have an almost constant demand. One example is the demand for paintbrushes (Fig. 9-31). Although the actual demand (in color) is not really constant, the fluctuations appear to be random. The *peaks* and *valleys* do not occur at the same time each year. On the whole, the sellers of this kind of item are fortunate. Orders, warehouse space, and personnel can be forecast fairly easily. We shall discuss this further later in this section.

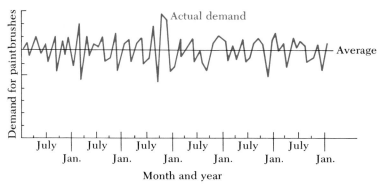

Fig. 9-31   A horizontal or constant item.

Trend Items

In some cases, average demand goes up or down steadily. This happened in the sales of transistor radios (Fig. 9-32). The average demand falls along a line called a *trend line*, and the fluctuations take place about this trend line (instead of about a horizontal line). We shall not discuss forecasting for trend items, but we wanted you to know that it can be done.

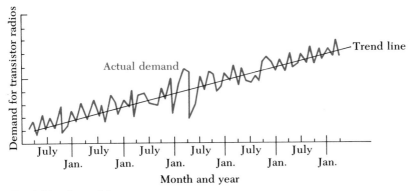

Fig. 9-32   A trend item.

Seasonal Variation

A very common type of variation is one in which demand appears to depend mainly upon the *season*. For example (Fig. 9-33), bathing suits sell all year long, but demand goes up sharply in preparation for the summer. A test of *seasonality* is accomplished by plotting the sales for successive years on the same set of axes. This is done for 2 years in Fig. 9-34. In spite of the fluctuations, it is clear from the graph that, for these 2 years, the peaks and valleys *coincide* (come at the same time or place). Variation for canned chicken soup is something like this except that the peak is in the winter months and the valley about 6 months later.

Methods of dealing with seasonal variation range from rule-of-thumb industrial methods to high-level methods such as *Fourier analysis*. We shall discuss a rule-of-thumb method for seasonal variation in Sec. 9-5.

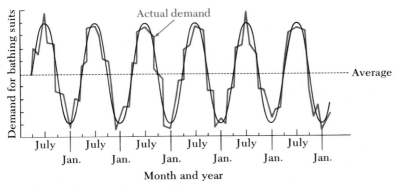

Fig. 9-33   A horizontal seasonal item.

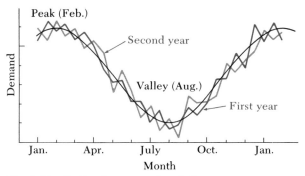

Fig. 9-34   Testing for seasonal variation.

Trend-Seasonal Variation

A common "mixed" variation is the combination of trend and seasonal. Figure 9-35 illustrates, in simplified form, the situation with overseas airline tickets. There are peaks and valleys at the same time each year but, in addition, there is a steady upward trend.

Other Variations

In actual industrial work, other types of demand patterns must be taken into account. Three of these are *low-volume lumpy, end-of-season*, and *irregular*.

   Low-volume lumpy demand usually deals wih very expensive items of which very few are sold, for example, multimillion-dollar computers. There is no way to forecast accurately. In general, these are made to order, and the customer has to wait for delivery. Some preparations still have to be made, however, and these are often done by simulation.

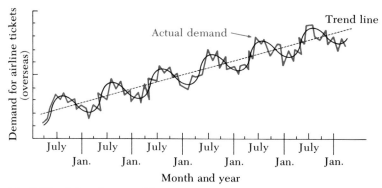

Fig. 9-35   A trend-seasonal item.

End-of-season demand deals with such items as snowsuits. These are not kept in stock the entire year. If a forecast is made, it is made for the short period when these are sold.

Irregular demand really means that we cannot forecast because we do not know why the graph of demand looks the way it does. It is a confession of failure to set up a "model."

Smoothing a Horizontal-demand Curve

As a practical matter, we shall now show how forecasting is done in commercial work for the simplest case, the horizontal-demand curve (refer to Fig. 9-31). The method is called *exponential smoothing* and uses the following formula:

Exponential Smoothing Formula: $\text{NFC} = \text{OFC} + \alpha E$ [7]

where NFC = new forecast, OFC = old forecast, α is the Greek letter *alpha* and is the exponential smoothing factor, and E = error = actual demand − OFC.

Commercial installations almost always use $\alpha = 0.1$ for horizontal-demand patterns, so that formula [7] becomes

$$\text{NFC} = \text{OFC} + 0.1(D - \text{OFC})$$ [8]

where D = actual demand.

illustrative problem 1

A mathematician has discovered that a certain item has horizontal demand. For January, it was forecast that the demand would be 150, but it was really 200. What is the forecast for February?

solution

NFC = OFC + 0.1(D − OFC)
NFC = 150 + 0.1(200 − 150)
NFC = 150 + 0.1(50)
NFC = 150 + 5
NFC = 155

The forecast for February is (a demand of) 155.

illustrative problem 2

The demand for a horizontal item is as follows: July, 120; August, 92; September, 81; October, 119; November, 111; and December, 82. The actual forecast for July was 100. Produce the forecasts for the other months, and for January.

solution

In the following, error = demand − OFC.

Month	Forecast	Demand	Error	Calculation
July	100	120	20	100 + 0.1(20)
August	102	92	−10	102 + 0.1(−10)
September	101	81	−20	101 + 0.1(−20)
October	99	119	20	99 + 0.1(20)
November	101	111	10	101 + 0.1(10)
December	102	82	−20	102 + 0.1(−20)
January	100			

illustrative problem 3

The demand for a horizontal item is March, 278; April, 266; May, 294. The forecast for March was 270. Make forecasts for April, May, and June.

solution

In the table, we obtain 270.8 for April and round it to 271 (forecasting is not accurate enough to carry so many figures). We obtain 270.5 for May and round it to 271. We obtain 273.3 for June and round it to 273.

Month	Forecast	Demand	Error	Calculation
March	270	278	8	270 + 0.1(8)
April	271	266	−5	271 + 0.1(−5)
May	271	294	23	271 + 0.1(23)
June	273			

Trend Forecasting

Although we shall not discuss trend forecasting, you should know that it is done by a similar method, using *two* previous values (to establish the slope of the trend line) and an exponential smoothing factor α equal to 0.05 instead of 0.1.

Starting a Series of Forecasts

It must have occurred to you that the *first* time a forecast must be made there is no actual demand (D) or old forecast (OFC) to go by. In such a case, the businessman has to guess, using any information he happens to have. After all, a sensible industry does not go into the production of an item without some estimate of how well it will sell.

PROBLEM SECTION 9.4

Part A. In each of the following cases, tell whether the demand is probably horizontal, trend, seasonal, trend-seasonal, or irregular. We are using 3-month intervals to simplify the problem (this is not good business practice).

Month	1	2	3	4	5	Problem 6	7	8	9	10
January	280	125	420	18	27	74	520	160	22,000	850
April	255	170	710	7	28	81	540	120	30,000	350
July	260	160	380	92	30	73	580	240	42,000	900
October	275	150	85	46	33	85	540	220	19,000	1,460
January	250	210	380	44	35	84	570	180	21,000	910
April	290	180	720	74	36	86	620	100	32,000	250
July	270	240	400	57	39	78	600	260	40,000	800
October	265	230	90	25	40	83	670	200	23,000	1,550

Part B. In the following, the demand pattern for 6 months and the old forecast for the first of these 6 months are given. Assuming these are horizontal and that $\alpha = 0.1$, make forecasts for the second through the seventh month.

11. The forecast for February was 50. The actual demands for February through July were 60, 41, 70, 42, 61, and 32. Make forecasts for March through August.
12. The forecast for June was 250. The actual demands for June through November were 280, 263, 274, 256, 246, and 285. Make forecasts for July through December.
13. The forecast for September was 1,000. The actual demands for September through February were 1200, 1100, 998, 1225, 945, 835. Make forecasts for October through March.
14. The forecast for April was 1,500. The actual demands for April through September were 1300, 1580, 1190, 1260, 1240, and 1220. Make forecasts for May through October.

Part C. These problems are similar to those in Part B except that rounding may be necessary.

15. The forecast for November was 150. The actual demands for November through April were 180, 160, 150, 140, 159, and 143. Make forecasts for December through May.
16. The forecast for January was 38. The actual demands for January through June were 32, 41, 38, 29, 31, and 30. Make forecasts for February through July.

9.5 FORECASTING (PART II)

For an item to be considered seasonal, the peaks and valleys must occur at about the same time each year and the peak demand must be at least 30 percent higher than the average demand. Usually there is an obvious reason for the seasonal demand, as in the case of radiator antifreeze for cars, or skis, or sunburn lotion. Often 5 full years of demand figures are needed to justify the claim that an item is seasonal. (These are rules of thumb developed by commerce rather than mathematical conclusions.)

   In the following, we shall assume that an item has been found to be of the horizontal-seasonal-demand type (see Fig. 9-33).

Base-index Method (Simplified)

Let us suppose that we have been in business about 2 years. It is now the end of June. Our actual demand in June was 115 (we just finished counting orders). We wish to forecast demand in July for this seasonal item.

   At the end of May, we made Table I which shows, in columns 2 and 3, the actual demand, month by month, for this item in the past 2 years. We shall explain all the columns presently.

   In column 4, we have calculated the average demand for each month. For example, to find the average for June we calculate

$$\frac{108 + 104}{2} = \frac{212}{2} = 106$$

TABLE 1

Month	Year 1	Year 2	Average	BI
June	108	104	106.0	0.91
July	102	92	97.0	0.83
August	67	39	53.0	0.45
September	124	173	148.5	1.27
October	147	126	136.5	1.17
November	152	171	161.5	1.39
December	179	163	171.0	1.47
January	111	92	101.5	0.87
February	92	96	94.0	0.81
March	82	64	73.0	0.63
April	113	103	108.0	0.93
May	127	171	149.0	1.28
Total			1,399.0	

(If we have been in business long enough, we use a 5-year average. This is found by adding the demands for 5 years and then dividing by 5.)

Now we add the averages and obtain a total of 1,399.0. Dividing by 12 (because we used 12 monthly averages), we obtain the average of the averages. This is called the *deseasonalized average (DED)*: The formula is

$$\text{DED} = \frac{\text{total}}{\text{no. of periods}} \qquad [9]$$

In this case,

$$\text{DED} = \frac{1,399.0}{12} = 116.6$$

This would be the estimated demand per month if the item were horizontal but not seasonal.

In the last column of Table I is found the *base index* (BI) for each month. This is found by the formula

$$\text{BI} = \frac{\text{average}}{\text{DED}} \qquad [10]$$

For June,

$$\text{BI} = \frac{106.0}{116.6} = 0.91$$

In short, this means that we expect the demand in June to be 91 percent of the DED.

Now we are ready to forecast for July, using the fact that the actual demand in June was 115. To forecast for July, we make the following table.

	Demand	BI
June	115	0.91
July	x	0.83

Then we set up a simple proportion:

$$115:x = 0.91:0.83 \qquad [11]$$

from which, by the *theorem of means and extremes,*

$$0.91x = (115)(0.83) \qquad [12]$$

$$x = \frac{(0.83)(115)}{0.91} \qquad [13]$$

This can be solved by hand, by slide rule, by logarithms, or by a machine to get $x = 105$. This simplified method tells us that the estimated demand for July is 105.

To forecast for any month, we set up the yearly table ending 2 months before. For example, to forecast for March, we would set up tables ending in January, calculate DED and BI through January (starting at the previous February), and then use the actual demand for February. In other words, the forecast is done month by month, using previous years' experience to calculate DED and BI and the present month's actual demand to estimate the next month's demand.

Long-range Forecasting

We can do some long-range forecasting, too, but it is not very reliable. Suppose it is, as before, the end of June and we have a table through May and the actual figures for June. We wish to forecast for August although we realize this cannot be very accurate. We make a table, using our Table I figures:

	Demand	BI
June	115	0.91
August	x	0.45

and set up the proportion:

$$115:x = 0.91:0.45 \tag{14}$$

from which

$$0.91x = (115)(0.45) \tag{15}$$

and

$$x = \frac{(115)(0.45)}{0.91} \tag{16}$$

The resulting forecast is a demand of 57 for August. As we said before, this is likely to be in considerable error, because it is based upon *June* figures. However, it is better than nothing.

Smoothing the Forecast (Optional)

Now suppose the item has been selling for some years and we have records of the DED and BI. To be specific, suppose the *old DED* (ODED) is 116.6 and the actual demand for June was 115. We assume for the moment that the BI is more *stable* than the DED. What would the DED really have to be to result in a demand of 115? We shall call this the *current DED* (CDED). Then

$$0.91 \, (CDED) = 115 \tag{17}$$

from which

$$CDED = \frac{115}{0.91} = 126.4 \tag{18}$$

This means that, if the BI is really 0.91, the DED should have been 126.4 to give us an actual demand of 115, since $0.91 \times 126.4 = 115$. What we have done corresponds to the formula

$$CDED = \frac{\text{actual demand}}{BI} \tag{19}$$

At any rate, we now have

CDED = 126.4
ODED = 116.6

which means that there is an *error* (E) equal to $126.4 - 116.6 = 9.8$. We used

$$E = CDED - ODED \tag{20}$$

Now, we can calculate the *new DED* (NDED) by

$$NDED = ODED + \alpha E \tag{21}$$

where α is the exponential smoothing factor, usually taken to equal 0.1. The result is

$$\begin{aligned} NDED &= 116.6 + 0.1(9.8) \\ &= 116.6 + 0.98 \\ &= 117.6 \end{aligned} \tag{22}$$

To forecast for July, we just use

$$\begin{aligned} \text{Demand} &= NDED \times BI \\ &= 117.6 \times 0.83 \\ &= 98 \end{aligned} \tag{23}$$

By the simplified method, the forecasted demand for July was 105. By the smoothing method, the forecast is 98. As you see, they are rather far apart. Which is right? Since commercial firms use smoothing, it must be useful in practice to use smoothing.

It is also possible to smooth the BI estimates by a formula which looks like Eq. [21], with $\alpha = 0.4$, but we shall not go into it. We just wanted you to see how people in industry make forecasts.

PROBLEM SECTION 9.5

Part A. Using Table I, make long-range forecasts by the simplified method for the following months.

1. September	2. October	3. November	4. December
5. January	6. February	7. March	8. April

Part B. Table II refers to a demand record for the last 2 years, from October through September. The numbers represent thousands of items.

TABLE II

Month	Year 1	Year 2
October	26	24
November	27	28
December	26	25
January	20	23
February	16	14
March	8	9
April	5	4
May	2	3
June	6	4
July	8	9
August	14	15
September	23	18

9. Show by graph that this is seasonal.
10. Identify the peak and valley months.
11. Find the DED.
12. Find the BI estimates.
13. If the actual demand in the current month (October) is 23.5, forecast the demand for November.

Part C

14. In Table II, assuming the actual demand in October was 23.5, calculate the CDED.
15. The ODED was found to be 14.0. Find the NDED.
16. Using this NDED, make a forecast for November. Is it the same as the result in Prob. 13?

an
introduction
to
computing

10 10 10 10 10 10

A man walks into a room which has the sign "Medical Laboratory." He places his arm in a slot; little instruments come out of sockets in the wall and painlessly take blood pressure readings and a blood sample. The blood is analyzed automatically, and the results are sent to the *memory* of a computer. A minute later, the man walks out and into another room which has x-ray facilities. By the time he reaches the end of the corridor where the internist (an M.D. with a specialization in diagnosis) has his office, the computer has given the doctor a complete report on the man's physical condition. With the report is included a listing of possible conditions to watch for. The printer has printed the information at the rate of about 1,500 lines (30 pages) per minute. The computer has spent a few *millionths* of a second in looking up the symptoms of all known diseases. The computer is extremely fast. However, the doctor has something the computer does not have: judgment. When the doctor reads the information from the computer, his mind (much better than the computer) is able to guide him to a conclusion. Possibly weeks of information-gathering time have been saved.

A lawyer needs precedents with reference to marine barratry on a freighter carrying perishable goods from New York to Calais. He leans over a small machine which looks like a typewriter and types, "Barratry, marine, perishable goods, 100." Immediately, the machine types back the 100 most recent cases appropriate to that heading. The lawyer has probably saved weeks of painstaking library research.

Now let us look at an engineer. What is he doing? He seems to be writing with something that looks like a pencil on something that looks like a glass plate. Oh yes, he seems to be sketching a building but, as he sketches it crudely, the computer is straightening the lines and correcting the errors. The engineer asks the computer to show him what the building would look like from another angle and to tell him about the stresses, needs, costs, and timing estimates (PERT). In millionths of a second, the computer obligingly redraws the same building from another view and displays all the facts requested. The engineer can make changes in his sketch, and the computer will pleasantly change all the calculations with lightning speed. Months of experimentation have been avoided by use of the *light-pen.*

The Vice President in charge of Everything wants a complete record of sales of the top-selling items. He wants it in tabular and graphical form for the past 10 years, and he wants smoothed forecasts of next year's demand pattern week by week. All this takes the computer a couple of minutes. At the same time, the same computer is keeping inventory; writing letters to manufacturers to order materials on the basis of *check-points;* writing memos to the management about items that do not satisfy specification limits; calculating payrolls, including taxes, overtime, and sick pay; forecasting personnel needs, and, perhaps, solving problems for the R and D (*Research and Development*) Division. These extra items are done in the "spare time" of the computer.

The world of tomorrow? No! This is the world of today. All the computer applications outlined above, and many, many more, are or could be in actual practice now. As a matter of fact, in its spare time, the computer could do all the problems in this book and recalculate all the Appendix tables in a matter of minutes.

How is this done? The whole story of programming a computer is much too long to condense into one chapter of a liberal arts book. In this chapter, we shall merely touch upon the language, components, and a method of computing for the computer of today. If you wish to learn more, take courses in *computer science*.

10.1 THE INTERNAL LANGUAGE OF THE COMPUTER

Most computers are wired in such a fashion that numbers $(0, 1, \ldots, 9)$, letters $(A, B, \ldots, Z)$, and special symbols $(, . \$ \ldots /)$ are represented by sets of on-and-off switches of one kind or another. Each switch is called a *bit* because it can be represented by a *bi*nary digi*t*, in other words, by a 1 (for ON) or a 0 (for OFF). There are variations, but we shall describe the type which is used in so-called *third-generation computers* such as the IBM 360.

Numbers in the Binary System

In the *decimal* system, a numeral like 101 stands for one hundred, no 10's, and one 1. The *place value* of the digits increases by a factor of 10 as we travel from right to left. For example, 1101 in the decimal system represents (reading from right to left) one 1, no 10's, one hundred, and one thousand.

In the *binary* system, the general idea is the same except that the place value of the digits increases by a factor of 2 as we travel leftward. Then 101 represents (reading from right to left) one 1, no 2's, and one 4; and 1101 represents one 1, no 2's, one 4, and one 8.

In shorthand notation, we shall say that

$$1101_2 = 13_{10} \tag{1}$$

meaning that the numeral 1101 in the binary system stands for the same number as the numeral 13 in the decimal system.

illustrative problem 1

What is 1110_2 in the decimal system?

solution

$0 \times 1 = 0$
$1 \times 2 = 2$
$1 \times 4 = 4$
$1 \times 8 = 8$

Therefore, $1110_2 = 14_{10}$.

illustrative problem 2

What is 1011_2 in the decimal system?

solution

$1 \times 1 = 1$
$1 \times 2 = 2$
$0 \times 4 = 0$
$1 \times 8 = 8$

Therefore, $1011_2 = 11_{10}$.

Converting from Decimal to Binary

We shall show you the following *algorithm* (method) without explanation. It involves repeated division by 2. This means that after the second division by 2, we have actually divided by 4; dividing by 2 three times is the same as dividing by 8.

illustrative problem 3

Convert 14_{10} to binary.

solution

2)14	Remainder
2)7	0
2)3	1
1	1

Answer: $14_{10} = 1110_2$

Explanation of procedure: Division is continued until the result is 0 or 1. Then the binary equivalent of the decimal number consists of the result followed by the remainders reading *upward*.

illustrative problem 4

Convert 11_{10} to binary.

solution

$$
\begin{array}{ll}
2\underline{)11} & \text{Remainder} \\
2\underline{)\ 5} & 1 \\
2\underline{)\ 2} & 1 \\
\quad 1 & 0 \\
\end{array}
$$

Answer: $11_{10} = 1011_2$

On the IBM 360, it is customary to consider sets of *eight* bits. Such a set is called a *byte*. In *byte* notation, we would convert the previous answer to 00001011. For practical purposes, we shall follow the usual custom of programmers and leave a space as follows: 0000 1011. The space does not really belong there but it makes the byte easier to read.

Converting from Decimal to Binary by Hex

We have just shown one method for converting from binary to decimal. For large numbers, this would be a lengthy procedure. Programmers use a faster method based upon the *hexadecimal system*. The word *hexadecimal* means that the system is based upon 16, just as *decimal* refers to 10 and *binary* to 2. Most professionals call it *hex* for short.

*TABLE I.   DECIMAL,
BINARY, AND HEX*

Decimal	Binary	Hex
0	0000	0
1	0001	1
2	0010	2
3	0011	3
4	0100	4
5	0101	5
6	0110	6
7	0111	7
8	1000	8
9	1001	9
10	1010	A
11	1011	B
12	1100	C
13	1101	D
14	1110	E
15	1111	F

The corresponding symbols for the first 16 decimal numbers are given in binary and in hex in Table I. Note that in hex the symbols A, $B, \ldots, F$ are *numerals*, not letters.

illustrative problem 5

Convert 527_{10} to hex.

solution

We use repeated division by 16 and continue to divide until the quotient is less than 16.

$$16\overline{)527}$$
$$16\underline{)\ 32} \qquad 15 = F$$
$$\qquad\ 2 \qquad\quad\ 0$$

Answer: $527_{10} = 20F_{16}$

We can check as follows, reading from right to left and increasing place value by a factor of 16:

$$F \times 1 = \quad 15_{10}$$
$$0 \times 16 = \quad\ 0_{10}$$
$$2 \times 256 = 512_{10} \qquad \text{(because } 16 \times 16 = 256\text{)}$$

But $512 + 0 + 15 = 527$, and so the answer checks.

illustrative problem 6

Convert 527_{10} to binary.

solution

We shall use the fact that

$$527_{10} = 20F_{16}$$

Now we merely change each hex digit to a binary number, using Table I:

$$2_{16} = 0010_2$$
$$0_{16} = 0000_2$$
$$F_{16} = 1111_2$$

Then

$$527_{10} = 0000 \qquad 0010_2 \qquad 0000 \qquad 1111$$

We added four (binary) zeros to make the answer two bytes (16 bits) long. The answer 001000001111 would have been correct but uncomfortable.

illustrative problem 7

Convert 1968_{10} to binary.

solution

First we convert to hex:

16) 1968

16) 123   0

       7   11 = B

Then $1968_{10} = 7B0_{16}$. Looking in Table I, we get

$1968_{10} = 7B0_{16} = 0000 \quad 0111 \quad 1011 \quad 0000_2$

There is a table method for converting from binary to decimal by means of hex, but we shall not go into it.

Adding in Binary

We know that $1 + 1 = 2$ in the decimal system. This means that $1 + 1 = 10$ in the binary system since 2_{10} and 10_2 mean exactly the same thing. Let us try a pair of larger numbers, for example, $23 + 34$ which should turn out to be 57. In the following, we use the fact that in binary

$$1 + 0 = 1$$
$$1 + 1 = 10$$
$$1 + 1 + 1 = 11$$

We are going to add 10111 ($= 23_{10}$) and 100010 ($= 34_{10}$). The numbers in color are the usual "carry."

```
        11
   0001 0111
 + 0010 0010
   ----------
   0011 1001
```

A quick check shows that 0011 1001 is, indeed, 57_{10}.

illustrative problem 8

Convert 51 and 27 to binary, add, and convert back to decimal.

solution

$51_{10} = 0011 \quad 0011_2$
$27_{10} = 0001 \quad 1011_2$

$$
\begin{array}{r}
11 \\
0011\ 0011 \\
+\ 0001\ 1011 \\
\hline
0100\ 1110
\end{array}
$$

$0100\ 1110_2 = 78_{10}$, which checks.

Arithmetic on High-speed Computers

There are methods for subtracting, multiplying, and dividing in binary but we shall not bother with them. We wanted to show you *one* example of how a high-speed computer does arithmetic. The *computer* (not the programmer) changes the numbers from decimal to binary, does the arithmetic (binary arithmetic is very easy for a computer), and then changes the answer back to decimal for us ordinary people. Why is the computer so fast? It is fast because the "addition table" is so easy to remember.

Nonnumeric Characters in Binary

As a matter of general information, we shall mention that each alphabetic and special symbol is represented by a set of eight bits (one byte). A few of the bytes are shown in Table II. When a programmer causes $ to be read into the computer, this character is instantly transformed to 0101 1011, using eight on-off switches. When the computer finds 0101 1011 in its memory, it can instantly read out $ to the programmer.

TABLE II. NONNUMERIC CHARACTERS

Character	Hex	Binary
A	C1	1100 0001
B	C2	1100 0010
J	D1	1101 0001
<	4C	0100 1100
(	4D	0100 1101
$	5B	0101 1011
?	6F	0110 1111

PROBLEM SECTION 10.1

Part A. Convert from binary to decimal.

1. 1111 0011	2. 1110 0001
3. 1100 1000	4. 1011 1010
5. 0110 1010	6. 1000 1101
7. 1010 1110	8. 1100 1111
9. 1011 1100	10. 1100 1011

Part B. Convert from decimal to hex and binary.

11. 193	12. 178
13. 216	14. 249
15. 58	16. 92
17. 155	18. 155
19. 250	20. 189

Part C. Convert to binary, add, and reconvert the result to decimal.

21. $193 + 27$	22. $61 + 25$
23. $75 + 137$	24. $115 + 125$

10.2   COMMUNICATING WITH THE COMPUTER

We shall touch lightly on the usual components of a computer center, including those machines which are used to prepare information going into or coming out of the computer. The function of getting information in or out of the computer is called *input-output*. Programmers usually call it *I/O*.

Ordinarily, everything begins with the preparation of a punched card.

Punched Cards

So far as we can tell, punched cards were first used early in the nineteenth century by textile manufacturers. These cards controlled the weaving of patterns in cloth. About 1885, the United States Bureau of the Census engaged a statistician, Dr. Herman Hollerith, to see whether he could adapt the punched-card principle (with which he had been experimenting) to assist in the census. By 1890, this had been done; by 1900, Dr. Hollerith developed a machine to handle the punched cards automatically. In 1903, Hollerith formed a company to manufacture and handle punched cards. By 1912, the International Business Machines

Company emerged from the company that Hollerith had founded. The *Hollerith card* is now almost always referred to as an *IBM card*.

Information is punched into these cards by a *key punch* like that shown in Fig. 10-1. A *deck* of cards is placed in the space at the top right. That space is called a *hopper*. When a button is pushed, a single card is *fed* by being lowered to the space just above the electric typewriter keyboard which you can see in the figure. When the card has been *registered* into the correct position, the *key-punch operator* may punch rectangular holes into the card by tapping the keys of the electric typewriter. The card has 80 *columns* (we shall illustrate) numbered from 1 to 80, and one column is punched at a time. It travels from right to left. When all the punching is done, a *release* button is pushed and the card travels to the left end. In Fig. 10-1, one card is on its way to the leftmost position, a second card is half-punched, and a third card is sitting in position ready to be started when the second card is finished.

The result of keypunching is a card like that shown in Fig. 10-2. There are many special kinds of IBM cards. The one shown in Fig. 10-2 is a *general-purpose card*. It happens to have a *cut* in the upper left corner. However, the cards may have a cut in some other corner, or may be rounded, or may be squared off at the corners. The purpose

Fig. 10-1   A key-punch machine. (IBM Corporation.)

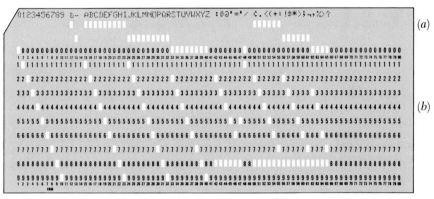

Fig. 10-2   A general-purpose IBM card. (a) Zone-punching area; (b) digit-punching area.

of having a corner cut is to make sure that all the cards in a deck are facing the same way.

   We have already mentioned that the card has 80 columns, usually numbered at the bottom and near the top. It has 12 rows, identified from top to bottom as follows:

1. The top row is the space in which the key punch types the equivalent of the holes, as shown in Fig. 10-2.
2. The next three rows are called the *zone-punching area.* Notice that
   they are, in order, the "12 punch," the "11 or X punch," and the
   "zero punch."
3. Rows 0 through 9 are the *digit-punching area.* Notice that 0 is both
   a zone punch and a digit punch.
4. The digits 0 through 9 are represented by single punches in the card.
   These are called *numeric characters.*
5. The alphabet (A through Z) is represented by a *double punch*
   in the same column, one punch being a zone punch (12, 11, or 0)
   and the other being a digit punch (1 through 9, but not 0). Table III
   gives the punch locations of the alphabet.
6. The *special characters* are represented by one, two, or three punches
   in a single column. The symbolism is somewhat different for different models of key punches. Table IV refers to the IBM model 029,
   shown in Fig. 10-1. The computer reads only the holes (not the
   typing) and so it does not matter which'key punch is used, so long
   as the correct holes are punched.
7. The top of the card is called the *twelve-edge,* and the bottom of the
   card is called the *nine-edge.*

TABLE III. ALPHABETIC CARD PUNCHING

Letter	Punches	Letter	Punches	Letter	Punches
A	12, 1	J	11, 1	S	0, 2
B	12, 2	K	11, 2	T	0, 3
C	12, 3	L	11, 3	U	0, 4
D	12, 4	M	11, 4	V	0, 5
E	12, 5	N	11, 5	W	0, 6
F	12, 6	O	11, 6	X	0, 7
G	12, 7	P	11, 7	Y	0, 8
H	12, 8	Q	11, 8	Z	0, 9
I	12, 9	R	11, 9		

It is possible to have a punched card which does not have the translation of the characters printed on it. For example, your electric-light bill may possibly be a punched card with some of the translation omitted. By reference to Tables III and IV, and using the fact that a single punch from 0 through 9 represents a digit, you can translate the card for yourself.

Industry uses many *special-purpose cards.* Two of them are shown in Figs. 10-3 and 10-4.

In Problem Section 10.2, you will have a chance to translate some general-purpose cards, using Tables III and IV. For example, in Fig. 10-3, if the translation were not already at the top, we could proceed column by column as shown (in part) in the following. The letter *b* stands for *blank column,* and *cc* stands for *card column.*

cc	Punches	Translation
1–17	*b*	*b*
18	11, 5	N
19	12, 5	E
20	0, 6	W
21	*b*	*b*
22	11, 4	M
⋮	⋮	⋮
30	5	5
⋮	⋮	⋮

Card Input

After the cards are punched, the information on them must be read into the computer. Most computers have a read-punch unit (Fig. 10-5)

TABLE IV.   SPECIAL-CHARACTER PUNCHING

Punches	Interpretation
12	&
0, 1	/
4, 8	@
5, 8	°
6, 8	=
0, 3, 8	,
11, 3, 8	$
11, 5, 8	)
12, 3, 8	.
12, 4, 8	<
12, 5, 8	(
12, 6, 8	+

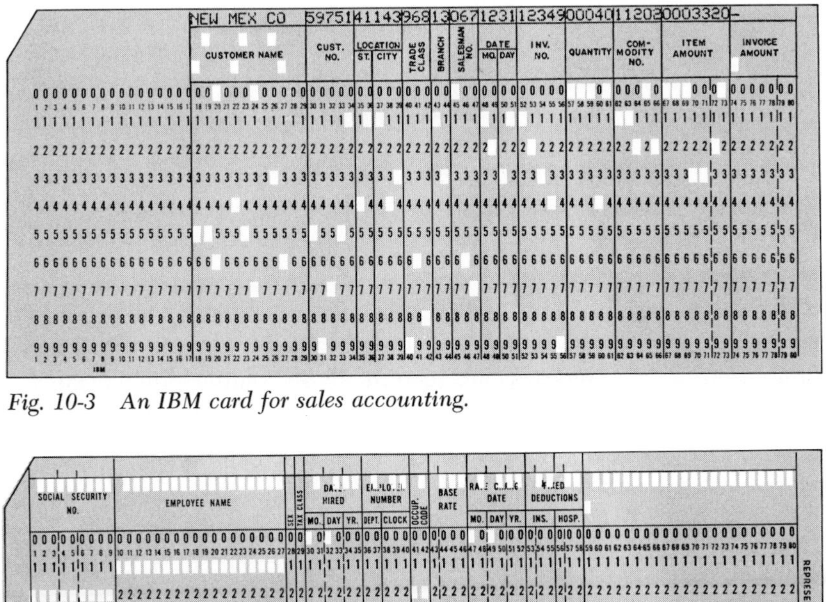

Fig. 10-3   An IBM card for sales accounting.

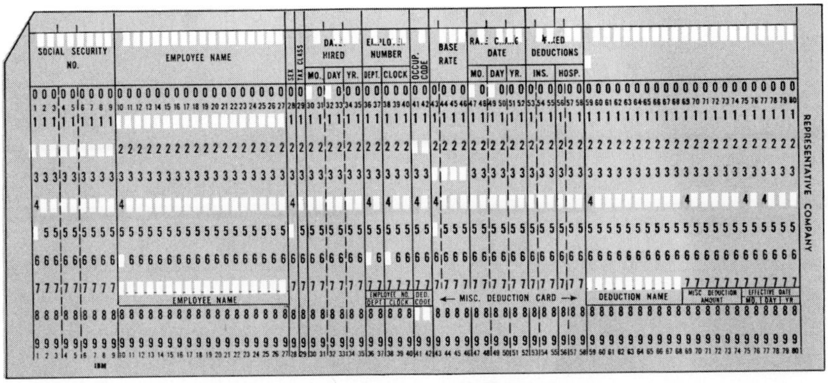

Fig. 10-4   A multiple-purpose card. This card cannot be translated by Tables III and IV. It is not designed for the usual kind of computer.

Fig. 10-5   Card read-punch unit for the IBM 2540.
(IBM Corporation.)

which reads in on one side and punches out on another. The one in the figure reads in cards by means of the upright hopper. (We shall mention *output* later.) The cards are read in, all 80 columns simultaneously, at various speeds on various models of various machines. The one in the figure reads several hundred cards a minute. There are some units rated at about a thousand cards per minute. If 400 cards per minute are used as a rough average, this means that $400 \times 80 = 32,000$ characters can be read in per minute on the average machine. If this book were punched on cards, it could be read into the computer in about an hour.

Memory and Storage

When the information on the cards has been read in, it must be *stored* somewhere. There are a great many ways of storing. We shall not be able to go into the mechanics of storage except to mention that each number, letter, or special symbol is *coded* in some way. (We mentioned *binary coding* in Sec. 10.1.) There are three main categories of storage:

1. Core storage
2. Direct-access storage
3. Serial-access storage

Core storage refers to storage inside the *central processing unit (CPU)* of the computer itself. We shall discuss the CPU later in this section. If there is a great deal of data to be stored, it is usually placed on a direct-access device, one type of which is shown in Fig. 10-6, or a serial device, one type of which is shown in Fig. 10-7. We shall describe these devices very briefly.

Direct-access Device (Disks)

The machine in Fig. 10-6 is called a *disk drive*. It has a *pack* of six *disks* in the top compartment. These disks look a little bit like a stack of long-playing phonograph records. Associated with each disk is a *read-write head* (like a phonograph needle, except that it does not touch the record). Each pack, for the disk drive shown in the figure, holds over 7 million bytes of data. We remind you that a byte consists of eight bits and that, speaking generally, you may think of a byte as a numeral, alphabetic character, or special symbol. (In some cases, *double* this amount of information can be stored on a single pack provided it is all numeric.) Most computer centers have many disk drives and, for

Fig. 10-6   Disk unit. (IBM Corporation.)

Fig. 10-7   Tape unit. (IBM Corporation.)

each, many disk packs. This whole book could easily be stored on both sides of one disk and one side of another, with plenty of room to spare.

On disks and other direct-access storage devices, any single item of information has an *address* which can be reached in thousandths of a second. The read-write head can be positioned to this address by a command from the programmer, and then about 156,000 bytes per second can be read.

Serial-access Device (Tapes)

The device in Fig. 10-7 is one kind of *magnetic-tape unit.* In some ways, it is like a tape recorder except that it records data instead of sounds. The information is read in on the magnetic tape which is wound on *spools.* It is possible to position the tape by command to a specified location and to read the material at the rate of 15,000 to 340,000 characters per second. However, it takes more time to position the tape than it does to position a read-write head for the disk. Therefore, the tape storage method is chiefly useful when a long series of items in serial order must be read in or out of the computer.

The Central Processing Unit (CPU)

When people speak of a computer, they usually have in mind the part shown in Fig. 10-8. This has a typewriter I/0 device used for special purposes (not programming) by the machine operator and by the computer. For example, it may be used for direct messages ("Whatever program you are working on now, computer, get rid of it. I have a more important one that I want you to do." or "There's something wrong with your data, operator. What do you want me to do?") The large unit at the right has a primary area of storage called *core storage* or, sometimes, the *memory.* The amount of "memory" depends upon the specific machine and model. The one in Fig. 10-8 has 32,768 bytes of storage. Others have from a few thousands to many millions of bytes. Access time varies so widely for various machines and models that it is impossible to make a general statement. The CPU in the figure is part of a small system and can find information in its core in about $1\frac{1}{2}$ *millionths* of a second.

It is in the CPU that the *arithmetic unit* and *logic unit* are located. Arithmetic units do problems in addition, subtraction, multiplication, division, and exponentiation. Logic units decide "if" types of questions such as, "If we have only 3 gloops left in warehouse 5, write a letter ordering 27 more," or "If we have read in all the data, do the calculations; if not, read some more data." Arithmetic and logical operations are done in *millionths* of a second.

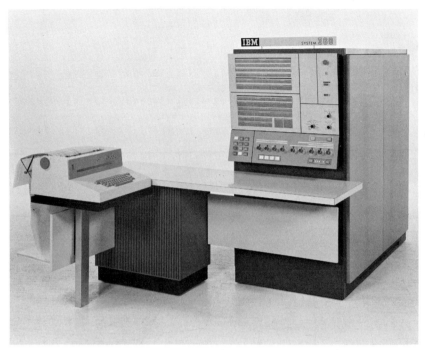

Fig. 10-8   The CPU of an IBM 360 model 30. (IBM Corporation.)

Output

Sometimes the results of the work of the computer are punched by the computer into cards. This is usually done by the same machine that does the reading (Fig. 10-5). For example, many of your utility and department-store bills are produced on punched cards by a computer.

The results may also be *printed* on a machine like the one in Fig. 10-9. The computer tells the printer what to print, and this is done at great speed. The speed depends upon the machine. Some machines will print about 1,000 *lines* (132 characters per line) each minute. The machine in the figure prints about 200 lines per minute, 120 characters per line, or about 24,000 characters per minute. If this book were stored in a computer, it could be printed in less than an hour.

Results can be printed and punched simultaneously with no loss of time.

Peripheral Machines

For your general information, we wish to tell you a little bit about some of the *peripheral machines* found in computing centers.

Fig. 10-9   An on-line printer for the IBM 360.
(IBM Corporation.)

We mentioned that computer output may be on punched cards. The *interpreter* in Fig. 10-10 reads the punched cards and, across the top, prints a translation of the holes in the card.

You are probably familiar (from TV) with the *sorter,* one model of which is shown in Fig. 10-11. A stack of cards is placed in the hopper at the right. At the touch of a button, the cards are separated according to alphabet or number into various *bins.* For example, if students have enrolled in classes by means of punched cards, the registration cards may then be sorted into classes and, within classes, into an alphabetic arrangement ready for listing.

Suppose you have a deck of cards and you want to list them. This listing can be done on the computer but it is often much cheaper to use a separate machine, like the one in Fig. 10-12. When the machine is used for *tabulating,* it is usually called a *tab* and the operators have come to be known as *tab operators.* Actually, this machine is able to do some arithmetic and make some logical decisions. It is a simple kind of computer, often used for billing and invoices. In the figure, the cards are stacked in the hopper at the left, and the printed listing is emerging at the center. This machine reads about 100 cards per minute and ordinarily prints a line from each card, at the same rate. It is fairly slow but also fairly inexpensive, as compared with a computer.

Figure 10-13 shows a *reproducing punch.* If a deck of punched cards is placed in the left hopper and a deck of blank cards on the

Fig. 10-10   *An interpreter. (IBM Corporation.)*

right hopper, it is possible to *copy* the left deck into the right deck. You get two decks for one. The new deck may be *edited;* i.e., the arrangement of the information may be altered in the new deck. This can be done on the computer, too, but the reproducing punch is a much cheaper machine. There are many other uses for this machine but we shall not be able to go into the matter any further. We just wanted you to get the general "feel" of the components of a computer center. If you can possibly visit a computer center, take this book along and see

Fig. 10-11   *A sorter. (IBM Corporation.)*

Fig. 10-12   *An accounting machine ("tab"). (IBM Corporation.)*

Fig. 10-13   A reproducing punch. (IBM Corporation.)

whether you can recognize the machines. The actual machines are far more interesting than their pictures.

PROBLEM SECTION 10.2

Translate each of the following punched cards. The easiest way to accomplish this is to cover all but one column and then use Tables III and IV. (You do not need a table for digit punches.)

1.

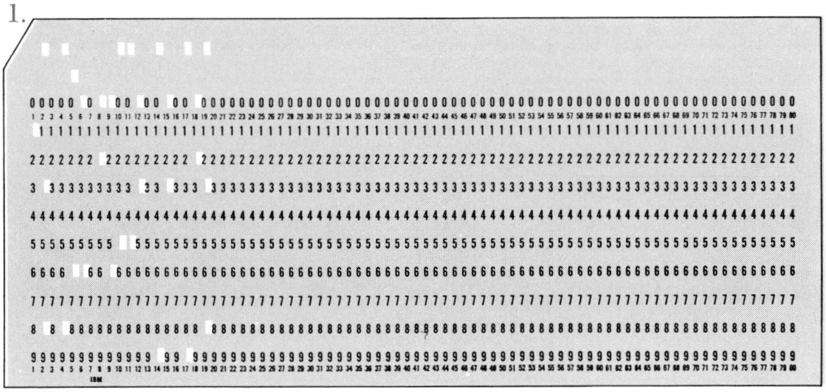

Fig. 10-14   Problem 1.

Fig. 10-15   Problem 2.

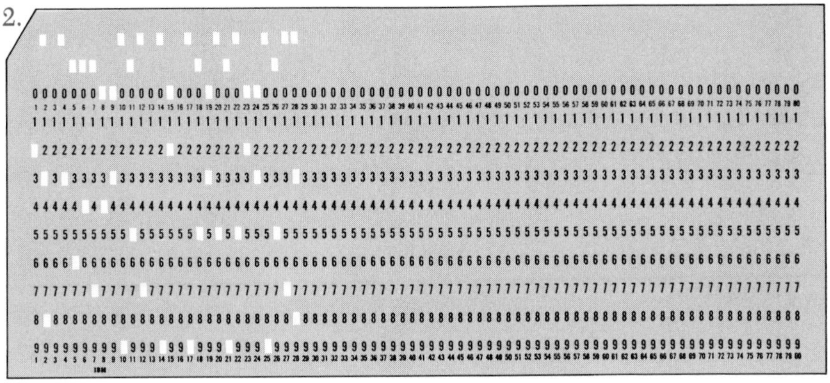

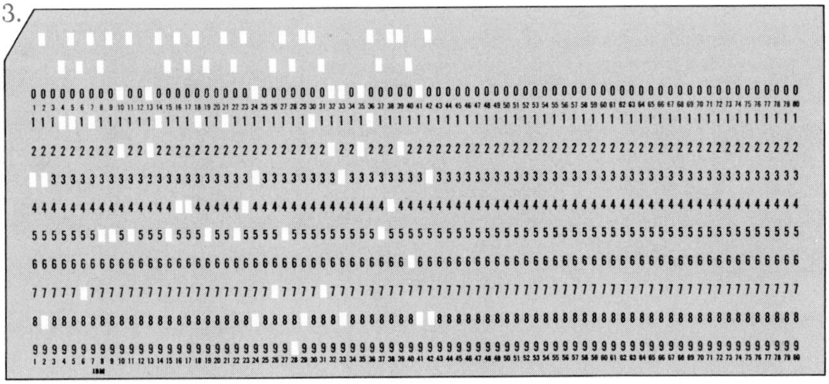

Fig. 10-16   Problem 3.

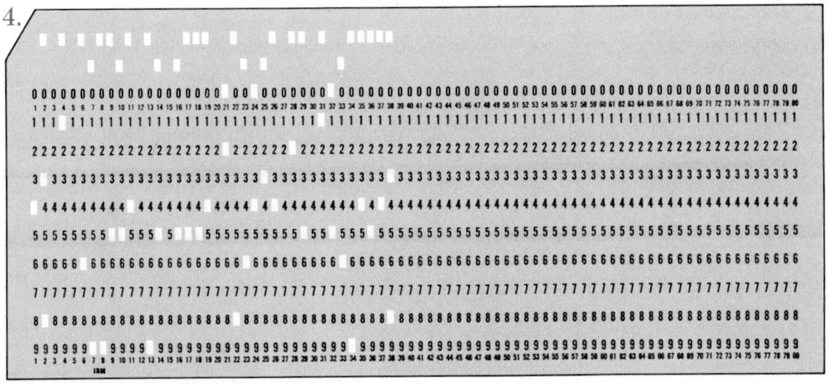

Fig. 10-17   Problem 4.

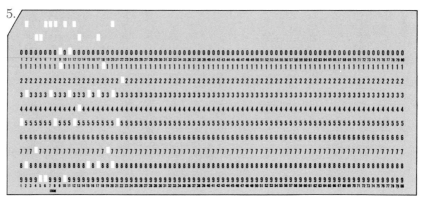

5.

Fig. 10-18 Problem 5.

6.

Fig. 10-19 Problem 6.

7.

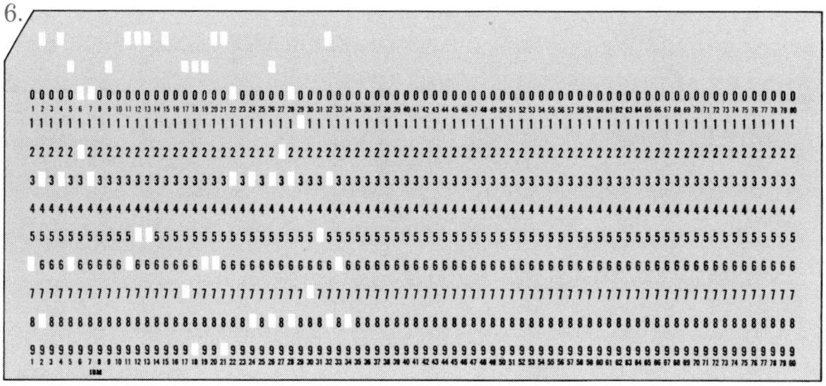

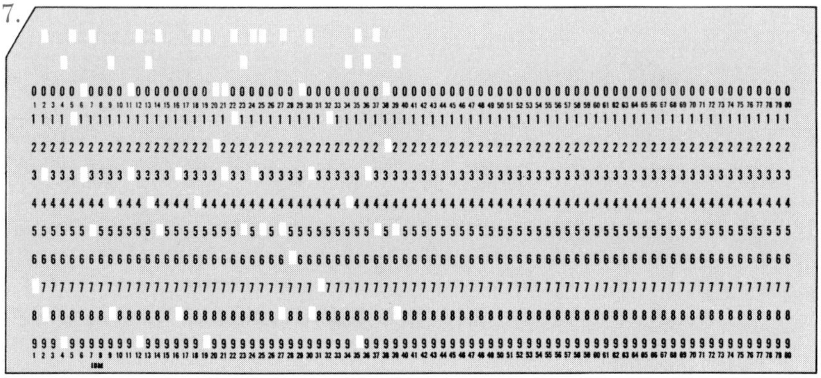

Fig. 10-20 Problem 7.

8.

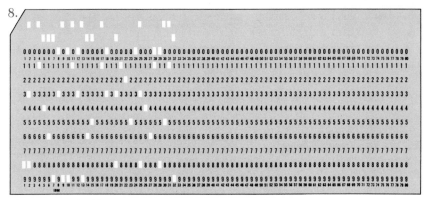

Fig. 10-21   *Problem 8.*

10.3   FORTRAN PROGRAMS

FORTRAN is a special language widely used throughout the world for mathematical and scientific programs. The name stands for FORmula TRANslation. In the remainder of this book, we shall illustrate some basic computer ideas by reference to programs in the FORTRAN language. There are small variations in FORTRAN for various machines. The type we are demonstrating is one "dialect" of FORTRAN IV. Other widely used special languages are COBOL (in business) and ALGOL (in Europe).

In this section, we shall discuss, very briefly, how to get information in and out of the computer and how to solve a formula by computer.

Input-Output (I / O)

Let us assume that our computer center has the following input-output machines. We have numbered them arbitrarily for identification throughout the remainder of the book.

Machine	Number
Card reader	1
Card punch	2
Printer	3
First disk pack	4
Second disk pack	5
First tape unit	7
Second tape unit	8

Numbers 1 and 3 are usually on the same machine, but they are at different ends and we shall treat each "end" as a separate machine.

Now suppose we are dealing with a stack of punched cards which have the following *fields* (sets of columns) set aside for information:

cc	Contents	Abbreviation
1–25	Name of employee	NAME
26–50	Street address	ADDR
51–60	Town or city	CITY
61–65	State	STATE
66–67	Number of dependents	NDEP
68–73	Hourly rate	RATE

An example of one such card for employee John Smith is shown in Fig. 10-22.

We wish to print a payroll. For this purpose, we need the name of the employee, the number of dependents, the hourly rate, and the number of hours he worked this week. The first three items are in cc 1–25, 66–67, and 68–73 on the card. We shall assume that the last item, number of hours worked this week, is on the first tape unit (machine 7).

We use a READ command to get the computer to accept the information. The READ command must include three items of information:

1. Which machine is being used to read the information?
2. Where is the information?
3. What do you wish to call the information after it is read into the computer?

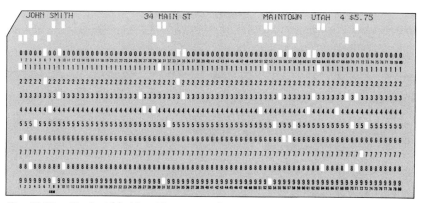

Fig. 10-22   Mr. Smith's identification card.

For example, to read the card in Fig. 10-22 into the computer, we might feed in a punched card with the following command:

5   READ (1, 100) NAME, NDEP, RATE

1. The 5 is the number of the statement and is, naturally, called a *statement number*. Not every statement is numbered. The programmer numbers the statements that are going to be used more than once. Then he can just refer to the statement number instead of repeating the command. Other statements may be numbered for other purposes.
2. READ is self-explanatory.
3. The 1 in the parentheses refers to the machine that is being used for input. Each computer center decides on its own numbering scheme, and the computer "knows" this scheme. We are using the table on page 353, so that machine 1 is the card reader.
4. The 100 in the parentheses refers to a FORMAT statement. We shall not be able to explain these important statements in detail. Briefly, the 100 says to the computer, "There is a statement numbered 100. Go look at that statement. It will tell you what parts of the punched card we are interested in." In this case FORMAT statement 100 would tell the computer that the programmer is interested in three parts of the punched card: cc 1–25, cc 66–67, and cc 68–73.
5. Now the computer knows it must read in the three items in those specific columns. How shall we refer to them? We shall call the first item NAME, the second item NDEP, and the third item RATE. The other material on the card is disregarded.

To read in the material on the first tape unit, we might punch a card with the following command:

READ (7, 105) HOURS

This would tell the computer to use the first tape unit, to look at FORMAT statement 105 to find out exactly where the item is that we want, and to call the item HOURS after it gets into the computer.

Let us skip over details, for the moment, and assume that we have succeeded in calculating that Mr. Smith is entitled to gross pay of $212.75 with deductions of $48.93, resulting in a net pay of $163.82. The deductions are for tax and pension. We shall call the items GROSS, DED, and TAKHOM. We have decided upon a certain way we want this printed, and we describe this specific way in a FORMAT statement, say, 153. Our output command might now be:

WRITE (3, 153) NAME, GROSS, DED, TAKHOM

You can probably understand the parts of this command by comparing it to the READ command. We apologize for not going into FORMAT. It is not particularly difficult, but there are several pages of rules. In the remainder of the problems, we shall just write

100 FORMAT STATEMENT

where, in place of "statement" there should be the specifications.

Mode

In FORTRAN, numbers without decimal points are called *fixed-point* constants or *integers,* and numbers with decimal points are called *floating-point* constants or *reals.* We shall use the former designations because it offends us, as mathematicians, to assign names as if integers were not real. Here are some examples:

Fixed Point	Floating Point
23	23.
−5	−5.16
7000	7000.48

These are said to be the two *modes* of constants.

We shall also use names for numbers, such as RATE or NUMBER. These also have two modes. By agreement, names beginning with the letters I, J, K, L, M, N are used for fixed point, and all the other letters are used for floating point. The names of numbers are called *fixed-point variables* and *floating-point variables.*

illustrative problem 1

Which of the following are incorrect?

	Constant	Name Assigned (Variable)
(*a*)	256	SUM
(*b*)	31.7	SUM
(*c*)	−26.8	NUMBER
(*d*)	85	TOTAL
(*e*)	85.	TOTAL

solution

(*a*), (*c*), and (*d*) are incorrect. (*a*) and (*d*) are fixed-point constants but have floating-point names. If we like, we can change the initial letter of the name to I, J, K, L, M, or N and then it will be correct. For example, in (*a*), we can change the name to JSUM; in (*d*), we can change the name to ITOTAL. (*c*) is incorrect because the constant is floating point whereas the variable is fixed point. We can correct it by giving the variable a different initial. For example, in (*c*) we can assign the name as ZNUMB. Unfortunately, we cannot use ZNUMBER because this has seven letters and *six* is the usual limit for a FORTRAN variable.

In doing arithmetic, the modes should not be mixed[1] except for one case (exponents) which we shall mention in Sec. 10.4. The following are not recommended:

Wrong	Should be
2 + 3.7	2. + 3.7
2. + 3	2. + 3.

The following are valid:

2 + 3
2. + 3.

When an error is made, the computer notifies the programmer, usually in print, and (when the error is serious enough) the program is stopped in order to avoid wasting time. The *mixed-mode* error is probably the most common among beginners. It is a very simple rule to remember but, unfortunately, equally easy to forget. We bothered to discuss it because, otherwise, you might wonder why we have such strange abbreviations for the names in the programs we are going to show you.

The Equals Sign in FORTRAN

The statement

X = 5.   [2]

means that from this point on (until we change our minds and notify the computer) we mean 5. when we write X.

The statement

Y = X + 1.   [3]

means that from this point on (until we change our minds and notify the computer) the value of Y is one more than the *current* value of X.

---

[1] Some large computers correct automatically for mixed-mode errors, but it is not safe to assume that this will be done.

If [2] and [3] are considered together, the result is X = 5. and Y = 6.

Now consider

$$X = X + 3. \tag{4}$$

which seems to make mathematical nonsense. There are two X's, one on the left side and one on the right. We shall call the left X the *new* X and the right X the *old* X. Then [4] tells the computer that the *new* value of X (until we change our minds and notify the computer) is three more than the *old* value of X. If [2], [3], and [4] are considered together, this means that, as a result, X = 8. (three more than the old value), and Y = 6. (the value of X had not been changed at the time this command was executed).

illustrative problem 2

What is the result of the following set of commands?

```
1   X = 7.
2   Y = X + 3.
3   X = X + 4.
4   Y = Y − 6.
5   X = X + Y
6   Y = X − Y
```

solution

We shall replace each X or Y by its current value, step-by-step (the way a computer does). Then

```
1   X = 7.
2   Y = 7. + 3. = 10.
3   X = 7. + 4. = 11.
4   Y = 10. − 6. = 4.
5   X = 11. + 4. = 15.
6   Y = 15. − 4. = 11.
```

The result is that X = 15. and Y = 11.

illustrative problem 3

What is the result of the following FORTRAN program if X is read in as 7. and Y as 9. (Note that we "sketch" in the FORMAT statements but do not really show them.)

```
1   READ (1, 150) X, Y
2   Z = X − Y
```

3   Z = Z + 12.
4   Z = Z − 3.
5   WRITE (2, 151) Z, X, Y
150   FORMAT STATEMENT
151   FORMAT STATEMENT
     CALL EXIT
     END

The last two statements end all the sample FORTRAN programs in this book. CALL EXIT or STOP is used to tell the computer to end this program and END is always the last card in a FORTRAN program, except for *job control* cards, which we shall not discuss. (In case you were wondering, the CALL EXIT may not be anywhere near the end of the cards which form the program.)

solution

1   Read a card according to FORMAT statement 150 and call the results X and Y. According to the problem, the numbers 7. and 9. are punched in the card, and so we have in the machine X = 7. and Y = 9. as soon as the card is read in.
2   Z = 7. − 9. = −2.
3   Z = −2. + 12. = 10.
4   Z = 10. − 3. = 7.
5   Punch a card according to FORMAT statement 151. On the card will be 7., 7., and 9. in that order. The specific card columns will depend upon the nature of the FORMAT statement 151.

PROBLEM SECTION 10.3

Part A. In Probs. 1 to 6, find out whether the expression is valid or invalid. If it is invalid, state why. In Probs. 7 to 12, tell whether the names given to the constants are valid or invalid. If a name is invalid, correct it.

1. 3.5 − 7   2. 2. + 3.
3. 3 + 5   4. 6 + 8.1 − 4.3
5. 3.5 − 8. + 6.3   6. 7 + 5. − 8.
7. −28.3, NUMB   8. 413, SUM
9. 176., TOTAL   10. 176, TOTAL
11. 97.3, DECIMAL   12. 814, WHOLENO

Part B. In each of the following, the actual input values are given in parentheses. Describe the nature of the input and output.

13.   READ (1, 125) A, B, C   (2., 8., 15.)
           D = A + B − C

```
           D = D + 6.
           D = D + A
           WRITE (3, 130) D, B
     125   FORMAT STATEMENT
           CALL EXIT
           END
14.        READ (7, 101) X, ZIN, ZYK        (25., 17., 6.)
           SUM = X + ZIN + ZYX
           SUM = SUM − 40.
           SUM = SUM + ZIN
           WRITE (2, 102) SUM
     102   FORMAT STATEMENT
           CALL EXIT
           END
15.        READ (5, 172) GROSS, DED         ($175.25, $62.13)
           ZNET = GROSS − DED
           CONTRB = 5.00
           ZNET = ZNET − CONTRB
           SAVING = 20.50
           ZNET = ZNET − SAVING
           WRITE (3, 173) ZNET, GROSS
     172   FORMAT STATMENT
     173   FORMAT STATEMENT
           CALL EXIT
           END
16.        READ (7, 100) ZNUM               (1500.)
           X = 700.
           Y = ZNUM + X
           Y = Y − 200.
           ZNUM = ZNUM + 400.
           Z = Y + ZNUM
           WRITE (4, 101) Z
     100   FORMAT STATEMENT
           CALL EXIT
           END
```

Part C. Write a program for each of the following, sketching in the FORMAT statements starting with 100.

17. A card has three numbers. We wish to read them in and call them A, B, and C. The second tape unit has a number which we wish to call D. Add B to A and call the result SUM. Increase SUM by 3.

Now subtract D from SUM. The results are to be printed in the order A, B, C, D, SUM.

18. The first disk pack has five numbers which we wish to call X1, X2, X3, X4, and X5. The second disk pack has a number which we wish to call C. Read them into the computer. Increase X1 by 1 and X2 by 8. Find the sum of X3, X4, and X5 and call the result TOTAL. Decrease TOTAL by 10. Add C to TOTAL. Write TOTAL, X_1, X_2, and C on the first tape unit.

10.4 FORTRAN MATHEMATICS

We distinguish between an *expression* (an indicated arithmetic operation with no equals sign), an *equation* (which has an equals sign but which, in FORTRAN, may not really be an equation) and a *function* (which we shall explain later in this section).

Arithmetic in FORTRAN

The arithmetic operations are *addition*, indicated by $+$; *subtraction*, indicated by $-$; *multiplication*, indicated by $*$; *division*, indicated by $/$; and *exponentiation*, indicated by $**$.

In the absence of other instructions, operations are performed *from left to right* and in the following order of precedence, by agreement among mathematicians:

1. Exponentiation
2. Multiplication and division in the order in which they are written
3. Addition and subtraction in the order in which they are written

Here are some examples:

```
1   2. + 3. * 5. / 10
    2. +   15.  / 10
    2. +        1.5
          3.5
2   2 ** 5 * 5 / 10
       32   * 5 / 10
          160   / 10
             16
3   3 + 12 / 6 / 2
    3 +    2  / 2
    3 +        1
          4
```

$$4 \quad 12 / 3 * 5 ** 2$$
$$12 / 3 * \quad 25$$
$$4 \quad * \quad 25$$
$$100$$
$$5 \quad 2 * 9 ** 1.5$$
$$2 * \quad 27$$
$$54$$

If there are parentheses, the part of the command which is inside the parentheses is done first. In students' language, parentheses are "removed" before the expression is "simplified."

illustrative problem 1

Translate into FORTRAN:

$$y \cdot \frac{(x + a)^3}{b}$$

solution

Y * (X + A) ** 3/B

Explanation: First the computer adds X and A because these are in parentheses. Then it raises the sum to the third power (*exponentiation* first). Then it multiplies the result by Y (*multiplication* and *division* take place from left to right in the order that they occur). Finally, it divides by B.

illustrative problem 2

Translate into FORTRAN:

$$x + \frac{yz^2}{p}$$

solution

X + Y * Z ** 2/P

Explanation: First the computer finds Z to the second power. Then it multiplies by Y and divides by P. Finally it adds X. Addition and subtraction take place last, left to right in the order of occurrence, unless there are parentheses which override this rule.

illustrative problem 3

Translate from FORTRAN into algebra.

A ** 2 * B * C − B ** 2 * C/X

solution

$$a^2bc - \frac{b^2c}{x}$$

Explanation: First, look for all exponents; this yields a^2 and b^2. Second, look for multiplications and divisions in the order of occurrence; this yields a^2bc and b^2c/x. Third, look for additions and subtractions in the order of occurrence.

illustrative problem 4

Translate from FORTRAN into algebra.

((X ** 2 * Y) ** 3)/(P ** 2 − Q)

solution

$$\frac{(x^2y)^3}{p^2 - q}$$

Explanation: Material in parentheses is done first, working from the inside out. (X ** 2 * Y ** 3 would have been x^2y^3.)

    In algebra, the expression xy means that two variables, x and y, are to be multiplied. In FORTRAN, to accomplish the same result, we have to write X * Y. The symbol XY would mean to the computer that we are giving this name to a number. A common error among beginners is to write something like 2X when they really mean 2. * X.

Nests of Parentheses

Parentheses are used, as we indicated above, to point to preferred operations. Sometimes this means that one or more sets of parentheses are inside other sets. We say that the parentheses are *nested*. Here are some examples:

Algebraic Expression	FORTRAN Expression
$[(-1)^3 5]^2$	((−1)**3*5)**2
$\dfrac{(3^5)^{n+2}}{7}$	((3**5)**(N + 2))/7
$\dfrac{-[(-3)^5]^{n+2}}{7}$	(−((−3)**5)**(N + 2))/7

To check, count the left parentheses, (, and the right parentheses,). There should be the same number of each.

FORTRAN distinguishes between the symbol — used as a *sign* and the same symbol used as an *operation* (subtracting). The expression

$$-3 * 5$$

is invalid because signed numbers are always enclosed in parentheses. This should be rewritten as

$$(-3) * 5$$

The following is all right as it stands:

$$5 - 3$$

because the symbol indicates subtraction.

FORTRAN Functions

There are many calculations, such as the calculation of *logarithms,* which are done at a single command by the computer. Among them are calculations of *absolute value,* various kinds of *exponentiation,* and *trigonometric values.* The following is a partial list of the *functions* built into the FORTRAN language.

Function	FORTRAN Name†	Example	Meaning
Log, base 10	ALOG10	Y = ALOG10 (X)	$y = \log x$
Square root	SQRT	Y = SQRT (X)	$y = \sqrt{x}$
Sine	SIN	Y = SIN (X)	$y = \sin x$
Cosine	COS	Y = COS (X)	$y = \cos x$

† The FORTRAN names of the various functions differ a bit for different computers.

illustrative problem 5

On page 236, we have the formula

$$y = 0.785 \times 10^{0.24t}$$

How would we command a computer to do this?

solution

$$Y = 0.785 * 10. ** (0.24 * T)$$

illustrative problem 6

Write in FORTRAN

$$y = 0.785 \times 10^{0.24n}$$

solution

Y = 0.785 * 10. ** (0.24 * ZN)

Remember that n is written as ZN in order to make sure the computer will recognize it as a floating-point variable. Any variable starting with I, J, K, L, M, or N is recognized by the computer as fixed-point (although some computers have built-in correction instructions).

illustrative problem 7

Write in FORTRAN: $P = 10^{-0.000182t}$ (from page 240).

solution

P = 10. ** ((−0.000182) * T)

illustrative problem 8

Write in FORTRAN: $f = 1,000,000/2\pi \sqrt{LC}$ (from page 249).

solution

F = 1000000./(2. * 3.1415927 * SQRT (ZL * C))

illustrative problem 9

Write in FORTRAN: $A = 625(1.03)^{24}$ (from page 256).

solution

A = 625. * 1.03 ** 24

In Illustrative Problem 9, you may think there is an error because two of the constants are in floating-point mode and the third is in fixed-point mode. However, this is the exception we mentioned previously. The rule is that the exponents may be either fixed or floating, regardless of the rest of the expression, but that each exponent should be all fixed or all floating.

illustrative problem 10

Write in FORTRAN: $S_n = a(m^n - 1)/(m - 1)$ (from page 261).

solution

$$SN = A * (ZM ** N - 1.)/(ZM - 1.)$$

illustrative problem 11

Write in FORTRAN formula [58] on page 285.

solution

We shall use Y for the Greek letter *gamma*.

$$V = SQRT (2. * G * Y/(Y - 1.) * R * T * (1. - PE/PC) ** ((Y - 1.)/Y))$$

PROBLEM SECTION 10.4

Part A. Translate the following into algebraic language.

1. A/B * C
2. (A/B) * C
3. A * B/C
4. A ** (B/C)
5. (A + B)/C * D ** (X + 2.)
6. A + B/C * D ** 2

Part B. Translate the following into FORTRAN.

7. $\dfrac{a + b^2}{c - d^3}$

8. $a + \dfrac{b^2}{c - d^3}$

9. $a + \dfrac{b}{c - d^3}$

10. $a + \dfrac{b^2}{c} - d^{3x-4}$

11. $\dfrac{a + b^{2(x-5)}}{c} - 5d$

12. $\left(\dfrac{ja + kb^{2y+m}}{c} - nd^{4(j-2)}\right)^3$

Part C. Write in FORTRAN the following formulas, all taken from physics.

13. $R = \dfrac{R_1 R_2}{R_1 + R_2}$

14. $W = I^2 R t$

15. $H = \dfrac{I(\sin t)L}{r^2}$

16. $F = \dfrac{BIL}{10} \sin t$

17. $q = EC(1 - e^{-t/RC})$, where $e =$ approximately 2.7183.

18. $E = I\sqrt{R^2 + (X_L - X_C)^2}$

10.5   PROGRAMS WITH LOOPS AND BRANCHES

We shall end the book with a brief introduction to *loops* and *branches* (we shall explain what these are). Consider the following problem. We have three cards sitting in the card reader. Each card has a number on it (in the same relative position on each of the cards), and we want to read in the three numbers, add them, and print the sums as we add them. The program might look like this:

Program I

SUM = 0.	We start with a sum of 0.
READ (1, 100) X	We read a card and identify the number read in as "X".
SUM = SUM + X	We add X to 0 and get a sum.
WRITE (3, 101) SUM	We print the sum.
READ (1, 100) X	We read the second card, again identifying the number read in as "X".
SUM = SUM + X	We add X to the previous sum, and get a new sum.
WRITE (3, 101) SUM	We print the sum.
READ (1, 100) X	We read the third card.
SUM = SUM + X	We add the new X to the previous sum.
WRITE (3, 101) SUM	We print the sum.
100 FORMAT STATEMENT	
101 FORMAT STATEMENT	
CALL EXIT	
END	

The Flow Chart

If we made a diagram of the procedure, it might look like Fig. 10-23. This kind of diagram, designed to show the logical steps of the program, is called a *flow chart* or *block diagram*. The type of flow in this problem is called *straight-line flow*.

The Simplest Loop: GO TO

Although the procedure illustrated will give the answers, it would be rather painful if this were an inventory of 100,000 items. Then about 300,000 program cards would be needed, and the process of reading the program in to the machine *before actually doing any useful work* would probably require several hours of machine time (depending upon the specific machine used).

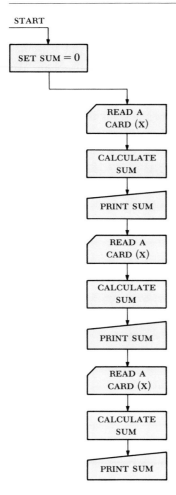

Fig. 10-23 A straight-line flow chart.

We can improve this considerably. Note that in Program I the steps *repeat*. Why not tell the computer to go back each time and do the three steps over again, reading a new card each time? The following program simplifies the program of telling the computer what to do. (There is, however, a serious flaw in it which we shall mention in this subsection and remove in the next one.)

Our plan of action is shown in the flow chart of Fig. 10-24. After the computer prints the first sum, it is to go back and do the entire process over and over again. Be sure to compare the flow charts in Figs. 10-23 and 10-24 to see why this is so. The program which follows has a new command, GO TO.

Program **II**

SUM = 0.

1   READ (1, 100) X   We need the statement number in
                             order to be able to tell the com-
                             puter where to go to.

SUM = SUM + X
WRITE (3, 101) SUM
GO TO 1   When the computer reaches this
                            command, it goes back and does
                            statement 1 again.

100   FORMAT STATEMENT
101   FORMAT STATEMENT
      CALL EXIT
      END

The GO TO command is called an *unconditional branch*. The result
of our program is called a *loop,* partly because of the way it looks in the
flow chart. Will this program of 9 cards read 100,000 cards? Yes, it will.
As a matter of fact, it will never stop going back, and that is the serious
flaw in the program. What we have is an *endless loop,* and this definitely
makes everyone very unhappy. Modern computers have clocks built in
so that any program which appears to be endless will be thrown off the
machine. We shall now cure the illness.

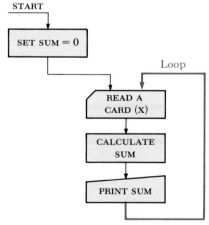

Fig. 10-24   *A simple loop using GO TO
for branching.*

Making a Decision with IF

To remove the flaw in the program, the computer must have some way to decide when all the cards have been read in. Then it can *branch on that condition* out of the loop. This can be done many different ways. We shall discuss only the IF statement. The following statement

IF (N − 3) 18, 20, 7

means:

If (N − 3) is negative (that is, N is less than 3), branch to statement 18.
If (N − 3) is zero (that is, N = 3), branch to statement 20.
If (N − 3) is positive (that is, N is more than 3), branch to statement 7.

To make use of the IF command, we must establish a *counter* in the computer to keep track of the cards that come in. We start with

N = 1

Every time we finish processing a card by going through the loop, we add 1 to the counter. Programmers say that we are *stepping* the counter.

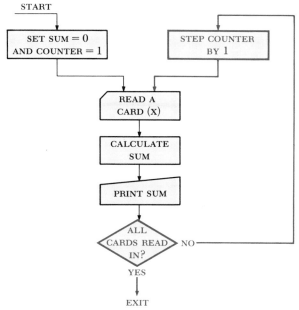

Fig. 10-25   A loop with an IF decision. Note the use of a counter.

To do this, we merely use

N = N + 1

which increases the value of N (the counter) by 1.

When *one* card has been processed, N = 1 and (N − 3) is negative. We want the computer to go back and read another card. When *two* cards have been read and processed, N = 2 and (N − 3) is still negative. We want the computer to go back and read another card. When the third card has been read and processed, N = 3 and (N − 3) = 0. At this point, we wish to get out of the loop.

In this particular program, (N − 3) never becomes positive but it is one of the rules of FORTRAN that we have to specify a branch even if the situation cannot occur. The explanation is too complicated to go into but it has to do with the way the language was written. Look at Fig. 10-25 and the following program very carefully, line by line. It will process exactly 100 cards.

Program III

```
      SUM = 0.
      N = 1                      This sets the counter.
  2   READ (1, 100) X
      SUM = SUM + X
      WRITE (3, 101) SUM
      IF (N − 100) 1, 3, 3       Branches out when N = 100.
  1   N = N + 1                  This steps the counter.
      GO TO 2                    Go back and read another card.
100   FORMAT STATEMENT
101   FORMAT STATEMENT
  3   CALL EXIT
      END
```

There are many different ways of writing this program. This is not the shortest way, but it is easiest to explain.

A Single-result Program

We end by showing the more common situation in which a single result is desired. Suppose we have 5,000 inventory cards and we want to punch one card with the total, instead of a series of printed items as in Program III. The flow chart for this program is shown in Fig. 10-26. You should compare it carefully with Fig. 10-25.

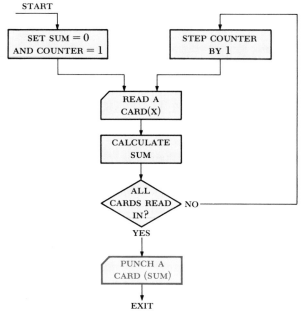

Fig. 10-26   *Punching a result after all the information is in.*

Program **IV**

```
    SUM = 0.
    N = 1
2   READ (1, 100) X
    SUM = SUM + X
    IF (N − 5000) 1, 3, 3
1   N = N + 1
    GO TO 2
3   WRITE (2, 101) SUM
100 FORMAT STATEMENT
101 FORMAT STATEMENT
    CALL EXIT
    END
```

PROBLEM SECTION 10.5

Part A. What does each of the following programs do?

1. TOTAL1 = 1.
    TOTAL2 = 0.
    N = 1

```
     3   READ (1, 100) X, Y
         TOTAL1 = TOTAL1 * X
         TOTAL2 = TOTAL2 + Y
         IF (N − 4) 1, 2, 2
     1   N = N + 1
         GO TO 3
     2   WRITE (4, 101) TOTAL1, TOTAL2
   100   FORMAT STATEMENT
   101   FORMAT STATEMENT
         CALL EXIT
         END
```

2.
```
         ZNET = 0.
         N = 1
     8   READ (1, 100) X, Y
         Z = X/Y
         ZNET = ZNET + Z
         IF (N − 5) 15, 16, 16
    15   N = N + 1
         GO TO 8
    16   WRITE (3, 101) X, Y, ZNET
   100   FORMAT STATEMENT
   101   FORMAT STATEMENT
         CALL EXIT
         END
```

3.
```
         SUM = 0.
         N = 1
         A = 1.
     3   B = A ** 3
         SUM = SUM + B
         IF (N − 25) 1, 2, 2
     1   A = A + 1.
         GO TO 3
     2   WRITE (2, 100) N, SUM
   100   FORMAT STATEMENT
         CALL EXIT
         END
```

4.
```
         N = 1
     3   READ (1, 100) A, B
         H = SQRT (A ** 2 + B ** 2)
         WRITE (3, 101) A, B, H
         IF (N − 50) 1, 2, 2
```

```
  1  N = N + 1
     GO TO 3
100  FORMAT STATEMENT
101  FORMAT STATEMENT
  2  CALL EXIT
     END
```

Part B. Write a program for each of the following.

5. To find the sum of the squares of the first 15 odd numbers and punch the result in a card.
6. To find the product of the logs (base 10) of the first 10 even numbers and write the result in the first tape unit.

APPENDIXES

tables;
answers
to odd-
numbered
problems

TABLE I. MANTISSAS OF COMMON LOGARITHMS†

N	0	1	2	3	4	5	6	7	8	9
10	0000	0043	0086	0128	0170	0212	0253	0294	0334	0374
11	0414	0453	0492	0531	0569	0607	0645	0682	0719	0755
12	0792	0828	0864	0899	0934	0969	1004	1038	1072	1106
13	1139	1173	1206	1239	1271	1303	1335	1367	1399	1430
14	1461	1492	1523	1553	1584	1614	1644	1673	1703	1732
15	1761	1790	1818	1847	1875	1903	1931	1959	1987	2014
16	2041	2068	2095	2122	2148	2175	2201	2227	2253	2279
17	2304	2330	2355	2380	2405	2430	2455	2480	2504	2529
18	2553	2577	2601	2625	2648	2672	2695	2718	2742	2765
19	2788	2810	2833	2856	2878	2900	2923	2945	2967	2989
20	3010	3032	3054	3075	3096	3118	3139	3160	3181	3201
21	3222	3243	3263	3284	3304	3324	3345	3365	3385	3404
22	3424	3444	3464	3483	3502	3522	3541	3560	3579	3598
23	3617	3636	3655	3674	3692	3711	3729	3747	3766	3784
24	3802	3820	3838	3856	3874	3892	3909	3927	3945	3962
25	3979	3997	4014	4031	4048	4065	4082	4099	4116	4133
26	4150	4166	4183	4200	4216	4232	4249	4265	4281	4298
27	4314	4330	4346	4326	4378	4393	4409	4425	4440	4456
28	4472	4487	4502	4518	4533	4548	4564	4579	4594	4609
29	4624	4639	4654	4669	4683	4698	4713	4728	4742	4757
30	4771	4786	4800	4814	4829	4843	4857	4871	4886	4900
31	4914	4928	4942	4955	4969	4983	4997	5011	5024	5038
32	5051	5065	5079	5092	5105	5119	5132	5145	5159	5172
33	5185	5198	5211	5224	5237	5250	5263	5276	5289	5302
34	5315	5328	5340	5353	5366	5378	5391	5403	5416	5428
35	5441	5453	5465	5478	5490	5502	5514	5527	5539	5551
36	5563	5575	5587	5599	5611	5623	5635	5647	5658	5670
37	5682	5694	5705	5717	5729	5740	5752	5763	5775	5786
38	5798	5809	5821	5832	5843	5855	5866	5877	5888	5899
39	5911	5922	5933	5944	5955	5966	5977	5988	5999	6010
40	6021	6031	6042	6053	6064	6075	6085	6096	6107	6117
41	6128	6138	6149	6160	6170	6180	6191	6201	6212	6222
42	6232	6243	6253	6263	6274	6284	6294	6304	6314	6325
43	6335	6345	6355	6365	6375	6385	6395	6405	6415	6425
44	6435	6444	6454	6464	6474	6484	6493	6503	6513	6522
45	6532	6542	6551	6561	6571	6580	6590	6599	6609	6618
46	6628	6637	6646	6656	6665	6675	6684	6693	6702	6712
47	6721	6730	6739	6749	6758	6767	6776	6785	6794	6803
48	6812	6821	6830	6839	6848	6857	6866	6875	6884	6893
49	6902	6911	6920	6928	6937	6946	6955	6964	6972	6981
50	6990	6998	7007	7016	7024	7033	7042	7050	7059	7067
51	7076	7084	7093	7101	7110	7118	7126	7135	7143	7152
52	7160	7168	7177	7185	7193	7202	7210	7218	7226	7235
53	7243	7251	7259	7267	7275	7284	7292	7300	7308	7316
54	7324	7332	7340	7348	7356	7364	7372	7380	7388	7396

† Decimal points omitted.

N	0	1	2	3	4	5	6	7	8	9
55	7404	7412	7419	7427	7435	7443	7451	7459	7466	7474
56	7482	7490	7497	7505	7513	7520	7528	7536	7543	7551
57	7559	7566	7574	7582	7589	7597	7604	7612	7619	7627
58	7634	7642	7649	7657	7664	7672	7679	7686	7694	7701
59	7709	7716	7723	7731	7738	7745	7752	7760	7767	7774
60	7782	7789	7796	7803	7810	7818	7825	7832	7839	7846
61	7853	7860	7868	7875	7882	7889	7896	7903	7910	7917
62	7924	7931	7938	7945	7952	7959	7966	7973	7980	7987
63	7993	8000	8007	8014	8021	8028	8035	8041	8048	8055
64	8062	8069	8075	8082	8089	8096	8102	8109	8116	8122
65	8129	8136	8142	8149	8156	8162	8169	8176	8182	8189
66	8195	8202	8209	8215	8222	8228	8235	8241	8248	8254
67	8261	8267	8274	8280	8287	8293	8299	8306	8312	8319
68	8325	8331	8338	8344	8351	8357	8363	8370	8376	8382
69	8388	8395	8401	8407	8414	8420	8426	8432	8439	8445
70	8451	8457	8463	8470	8476	8482	8488	8494	8500	8506
71	8513	8519	8525	8531	8537	8543	8549	8555	8561	8567
72	8573	8579	8585	8591	8597	8603	8609	8615	8621	8627
73	8633	8639	8645	8651	8657	8663	8669	8675	8681	8686
74	8692	8698	8704	8710	8716	8722	8727	8733	8739	8745
75	8751	8756	8762	8768	8774	8779	8785	8791	8797	8802
76	8808	8814	8820	8825	8831	8837	8842	8848	8854	8859
77	8865	8871	8876	8882	8887	8893	8899	8904	8910	8915
78	8921	8927	8932	8938	8943	8949	8954	8960	8965	8971
79	8976	8982	8987	8993	8998	9004	9009	9015	9020	9025
80	9031	9036	9042	9047	9053	9058	9063	9069	9074	9079
81	9085	9090	9096	9101	9106	9112	9117	9122	9128	9133
82	9138	9143	9149	9154	9159	9165	9170	9175	9180	9186
83	9191	9196	9201	9206	9212	9217	9222	9227	9232	9238
84	9243	9248	9253	9258	9263	9269	9274	9279	9284	9289
85	9294	9299	9304	9309	9315	9320	9325	9330	9335	9340
86	9345	9350	9355	9360	9365	9370	9375	9380	9385	9390
87	9395	9400	9405	9410	9415	9420	9425	9430	9435	9440
88	9445	9450	9455	9460	9465	9469	9474	9479	9484	9489
89	9494	9499	9504	9509	9513	9518	9523	9528	9533	9538
90	9542	9547	9552	9557	9562	9566	9571	9576	9581	9586
91	9590	9595	9600	9605	9609	9614	9619	9624	9628	9633
92	9638	9643	9647	9652	9657	9661	9666	9671	9675	9680
93	9685	9689	9694	9699	9703	9708	9713	9717	9722	9727
94	9731	9736	9741	9745	9750	9754	9759	9763	9768	9773
95	9777	9782	9786	9791	9795	9800	9805	9809	9814	9818
96	9823	9827	9832	9836	9841	9845	9850	9854	9859	9863
97	9868	9872	9877	9881	9886	9890	9894	9899	9903	9908
98	9912	9917	9921	9926	9930	9934	9939	9943	9948	9952
99	9956	9961	9965	9969	9974	9978	9983	9987	9991	9996

TABLE II.   COMPOUND AMOUNT TABLE: $(1 + r)^n$

n	1%	1½%	2%	2½%	3%	3½%	4%	5%	6%
1	1.0100	1.0150	1.0200	1.0250	1.0300	1.0350	1.0400	1.0500	1.0600
2	1.0201	1.0302	1.0404	1.0506	1.0609	1.0712	1.0816	1.1025	1.1236
3	1.0303	1.0457	1.0612	1.0769	1.0927	1.1087	1.1249	1.1576	1.1910
4	1.0406	1.0614	1.0824	1.1038	1.1255	1.1475	1.1699	1.2155	1.2625
5	1.0510	1.0773	1.1041	1.1314	1.1593	1.1877	1.2167	1.2763	1.3382
6	1.0615	1.0934	1.1262	1.1597	1.1941	1.2293	1.2653	1.3401	1.4185
7	1.0721	1.1098	1.1487	1.1887	1.2299	1.2723	1.3159	1.4071	1.5036
8	1.0829	1.1265	1.1717	1.2184	1.2668	1.3168	1.3686	1.4775	1.5938
9	1.0937	1.1434	1.1951	1.2489	1.3048	1.3629	1.4233	1.5513	1.6895
10	1.1046	1.1605	1.2190	1.2801	1.3439	1.4106	1.4802	1.6289	1.7908
11	1.1157	1.1779	1.2434	1.3121	1.3842	1.4600	1.5395	1.7103	1.8983
12	1.1268	1.1956	1.2682	1.3449	1.4258	1.5111	1.6010	1.7959	2.0122
13	1.1381	1.2136	1.2936	1.3785	1.4685	1.5640	1.6651	1.8856	2.1329
14	1.1495	1.2318	1.3195	1.4130	1.5126	1.6187	1.7317	1.9799	2.2609
15	1.1610	1.2502	1.3459	1.4483	1.5580	1.6753	1.8009	2.0789	2.3966
16	1.1726	1.2690	1.3728	1.4845	1.6047	1.7340	1.8730	2.1829	2.5404
17	1.1843	1.2880	1.4002	1.5216	1.6528	1.7947	1.9479	2.2920	2.6928
18	1.1961	1.3073	1.4282	1.5597	1.7024	1.8575	2.0258	2.4066	2.8543
19	1.2081	1.3270	1.4568	1.5987	1.7535	1.9225	2.1068	2.5270	3.0256
20	1.2202	1.3469	1.4859	1.6386	1.8061	1.9898	2.1911	2.6533	3.2071
21	1.2324	1.3671	1.5157	1.6796	1.8603	2.0594	2.2788	2.7860	3.3996
22	1.2447	1.3876	1.5460	1.7216	1.9161	2.1315	2.3699	2.9253	3.6035
23	1.2572	1.4084	1.5769	1.7646	1.9736	2.2061	2.4647	3.0715	3.8197
24	1.2697	1.4295	1.6084	1.8087	2.0328	2.2833	2.5633	3.2251	4.0489
25	1.2824	1.4509	1.6406	1.8539	2.0938	2.3632	2.6658	3.3864	4.2919
26	1.2953	1.4727	1.6734	1.9003	2.1566	2.4460	2.7725	3.5557	4.5494
27	1.3082	1.4948	1.7069	1.9478	2.2213	2.5316	2.8834	3.7335	4.8223
28	1.3213	1.5172	1.7410	7.9965	2.2879	2.6202	2.9987	3.9201	5.1117
29	1.3345	1.5400	1.7758	2.0464	2.3566	2.7119	3.1187	4.1161	5.4184
30	1.3478	1.5631	1.8114	2.0976	2.4273	2.8068	3.2434	4.3219	5.7435
31	1.3613	1.5865	1.8476	2.1500	2.5001	2.9050	3.3731	4.5380	6.0881
32	1.3749	1.6103	1.8845	2.2038	2.5751	3.0067	3.5081	4.7649	6.4534
33	1.3887	1.6345	1.9222	2.2589	2.6523	3.1119	3.6484	5.0032	6.8406
34	1.4026	1.6590	1.9607	2.3153	2.7319	3.2209	3.7943	5.2533	7.2510
35	1.4166	1.6839	1.9999	2.3732	2.8139	3.3336	3.9461	5.5160	7.6861
36	1.4308	1.7091	2.0399	2.4325	2.8983	3.4503	4.1039	5.7918	8.1473
37	1.4451	1.7348	2.0807	2.4933	2.9852	3.5710	4.2681	6.0814	8.6361
38	1.4595	1.7608	2.1223	2.5557	3.0748	3.6960	4.4388	6.3855	9.1543
39	1.4741	1.7872	2.1647	2.6196	3.1670	3.8254	4.6164	6.7048	9.7035
40	1.4889	1.8140	2.2080	2.6851	3.2620	3.9593	4.8010	7.0400	10.2857
41	1.5038	1.8412	2.2522	2.7522	3.3599	4.0978	4.9931	7.3920	10.9029
42	1.5188	1.8688	2.2972	2.8210	3.4607	4.2413	5.1928	7.7616	11.5570
43	1.5340	1.8969	2.3432	2.8915	3.5645	4.3897	5.4005	8.1497	12.2505
44	1.5493	1.9253	2.3901	2.9638	3.6715	4.5433	5.6165	8.5572	12.9855
45	1.5648	1.9542	2.4379	3.0379	3.7816	4.7024	5.8412	8.9850	13.7646
46	1.5805	1.9835	2.4866	3.1139	3.8950	4.8669	6.0748	9.4343	14.5905
47	1.5963	2.0133	2.5363	3.1917	4.0119	5.0373	6.3178	9.9060	15.4659
48	1.6122	2.0435	2.5871	3.2715	4.1323	5.2136	6.5705	10.4013	16.3939
49	1.6283	2.0741	2.6388	3.3533	4.2562	5.3961	6.8333	10.9213	17.3775
50	1.6446	2.1052	2.6916	3.4371	4.3839	5.5849	7.1067	11.4674	18.4202

TABLE III.   CUMULATED AMOUNTS (ANNUITIES)

n	1%	1½%	2%	2½%	3%	3½%	4%	5%	6%
1	1.0000	1.0000	1.0000	1.0000	1.0000	1.0000	1.0000	1.0000	1.0000
2	2.0100	2.0150	2.0200	2.0250	2.0300	2.0350	2.0400	2.0500	2.0600
3	3.0301	3.0452	3.0604	3.0756	3.0909	3.1062	3.1216	3.1525	3.1836
4	4.0604	4.0909	4.1216	4.1525	4.1836	4.2149	4.2465	4.3101	4.3746
5	5.1010	5.1523	5.2040	5.2563	5.3091	5.3625	5.4163	5.5256	5.6371
6	6.1520	6.2296	6.3081	6.3877	6.4684	6.5502	6.6330	6.8019	6.9753
7	7.2135	7.3230	7.4343	7.5474	7.6625	7.7794	7.8983	8.1420	8.3938
8	8.2857	8.4328	8.5830	8.7361	8.8923	9.0517	9.2142	9.5491	9.8975
9	9.3685	9.5593	9.7546	9.9545	10.1591	10.3685	10.5828	11.0266	11.4913
10	10.4622	10.7027	10.9497	11.2034	11.4639	11.7314	12.0061	12.5779	13.1808
11	11.5668	11.8633	12.1687	12.4835	12.8078	13.1420	13.4864	14.2068	14.9716
12	12.6825	13.0412	13.4121	13.7956	14.1920	14.6020	15.0258	15.9171	16.8699
13	13.8093	14.2368	14.6803	15.1404	15.6178	16.1130	16.6268	17.7130	18.8821
14	14.9474	15.4504	15.9739	16.5190	17.0863	17.6770	18.2919	19.5986	21.0151
15	16.0969	16.6821	17.2934	17.9319	18.5989	19.2957	20.0236	21.5786	23.2760
16	17.2579	17.9324	18.6393	19.3802	20.1569	20.9710	21.8245	23.6575	25.6725
17	18.4304	19.2014	20.0121	20.8647	21.7616	22.7050	23.6975	25.8404	28.2129
18	19.6147	20.4894	21.4123	22.3863	23.4144	24.4997	25.6454	28.1324	30.9057
19	20.8109	21.7967	22.8406	23.9460	25.1169	26.3572	27.6712	30.5390	33.7600
20	22.0190	23.1237	24.2974	25.5447	26.8704	28.2797	29.7781	33.0660	36.7856
21	23.2392	24.4705	25.7833	27.1833	28.6765	30.2695	31.9692	35.7193	39.9927
22	24.4716	25.8376	27.2990	28.8629	30.5368	32.3289	34.2480	38.5052	43.3923
23	25.7163	27.2251	28.8450	30.5844	32.4529	34.4604	36.6179	41.4305	46.9958
24	26.9735	28.6335	30.4219	32.3490	34.4265	36.6665	39.0826	44.5020	50.8156
25	28.2432	30.0630	32.0303	34.1578	36.4593	38.9499	41.6459	47.7271	54.8645
26	29.5256	31.5140	33.6709	36.0117	38.5530	41.3131	44.3117	51.1135	59.1564
27	30.8209	32.9867	35.3443	37.9120	40.7096	43.7591	47.0842	54.6691	63.7058
28	32.1291	34.4815	37.0512	39.8598	42.9309	46.2906	49.9676	58.4026	68.5281
29	33.4504	35.9987	38.7922	41.8563	45.2189	48.9108	52.9663	62.3227	73.6398
30	34.7849	37.5387	40.5681	43.9027	47.5754	51.6227	56.0849	66.4388	79.0582
31	36.1327	39.1018	42.3794	46.0003	50.0027	54.4295	59.3283	70.7608	84.8017
32	37.4941	40.6883	44.2270	48.1503	52.5028	57.3345	62.7015	75.2988	90.8898
33	38.8690	42.2986	46.1116	50.3540	55.0778	60.3412	66.2095	80.0638	97.3432
34	40.2577	43.9331	48.0338	52.6129	57.7302	63.4532	69.8579	85.0670	104.1838
35	41.6603	45.5921	49.9945	54.9282	60.4621	66.6740	73.6522	90.3203	111.4348
36	43.0769	47.2760	51.9944	57.3014	63.2759	70.0076	77.5983	95.8363	119.1209
37	44.5076	48.9851	54.0343	59.7339	66.1742	73.4579	81.7022	101.6281	127.2681
38	45.9527	50.7199	56.1149	62.2273	69.1594	77.0289	85.9703	107.7095	135.9042
39	47.4123	52.4807	58.2372	64.7830	72.2342	80.7249	90.4091	114.0950	145.0585
40	48.8864	54.2679	60.4020	67.4026	75.4013	84.5503	95.0255	120.7998	154.7620
41	50.3752	56.0819	62.6100	70.0876	78.6633	88.5095	99.8265	127.8398	165.0477
42	51.8790	57.9231	64.8622	72.8398	82.0232	92.6074	104.8196	135.2318	175.9505
43	53.3978	59.7920	67.1595	75.6608	85.4839	96.8486	110.0124	142.9933	187.5076
44	54.9318	61.6889	69.5027	78.5523	89.0484	101.2383	115.4129	151.1430	199.7580
45	56.4811	63.6142	71.8927	81.5161	92.7199	105.7817	121.0294	159.7002	212.7435
46	58.0459	65.5684	74.3306	84.5540	96.5015	110.4840	126.8706	168.6852	226.5081
47	59.6263	67.5519	76.8172	87.6679	100.3965	115.3510	132.9454	178.1194	241.0986
48	61.2226	69.5652	79.3535	90.8596	104.4084	120.3883	139.2632	188.0254	256.5645
49	62.8348	71.6087	81.9406	94.1311	108.5406	125.6018	145.8337	198.4267	272.9584
50	64.4632	73.6828	84.5794	97.4843	112.7969	130.9979	152.6671	209.3480	290.3359

TABLE IV.   PRESENT VALUE OF $1 AFTER n PERIODS: $(1 + r)^{-n}$

n	1%	1½%	2%	2½%	3%	3½%	4%	5%	6%
1	0.99010	0.98522	0.98039	0.97561	0.97087	0.96618	0.96154	0.95238	0.94340
2	0.98030	0.97066	0.96117	0.95181	0.94260	0.93351	0.92456	0.90703	0.89000
3	0.97059	0.95632	0.94232	0.92860	0.91514	0.90194	0.88900	0.86384	0.83962
4	0.96098	0.94218	0.92385	0.90595	0.88849	0.87144	0.85480	0.82270	0.79209
5	0.95147	0.92826	0.90573	0.88385	0.86261	0.84197	0.82193	0.78353	0.74726
6	0.94205	0.91454	0.88797	0.86230	0.83748	0.81350	0.79031	0.74622	0.70496
7	0.93272	0.90103	0.87056	0.84127	0.81309	0.78599	0.75992	0.71068	0.66506
8	0.92348	0.88771	0.85349	0.82075	0.78941	0.75941	0.73069	0.67684	0.62741
9	0.91434	0.87459	0.83676	0.80073	0.76642	0.73373	0.70259	0.64461	0.59190
10	0.90529	0.86167	0.82035	0.78120	0.74409	0.70892	0.67556	0.61391	0.55839
11	0.89632	0.84893	0.80426	0.76214	0.72242	0.68495	0.64958	0.58468	0.52679
12	0.88745	0.83639	0.78849	0.74356	0.70138	0.66178	0.62460	0.55684	0.49697
13	0.87866	0.82403	0.77303	0.72542	0.68095	0.63940	0.60057	0.53032	0.46884
14	0.86996	0.81185	0.75788	0.70773	0.66112	0.61778	0.57748	0.50507	0.44230
14	0.86135	0.79985	0.74301	0.69047	0.64186	0.59689	0.55526	0.48102	0.41727
16	0.85282	0.78803	0.72845	0.67362	0.62317	0.57671	0.53391	0.45811	0.39365
17	0.84438	0.77639	0.71416	0.65720	0.60502	0.55720	0.51337	0.43630	0.37136
18	0.83602	0.76491	0.70016	0.64117	0.58739	0.53836	0.49363	0.41552	0.35034
19	0.82774	0.75361	0.68643	0.62553	0.57029	0.52016	0.47464	0.39573	0.33051
20	0.81954	0.74247	0.67297	0.61027	0.55368	0.50257	0.45639	0.37689	0.31180
21	0.81143	0.73150	0.65978	0.59539	0.53755	0.48557	0.43883	0.35894	0.29416
22	0.80340	0.72069	0.64684	0.58086	0.52189	0.46915	0.42196	0.34185	0.27751
23	0.79544	0.71004	0.63416	0.56670	0.50669	0.45329	0.40573	0.32557	0.26180
24	0.78757	0.69954	0.62172	0.55288	0.49193	0.43796	0.39012	0.31007	0.24698
25	0.77977	0.68921	0.60953	0.53939	0.47761	0.42315	0.37512	0.29530	0.23300
26	0.77205	0.67902	0.59758	0.52623	0.46369	0.40884	0.36069	0.28124	0.21981
27	0.76440	0.66899	0.58586	0.51340	0.45019	0.39501	0.34682	0.26785	0.20737
28	0.75684	0.65910	0.57437	0.50088	0.43708	0.38165	0.33348	0.25509	0.19563
29	0.74934	0.64936	0.56311	0.48866	0.42435	0.36875	0.32065	0.24295	0.18456
30	0.74192	0.63976	0.55207	0.47674	0.41199	0.35628	0.30832	0.23138	0.17411
31	0.73458	0.63031	0.54125	0.46511	0.39999	0.34423	0.29646	0.22036	0.16425
32	0.72730	0.62099	0.53063	0.45377	0.38834	0.33259	0.28506	0.20987	0.15496
33	0.72010	0.61182	0.52023	0.44270	0.37703	0.32134	0.27409	0.19987	0.14619
34	0.71297	0.60277	0.51003	0.43191	0.36604	0.31048	0.26355	0.19035	0.13791
35	0.70591	0.59387	0.50003	0.42137	0.35538	0.29998	0.25342	0.18129	0.13011
36	0.69892	0.58509	0.49022	0.41109	0.34503	0.28983	0.24367	0.17266	0.12274
37	0.69200	0.57644	0.48061	0.40107	0.33498	0.28003	0.23430	0.16444	0.11579
38	0.68515	0.56792	0.47119	0.39128	0.32523	0.27056	0.22529	0.15661	0.10924
39	0.67837	0.55953	0.46195	0.38174	0.31575	0.26141	0.21662	0.14915	0.10306
40	0.67165	0.55126	0.45289	0.37243	0.30656	0.25257	0.20829	0.14205	0.09722
41	0.66500	0.54312	0.44401	0.36335	0.29763	0.24403	0.20028	0.13528	0.09172
42	0.65842	0.53509	0.43530	0.35448	0.28896	0.23578	0.19257	0.12884	0.08653
43	0.65190	0.53718	0.42677	0.34584	0.28054	0.22781	0.18517	0.12270	0.08163
44	0.64545	0.51939	0.41840	0.33740	0.27237	0.22010	0.17805	0.11686	0.07701
45	0.63905	0.51171	0.41020	0.32917	0.26444	0.21266	0.17120	0.11130	0.07265
46	0.63273	0.50415	0.40215	0.32115	0.25674	0.20547	0.16461	0.10600	0.06854
47	0.62646	0.49670	0.39427	0.31331	0.24926	0.19852	0.15828	0.10095	0.06466
48	0.62026	0.48936	0.38654	0.30567	0.24200	0.19181	0.15219	0.09614	0.06100
49	0.61412	0.48213	0.37896	0.29822	0.23495	0.18532	0.14634	0.09156	0.05755
50	0.60804	0.47500	0.37153	0.29094	0.22811	0.17905	0.14071	0.08720	0.05429

TABLE V. *PRESENT VALUE OF AN ANNUITY*

n	1%	1½%	2%	2½%	3%	3½%	4%	5%	6%
1	0.9901	0.9852	0.9804	0.9756	0.9709	0.9662	0.9615	0.9524	0.9434
2	1.9704	1.9559	1.9416	1.9274	1.9135	1.8997	1.8861	1.8594	1.8334
3	2.9410	2.9122	2.8839	2.8560	2.8286	2.8016	2.7751	2.7232	2.6730
4	3.9020	3.8544	3.8077	3.7620	3.7171	3.6731	3.6299	3.5460	3.4651
5	4.8534	4.7826	4.7135	4.6458	4.5797	4.5151	4.4518	4.3295	4.2124
6	5.7955	5.6972	5.6014	5.5081	5.4172	5.3286	5.2421	5.0757	4.9173
7	6.7282	6.5982	6.4720	6.3494	6.2303	6.1145	6.0021	5.7864	5.5824
8	7.6517	7.4859	7.3255	7.1701	7.0197	6.8740	6.7327	6.4632	6.2098
9	8.5660	8.3605	8.1622	7.9709	7.7861	7.6077	7.4353	7.1078	6.8017
10	9.4713	9.2222	8.9826	8.7521	8.5302	8.3166	8.1109	7.7217	7.3601
11	10.3676	10.0711	9.7868	9.5142	9.2526	9.0016	8.7605	8.3064	7.8869
12	11.2551	10.9075	10.5753	10.2578	9.9540	9.6633	9.3851	8.8633	8.3838
13	12.1337	11.7315	11.3484	10.9832	10.6350	10.3027	9.9856	9.3936	8.8527
14	13.0037	12.5434	12.1062	11.6909	11.2961	10.9205	10.5631	9.8986	9.2950
15	13.8651	13.3432	12.8493	12.3814	11.9379	11.5174	11.1184	10.3797	9.7122
16	14.7179	14.1313	13.5777	13.0550	12.5611	12.0941	11.6523	10.8378	10.1059
17	15.5623	14.9076	14.2919	13.7122	13.1661	12.6513	12.1657	11.2741	10.4773
18	16.3983	15.6726	14.9920	14.3534	13.7535	13.1897	12.6593	11.6896	10.8276
19	17.2260	16.4262	15.6785	14.9789	14.3238	13.7098	13.1339	12.0853	11.1581
20	18.0456	17.1686	16.3514	15.5892	14.8775	14.2124	13.5903	12.4622	11.4699
21	18.8570	17.9001	17.0112	16.1845	15.4150	14.6980	14.0292	12.8212	11.7641
22	19.6604	18.6208	17.6580	16.7654	15.9369	15.1671	14.4511	13.1630	12.0416
23	20.4558	19.3309	18.2922	17.3321	16.4436	15.6204	14.8568	13.4886	12.3034
24	21.2434	20.0304	18.9139	17.8850	16.9355	16.0584	15.2470	13.7986	12.5504
25	22.0232	20.7196	19.5235	18.4244	17.4131	16.4815	15.6221	14.0939	12.7834
26	22.7952	21.3986	20.1210	18.9506	17.8768	16.8904	15.9828	14.3752	13.0032
27	23.5596	22.0676	20.7069	19.4640	18.3270	17.2854	16.3296	14.6430	13.2105
28	24.3164	22.7267	21.2813	19.9649	18.7641	17.6670	16.6631	14.8981	13.4062
29	25.0658	23.3761	21.8444	20.4535	19.1885	18.0358	16.9837	15.1411	13.5907
30	25.8077	24.0158	22.3965	20.9303	19.6004	18.3920	17.2920	15.3725	13.7648
31	26.5423	24.6461	22.9377	21.3954	20.0004	18.7363	17.5885	15.5928	13.9291
32	27.2696	25.2671	23.4683	21.8492	20.3888	19.0689	17.8736	15.8027	14.0840
33	27.9897	25.8790	23.9886	22.2919	20.7658	19.3902	18.1476	16.0025	14.2302
34	28.7027	26.4817	24.4986	22.7238	21.1318	19.7007	18.4112	16.1929	14.3681
35	29.4086	27.0756	24.9986	23.1452	21.4872	20.0007	18.6646	16.3742	14.4982
36	30.1075	27.6607	25.4888	23.5563	21.8323	20.2905	18.9083	16.5469	14.6210
37	30.7995	28.2371	25.9695	23.9573	22.1672	20.5705	19.1426	16.7113	14.7368
38	31.4847	28.8051	26.4406	24.3486	22.4925	20.8411	19.3679	16.8679	14.8460
39	32.1630	29.3646	26.9026	24.7303	22.8082	21.1025	19.5845	17.0170	14.9491
40	32.8347	29.9158	27.3555	25.1028	23.1148	21.3551	19.7928	17.1591	15.0463
41	33.4997	30.4590	27.7995	25.4661	23.4124	21.5991	19.9931	17.2944	15.1380
42	34.1581	30.9941	28.2348	25.8206	23.7014	21.8349	20.1856	17.4232	15.2245
43	34.8100	31.5212	28.6616	26.1664	23.9819	22.0627	20.3708	17.5459	15.3062
44	35.4555	32.0406	29.0800	26.5038	24.2543	22.2828	20.5488	17.6628	15.3832
45	36.0945	32.5523	29.4902	26.8330	24.5187	22.4955	20.7200	17.7741	15.4558
46	36.7272	33.0565	29.8923	27.1542	24.7754	22.7009	20.8847	17.8801	15.5244
47	37.3537	33.5532	30.2866	27.4675	25.0247	22.8994	21.0429	17.9810	15.5890
48	37.9740	34.0426	30.6731	27.7732	25.2667	23.0912	21.1951	18.0772	15.6500
49	38.5881	34.5247	31.0521	28.0714	25.5017	23.2766	21.3415	18.1687	15.7076
50	39.1961	34.9997	31.4236	28.3623	25.7298	23.4556	21.4822	18.2559	15.7619

Answers to Odd-numbered Problems

CHAPTER 1

1.1   The Language of Sets
The first set given is the *union;* the second set is the *intersection.*

1. {A,B,C,D}, {B,C}   3. {A,B,C,E,M}, Ø   5. {A,B,C}, {A,B,C}
7. {A,B,C,D}, {B,C}   9. {A,B,C,D}, Ø

In the following, the four numbers are (*a*) the cardinal number of set A; (*b*) the cardinal number of set B; (*c*) the cardinal number of the union; and (*d*) the cardinal number of the intersection.

11. 3, 4, 6, 1   13. 7, 5, 9, 3   15. 2, 5, 5, 2   17. 3, 2, 5, 0

In the following, the five numbers are (*a*) the cardinal number of set A; (*b*) the cardinal number of set B; (*c*) the cardinal number of set C; (*d*) the cardinal number of the union of the three sets; and (*e*) the cardinal number of the intersection of the three sets.

19. 6, 7, 7, 13, 2   21. 5, 7, 3, 9, 0

1.2   Incomplete Polls
1. 21   3. 26   5. 39   7. 5

1.3   Linear Graphs
1 to 9.

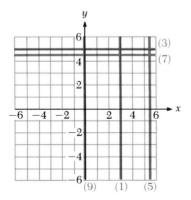

11 a. $(1, 1)$ I b. $(3, 3)$ I c. $(-3, 4)$ II d. $(-5, 2)$ II e. $(-5, -4)$ III
f. $(-1, -5)$ III g. $(1, -4)$ IV h. $(5, -3)$ IV i. $(4, 0)$ I and IV
j. $(-3, 0)$ II and III k. $(0, -2)$ III and IV l. $(0, 4)$ I and II

13 to 25.

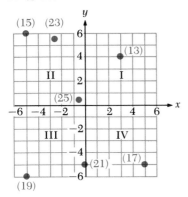

27.

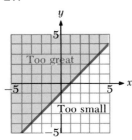

29.

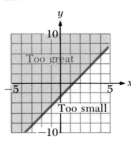

31.

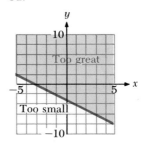

33.

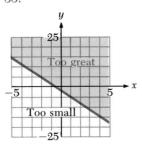

[(a) only] 35a. $y = -x$ 37a. $y = 3x$ 39a. $y = 3x + 1$

1.4 Polygon Graphs

1.

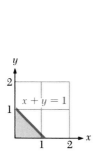

3.

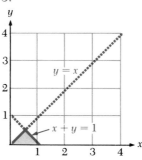

5.

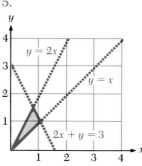

7.

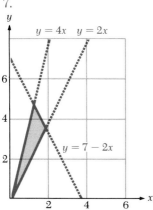

9.

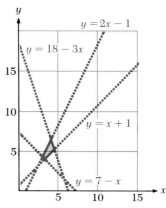

1.5 Linear Programming (Part I)

1.

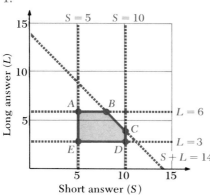

Point	S	L	Credits (S)	Credits (L)	Total Credits
A	5	6	15	42	57
B	8	6	24	42	66✔
C	10	4	30	28	58
D	10	3	30	21	51
E	5	3	15	21	36

The best score results from eight short-answer and six long-answer questions (if they are done correctly).

3.

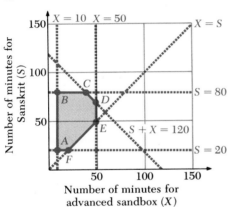

Number of minutes for Sanskrit (S)

Number of minutes for advanced sandbox (X)

Point	X	S	Raise (X)	Raise (S)	Total Raise
A	10	20	2	10	12
B	10	80	2	40	42
C	40	80	8	40	48✔
D	50	70	10	35	45
E	50	50	10	25	35
F	20	20	4	10	14

He can raise his average best by studying Advanced Sandbox for 40 minutes (raising it from 80 to 88 percent) and Sanskrit for 80 minutes (raising it from 55 to 95 percent).

5.

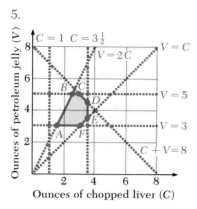

Point	C	V	Cost (C)	Cost (V)	Total Cost
A	1½	6	$0.07½	$0.12	$0.19½ ✔
B	2½	5	$0.12½	$0.10	$0.22½
C	3	5	$0.15	$0.10	$0.25
D	3½	4½	$0.17½	$0.09	$0.26½
E	3½	3½	$0.17½	$0.07	$0.24½
F	3	3	$0.15	$0.06	$0.21

The cheapest mixture contains 1½ ounces of chopped liver and 6 ounces of petroleum jelly.

1.6 Linear Programming (Part II)

1. 5 problems in set S, 3 in set L, and 5 in set P, making a total of 96.
3. 10 minutes on Advanced Sandbox (raising the mark from 80 to 82), 80 minutes on Sanskrit (raising the mark from 55 to 95), and 30 minutes on Chicken Plucking (raising the mark from 65 to 75).
5. 3 ounces of chopped liver, 5 ounces of petroleum jelly, no water, with a final cost of 25¢.

CHAPTER 2

2.1 Dice Combinations

1. 1, 2.78%   3. 3, 8.33%   5. 5, 13.89%   7. 4, 11.11%   9. 2, 5.56%
11. 10, 27.78%   13. 2, 5.56%   15. 8, 22.22%   17. 18, 50.00%
19. 9, 25.00%
21. $\frac{2}{36} \times \frac{4}{36} \times \frac{2}{36} = \frac{16}{46,656}$, about 0.034%
23. $\frac{5}{36} \times \frac{2}{36} \times \frac{2}{36} \times \frac{3}{36} = \frac{60}{1,679,616}$, about 0.0036%

2.2   Tossing Coins

1. $\frac{6}{16} = 37.5\%$ 3. $\frac{11}{16} = 68.75\%$ 5. 3.125% 7. 31.25% 9. 15.625%
11. 50.00% 13. $(0.6)^4 = 0.1296$, about 13% 15. $6(0.6)^2(0.4)^2 = 0.3456$,
about 35% 17. $(0.4)^4 = 0.0256$, about 2.6%

2.3   Shuffling

1. 120 3. $5{,}040$ 5. $362{,}880$ 7. 120 9. 720 11. $5{,}040$ 13. 4
15. $\frac{12}{120}$ or 10%

2.4   Equal-suit Games

1. 10 3. 6 5. 120 7. $75{,}600$ 9. 35 11. $\frac{2}{5}$ 13. $\frac{5}{6}$ 15. $\frac{5}{6} \times \frac{4}{5}$

2.5   Pick a Card

1. $\frac{4}{52} \times \frac{3}{51} \times \frac{2}{50}$ 3. $\frac{1}{52} \times \frac{1}{51} \times \frac{1}{50}$ 5. $\frac{26}{52} \times \frac{25}{51} \times \frac{24}{50} \times \frac{23}{49}$
7. $\frac{26}{52} \times \frac{26}{51} \times \frac{25}{50}$ 9. $\frac{52}{52} \times \frac{12}{51} \times \frac{11}{50} \times \frac{10}{49} \times \frac{9}{48}$

2.6   Complicated Games

1. $(\frac{1}{2} \times \frac{2}{5}) + (\frac{1}{2} \times \frac{1}{5}) = 30\%$ 3. $(\frac{1}{6} \times \frac{4}{36}) + (\frac{5}{6} \times \frac{3}{36}) = $ approximately 8.80%

5.

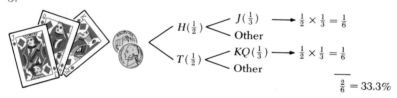

$$H(\tfrac{1}{2}) < \begin{array}{l} J(\tfrac{1}{3}) \longrightarrow \tfrac{1}{2} \times \tfrac{1}{3} = \tfrac{1}{6} \\ \text{Other} \end{array}$$

$$T(\tfrac{1}{2}) < \begin{array}{l} KQ(\tfrac{1}{3}) \longrightarrow \tfrac{1}{2} \times \tfrac{1}{3} = \tfrac{1}{6} \\ \text{Other} \end{array}$$

$$\overline{\tfrac{2}{6} = 33.3\%}$$

7.

$$R(\tfrac{1}{3}) < \begin{array}{l} R(\tfrac{3}{5}) \longrightarrow \tfrac{1}{3} \times \tfrac{3}{5} = \tfrac{1}{5} \\ W \end{array}$$

$$W(\tfrac{2}{3}) < \begin{array}{l} WW(\tfrac{2}{5} \times \tfrac{1}{4}) \longrightarrow \tfrac{2}{3} \times \tfrac{1}{10} = \tfrac{1}{15} \\ \text{Other} \end{array}$$

$$\overline{\tfrac{4}{15} = \text{approx. } 26.67\%}$$

CHAPTER 3

3.1   The Simple-explosion Problem

1a.

	Fat books	Thin books
Pages	320	192
Covers	2	2

b. $\begin{pmatrix} 320 & 192 \\ 2 & 2 \end{pmatrix} \begin{pmatrix} 100 \\ 50 \end{pmatrix} = \begin{pmatrix} 41{,}600 \\ 300 \end{pmatrix}$ (pages)
(covers)

3a.

	C	T
W	20	2
M	5	18

b. $\begin{pmatrix} 20 & 2 \\ 5 & 18 \end{pmatrix}\begin{pmatrix} 10 \\ 12 \end{pmatrix} = \begin{pmatrix} 224 \\ 266 \end{pmatrix}$ (women)
(men)

5a.

	Size 1	Size 2
Wire	4	6
Tubes	1	2
Switches	1	2

b. $\begin{pmatrix} 4 & 6 \\ 1 & 2 \\ 1 & 2 \end{pmatrix}\begin{pmatrix} 30 \\ 2 \end{pmatrix} = \begin{pmatrix} 132 \\ 34 \\ 34 \end{pmatrix}$ (wire)
(tubes)
(switches)

7a.

	Cheap	Expensive
Steel	1	0
Gold	0	1
Hands	2	3
Jewels	6	17
Gears	25	30

b. $\begin{pmatrix} 1 & 0 \\ 0 & 1 \\ 2 & 3 \\ 6 & 17 \\ 25 & 30 \end{pmatrix}\begin{pmatrix} 500 \\ 300 \end{pmatrix} = \begin{pmatrix} 500 \\ 300 \\ 1,900 \\ 8,100 \\ 21,500 \end{pmatrix}$ (steel cases)
(gold cases)
(hands)
(jewels)
(gears)

9a.

	I	M	E
M	3	4	5
T	4	5	7
B	6	3	2
P	4	2	0

b. $\begin{pmatrix} 3 & 4 & 5 \\ 4 & 5 & 7 \\ 6 & 3 & 2 \\ 4 & 2 & 0 \end{pmatrix}\begin{pmatrix} 12 \\ 6 \\ 3 \end{pmatrix} = \begin{pmatrix} 75 \\ 99 \\ 96 \\ 60 \end{pmatrix}$ (material)
(thread)
(buttons)
(pads)

3.2 Operations with Matrices (Part I)

1. $\begin{pmatrix} 5 & 4 \\ 8 & 17 \end{pmatrix}; \begin{pmatrix} 1 & 4 \\ 6 & 1 \end{pmatrix}$ 3. $\begin{pmatrix} 11 & 2 \\ 1 & 12 \end{pmatrix}; \begin{pmatrix} -7 & -2 \\ 1 & 4 \end{pmatrix}$

5. $\begin{pmatrix} 9 & -8 & 2 \\ -14 & -1 & 15 \\ -8 & -7 & -7 \end{pmatrix}$ 7. $\begin{pmatrix} -7 & 2 & 12 \\ -4 & 5 & 7 \\ 12 & 7 & -1 \end{pmatrix}$

3.3   Operations with Matrices (Part II)

1. $\begin{pmatrix} 0 & 2 \\ 15 & 8 \end{pmatrix}; \begin{pmatrix} 3 & 5 \\ 9 & 5 \end{pmatrix}$ 3. $\begin{pmatrix} 1 & 0 \\ 7 & 9 \end{pmatrix}; \begin{pmatrix} 9 & 6 \\ 0 & 1 \end{pmatrix}$

5. $\begin{pmatrix} 0 & 8 & 2 \\ 9 & 19 & 0 \\ 18 & 6 & 10 \end{pmatrix}; \begin{pmatrix} 10 & 12 & 0 \\ 3 & 3 & 10 \\ 0 & 12 & 16 \end{pmatrix}$ 7. $\begin{pmatrix} 10 & 12 & 2 \\ 10 & 3 & 0 \\ 16 & 12 & 0 \end{pmatrix}; \begin{pmatrix} 0 & 0 & 4 \\ 9 & 3 & 8 \\ 18 & 10 & 10 \end{pmatrix}$

9. $\begin{pmatrix} 4 & 0 \\ 21 & 25 \end{pmatrix}; \begin{pmatrix} 8 & 0 \\ 117 & 125 \end{pmatrix}$

3.4   Transitions

1a.

b.

$$\begin{array}{c c c} & D & R \\ D & \begin{pmatrix} 80\% & 20\% \\ R & 10\% & 90\% \end{pmatrix} \end{array}$$

3a.

b.

$$\begin{array}{c c c} & C & S \\ C & \begin{pmatrix} 90\% & 10\% \\ S & 5\% & 95\% \end{pmatrix} \end{array}$$

5a.

b.

$$\begin{array}{c c c c} & R & G & B \\ R & \begin{pmatrix} 0 & 30\% & 70\% \\ G & 20\% & 20\% & 60\% \\ B & 10\% & 30\% & 60\% \end{pmatrix} \end{array}$$

3.5 Markov Chains

1a. $(0.66, 0.34)$ b. $\begin{pmatrix} 0.66 & 0.34 \\ 0.17 & 0.83 \end{pmatrix}$ c. $(0.562, 0.438)$

3a. $(0.56, 0.44)$ b. $\begin{pmatrix} 0.815 & 0.185 \\ 0.0925 & 0.9075 \end{pmatrix}$ c. $(0.526, 0.474)$

5a. $(0.09, 0.28, 0.63)$ b. $\begin{pmatrix} 0.13 & 0.27 & 0.60 \\ 0.10 & 0.28 & 0.62 \\ 0.12 & 0.27 & 0.61 \end{pmatrix}$ c. $(0.119, 0.272, 0.609)$

CHAPTER 4

4.1 The Game Matrix

1. If George matches Pete, he pays 2¢. Otherwise, he wins 3¢.
3. If the choices match, there is no payoff. If Lance chooses paper and Eric chooses scissors, Lance loses 1 point. If Lance chooses paper and Eric chooses stone, Lance gains 1 point, etc.

5.

		Y	
		Odd	Even
X	Odd	1	-1
	Even	-1	1

7.

		Charles writes		
		2	3	4
	2	4	-5	6
Richard writes	3	-5	6	-7
	4	6	-7	8

4.2 Saddle-point Games (2 × 2)

1. $(2,1),3$ 3. $(2,1),9$ 5. $(1,1),-\frac{3}{4}$ 7. $(2,1),\frac{1}{5}$

9.

		Enemy	
		Consonant	Vowel
We	C	-3	2
	V	0	3

$(2,1), 0$ (fair game)

11.

Nature

		Sunny	Rain
Guess	Sunny	$50	$30
	Rain	$ 0	$20

(1,2), $30

4.3   Larger Saddle-point Games

1. $(2,1), -1$ 3. $(3,2),15$ 5. $(2,1),0$ (fair game)   7. $(1,2),2.5$

9.

She

		Early	On time	Late
We	Early	5	0	9
	On time	-5	5	0
	Late	-15	-10	10

Saddle point at $(1,1)$; value $= 5$

4.4   Dominance

1. Column 2 is dominated by columns 1 and 4 (delete columns 1 and 4).
   Row 2 dominates row 3 (delete row 3). The result is

	2	3
1	5	10
2	8	7

3. Row 1 dominates row 2 (delete row 2).
   Column 1 dominates column 2 (delete column 1).
   Row 1 dominates row 4 (delete row 4).
   Row 1 dominates row 3 (delete row 3).
   The result is

	2	3
1	29	26
4	3	25

5. It is advisable first to add 3 to each entry.
   Row 2 dominates rows 4 and 5 (delete rows 4 and 5).
   Column 3 dominates column 2 (delete column 3).

Column 6 dominates column 4 (delete column 6).
Row 2 dominates row 1 (delete row 1).
Column 1 dominates column 5 (delete column 1).
Column 5 dominates column 4 (delete column 5).
Row 3 dominates row 6 (delete row 6).
Saddle point at (2,4); value = 2.

4.5 Evaluating Determinants

1. (2.8,1.8) 3. (2.2,4.2) 5. $(\frac{1}{5},\frac{4}{5})$ 7. $\begin{pmatrix}4.1\\1.6\end{pmatrix}$ 9. $\begin{pmatrix}3.5\\2.0\end{pmatrix}$ 11. $\begin{pmatrix}-1\\-1\end{pmatrix}$

13. 4 15. 34 17. −55 19. 25 21. −49 23. −5

CHAPTER 5

5.1 Mixed Strategy (Part I)

1. (6,54) 3. (20,40) 5. (16,44) 7. $(\frac{1}{2},\frac{1}{2})$; $\begin{pmatrix}\frac{1}{2}\\\frac{1}{2}\end{pmatrix}$; ½¢. George should play heads and tails equally, at random. He will average out winning 0.5¢ per play. 9. $(\frac{1}{2},\frac{1}{2})$; $\begin{pmatrix}\frac{1}{2}\\\frac{1}{2}\end{pmatrix}$; 0. X should stick out an odd or an even number of fingers equally, at random, in order to break even.

11. $(0,\frac{1}{6},\frac{5}{6},0)$; $\begin{pmatrix}0\\\frac{1}{2}\\\frac{1}{2}\\0\end{pmatrix}$; 7½

5.2 Mixed Strategy (Part II)

1. Saddle point at (1,1); value 4; $2\frac{5}{6}$ 3. $(\frac{4}{5},\frac{1}{5})$; $\begin{pmatrix}\frac{1}{2}\\\frac{1}{2}\end{pmatrix}$; 4; $3\frac{3}{5}$

5. $(\frac{1}{5},\frac{4}{5})$; $\begin{pmatrix}\frac{1}{2}\\\frac{1}{2}\end{pmatrix}$; 2; 1½ 7. $(\frac{1}{2},\frac{1}{2})$; $\begin{pmatrix}\frac{3}{10}\\\frac{7}{10}\end{pmatrix}$; ½; 0 9. $(\frac{3}{5},\frac{2}{5})$; $\begin{pmatrix}\frac{1}{5}\\\frac{4}{5}\end{pmatrix}$; 0; $\frac{11}{40}$

5.3 $2 \times m$ and $m \times 2$ Games; Trial-and-Error Method

1. (0.7,0.3); $\begin{pmatrix}0.3\\0\\0.7\end{pmatrix}$; 5.1 3. $(\frac{1}{2},\frac{1}{2})$; $\begin{pmatrix}\frac{2}{3}\\\frac{1}{3}\\0\end{pmatrix}$; $\frac{4}{5}$ 5. $(\frac{8}{11},\frac{3}{11},0)$; $\begin{pmatrix}\frac{4}{11}\\\frac{7}{11}\end{pmatrix}$; $2\frac{10}{11}$

5.4 2 × m and m × 2 Games; Graphical Method

Answers are the same as those in Problem Section 5.3.

5.5 3 × 3 Games

1. Saddle point (row 2, column 3); value $= -7$ 3. $(0,\tfrac{3}{4},\tfrac{1}{4})$; $\begin{pmatrix} \tfrac{1}{2} \\ \tfrac{1}{2} \\ 0 \end{pmatrix}$; 0

5. $(0,\tfrac{1}{2},\tfrac{1}{2})$, $\begin{pmatrix} 2\tfrac{1}{34} \\ \tfrac{4}{34} \\ \tfrac{9}{34} \end{pmatrix}$, $7\tfrac{1}{2}$ 7. $(\tfrac{1}{3},\tfrac{1}{3},\tfrac{1}{3})$, $\begin{pmatrix} \tfrac{1}{3} \\ \tfrac{1}{3} \\ \tfrac{1}{3} \end{pmatrix}$, 0   9. $(0,\tfrac{3}{7},\tfrac{4}{7})$, $\begin{pmatrix} 0 \\ \tfrac{1}{7} \\ \tfrac{6}{7} \end{pmatrix}$, $-\tfrac{3}{7}$

CHAPTER 6

6.1 Arithmetic by Slide Rule

1. The value of the left index, whether or not the scales match, and the spacing of the numbers on the scales
3. The following tables are some sample calculations:

Fig. (a)	Fig. (b)
2 ? 0 = 2	3 ? 0 = 3
2 ? 5 = 3	3 ? 5 = 4
2 ? 10 = 4	3 ? 10 = 5
2 ? 15 = 5	3 ? 15 = 6

To each number under the C index, add $\tfrac{1}{5}$ of the number on the C scale under the hairline. For example, in Fig. (b), the number under the C index is 3. Read across to 20. One-fifth of this is 4. The result, 7, is found under the hairline on the D scale.

6.2 Reading the Slide Rule

1. 1.02, 1.17, 1.335, 1.896   3. 20.10, 22.00, 25.05, 29.98
5. 306.0, 308.5, 351.0, 367.5   7. 0.807, 0.830, 0.865, 0.895

6.3 Multiplying by Slide Rule

1. 0.000,016   3. 2,400,000,000   5. 54.6   7. 0.000,457,075   9. 29.6244
11. 134.1295

6.4 Continued Products (Optional)

1. 48.960,626   3. 14.235,905,2   5. 771.516   7. 68,335,176.0
9. 131.863,360,200

6.5 Division by Slide Rule

1. 34.83740   3. 0.637655   5. 0.0184867   7. 0.000,436,800
9. 0.301,481,5   11. 65.9115

6.6 Mixed Multiplication and Division (Optional)

1. 45.38182   3. 62.9216   5. 35.1413   7. 0.021,715,5   9. 10.15561
11. 0.175,788,7

CHAPTER 7

7.1 A Taste of Theory

1c. 9,683   3. $3^4 = 81, 2^4 = 16$ 5. $10^3 = 1,000, 10^1 = 10$ 7. 117,147
9. 1,024   11. 9

7.2 The Laws of Logarithms

1. 59,049   3. 177,147   5. 4,096   7. 4,096   9. 81   11. 9   13. $1/6,561$
15. $1/81$

7.3 The Table of Mantissas

1. 0.0253   3. 0.8639   5. 0.6465   7. 0.2989   9. 0.7490   11. 0.9227
13. 0.8248   15. 0.6821   17. 362   19. 505   21. 542   23. 103   25. 151
27. 352   29. 509   31. 0.4099   33. 0.4116   35. 503   37. 417

7.4 Finding Characteristics

1. $0.0253 + 4$ 3. $0.8639 + 3$ 5. $0.6425 + 2$ 7. $0.2989 + 1$
9. 0.7490   11. $0.9227 - 1$ 13. $0.8248 - 2$ 15. $0.6821 - 3$
17. 36.2   19. 505   21. 5420   23. 1,030   25. 0.151   27. 0.0382
29. 0.00509   31. $0.4099 + 1$ 33. $0.4116 + 1$ 35. 0.00503   37. 41.7

7.5 Multiplication by Logarithms

1. 11.4   3. 14,700   5. 27.6

7.6 Division by Logarithms

1. 2.42   3. 28.7   5. 3.02   7. 1.44   9. 13.9   11. 0.167   13. 2.85
15. 0.0332   17. 0.0754   19. 0.00550

7.7   Growth and Decay Problems

1. 73%   3. 48%   5. 250   7. 2,200   9c. 0.14 second   11c. 17.3 hours
11d. 173 hours

CHAPTER 8

8.1   Mixed Multiplication and Division

1. 46.3   3. 4,130   5. 0.0140   7. 0.0183   9. 2.23   11. 573   13. 0.183
15. 15.1   17. 0.000,004,98

8.2   Powers

1. 1,260   3. 0.000,002,14   5. 422   7. $25(1.01)^{40} = \$37.20$
9. $\$1(1.0125)^{400} = \$143$ 11. $\$5,000(1.015)^{84} = \$17,500$

8.3   Savings Plans

1. $\dfrac{2(3^{20} - 1)}{2} =$ about 3,480,000,000   3. $\dfrac{8(0.5^{10} - 1)}{0.5 - 1} =$ about 15.98
5. 47; $13,150.19   7. 50; $84,579.40   9. Deduct $374.00; $12,776.19

8.4   Annuities

1. $500; $7,090.575   3. $1,500; $15,336.55   5.† $800; $2,720.10
7.† $1,500; $6,068.85

8.5   Amortization

1. $1,000 ÷ 5.6972 = $175.52; $1,053.12
3. $20,000 ÷ 12.4622 = $1,604.85, $1,604.85 × 20 = $32,097,
   $32,097 + $5,000 = $37,097
5. $50,000 − $5,000 = $45,000, $45,000 ÷ 7.3601 = $6,114.05,
   $6,114.05 × 10 = $61,140.50; $61,140.50 + $5,000 = $66,140.50

8.6   Roots

1. 9.12; 4.36   3. 0.647; 0.748   5. 0.0962; 0.392   7. 0.00814; 0.201

8.7   Fractional Exponents

1. 2   3. 8   5.   216   7. ⅛   9. ½   11. 5.79   13. 1.50   15. 0.513
17. 3.86   19. 308   21. 0.173   23. 0.259

† From a more complete table.

8.8   Combined Operations (Optional)

1. $T = 1.62$ seconds   3. $r = 0.992$ inch   5. $m = 203$ tons

CHAPTER 9

9.3   PERT

1. 1 hour, 55 minutes, 6:55 p.m.   3. 1 hour, 53 minutes, 3:33 p.m.
5. 1 day, 21 hours, 50 minutes, 4:10 p.m. Monday
7. 1-8-11-12-14-15-16, 1 day, 23 hours, 30 minutes, 6:12 p.m. Friday
9. 1-5-6-4-12-13, 3 days, 9 hours, 0 minutes, Jan. 21 at 4:15 p.m.

9.4   Forecasting (Part I)

1. H   3. S   5. T   7. T   9. TS   11. 51, 50, 52, 51, 52, 50
13. 1020, 1028, 1025, 1045, 1035, 1015
15. 153, 154, 154, 153, 154, 153

9.5   Forecasting (Part II)

1. 160   3. 176   5. 110   7. 80
   The following table has the calculations for Probs. 9 to 15.

Month	Year 1	Year 2	Average	BI
October	26	24	25.0	1.79
November	27	28	27.5	1.96
December	26	25	25.5	1.82
January	20	23	21.5	1.54
February	16	14	15.0	1.07
March	8	9	8.5	0.61
April	5	4	4.5	0.32
May	2	3	2.5	0.18
June	6	4	5.0	0.36
July	8	9	8.5	0.61
August	14	15	14.5	1.04
September	23	18	10.5	0.75
			168.5	

11. 14.0   13. 25.7   15. −0.9, 13.9

CHAPTER 10

10.1   The Internal Language of the Computer

1. 243   3. 200   5. 106   7. 174   9. 188   11. C1, 1100 0001

13. *D8*, 1101 1000   15. *3A*, 0011 1010   17. *9B*, 1001 1011
19. *FA*, 1111 1010   21. 220, 1101 1100   23. 212, 1101 0100

10.2   Communicating with the Computer

1. HOW SWEET IT IS.
3. JAPANESE SANDMAN AND, PERHAPS, SANDBOY.
5. PRICE/ITEM = $17.52
7. RATE * TIME = DISTANCE (60.71 MILES)

10.3   FORTRAN Programs

1. Invalid, mixed   3. Valid   5. Valid   7. Invalid, mixed, ZNUM
9. Valid   11. Invalid, too long, use DECMAL   13. Input on cards;
printer output is 3,8   15. Input from second disk pack; printer output
$87.62, $175.25

17.
```
        READ (1, 100) A,B,C
        READ (8, 101) D
        SUM = A + B
        SUM = SUM + 3.
        SUM = SUM − D
        WRITE (3, 102) A, B, C, D, SUM
   100  FORMAT statement
   101  FORMAT statement
        CALL EXIT
        END
```

10.4   FORTRAN Mathematics

1. $\dfrac{ac}{b}$ 3. $\dfrac{ab}{c}$ 5. $\dfrac{a+b}{c} \cdot d^{x+2}$ 7. $(A + B ** 2)/(C - D ** 3)$

9. $A + B/(C - D ** 3)$ 11. $(A + B ** (2. * (X - 5.)))/C - 5. * D$
13. $R = R1 * R2/(R1 + R2)$ 15. $H = ZI * SIN (T) * ZL/(R ** 2)$
17. $Q = E *C * (1. - 2.7183 ** ((-T)/(R * C)))$

10.5   Programs with Loops and Branches

1. Reads in four cards, finds product of one set and sum of another,
   writes them on the first disk pack.
3. No data are read in, the program finds the sum of the cubes of the
   first 25 whole numbers and punches 25 and the sum into a card.

5.   SUM = 0.
          $N = 1$
          $X = 1.$
   3   SUM = SUM + $X ** 2$
        IF $(N - 15)$ 1,2,2
   1    $N = N + 1$
        $X = X + 2.$
        GO TO 3
   2   WRITE (2, 100) SUM
100   FORMAT statement
        CALL EXIT
        END

index